MANAGERS WHO LEAD

OTHER PUBLICATIONS BY
MANAGEMENT SCIENCES FOR HEALTH

Community-Based Health Care: Lessons from Bangladesh to Boston
    ed. Jon Rohde and John Wyon

CORE—A Tool for Cost and Revenue Analysis

The Family Planning Manager's Handbook: Basic Skills and
Tools for Managing Family Planning Programs
    ed. James A. Wolff, Linda J. Suttenfield, and Susanna C. Binzen

FIMAT—Financial Management Assessment Tool

Human Resource Management Rapid Assessment Tool for HIV/AIDS
Environments: A Guide for Strengthening HRM Systems

Lessons from MSH: Strategic Planning: Reflections on Process and Practice
    Sylvia Vriesendorp

Managing Drug Supply: The Selection, Procurement,
Distribution, and Use of Pharmaceuticals, 2nd edition
    with the World Health Organization

Management Strategies for Improving Family Planning Services:
The Family Planning Manager Compendium (Vols. I–IV)
    ed. Janice Miller and James A. Wolff

Management Strategies for Improving Health and Family Planning Services:
A Compendium of *The Manager* Series, Vols. V–IX
    ed. Janice Miller, Claire Bahamon, Laura Lorenz, and Kim Atkinson

MOST—Management and Organizational Sustainability Tool:
A Guide for Users and Facilitators, 2nd edition

Scaling Up HIV/AIDS Programs: A Manual for Multisectoral Planning
    Saul Helfenbein and Catherine Severo

MANAGERS WHO LEAD

A Handbook for Improving Health Services

MANAGEMENT SCIENCES *for* HEALTH
Cambridge, Massachusetts

Management Sciences for Health   Tel.: 617.250.9500
784 Memorial Drive   Fax: 617.250.9090
Cambridge, MA 02139-4613 USA   Web site: www.msh.org

ISBN 0-913723-95-9

Interior design and composition: Jenna Dixon
Indexer: Barbara K. Timmons
Proofreader: Ceallaigh Reddy

Funding for this publication was provided by the Office of Population and Reproductive Health, Bureau for Global Health, US Agency for International Development, under the terms of the Management and Leadership Program, award number HRN-A-00-00-00014-00. The opinions expressed herein are those of the authors and do not necessarily reflect the views of USAID.

Printed in the United States of America on acid-free paper by Quebecor World with vegetable-oil-based ink.

♾ The paper used in this publication meets the minimum requirements of the American National Standard for Information Sciences—Permanence of Paper for Printed Library Materials, ANSI Z39.48-1992.

Library of Congress Cataloging-in-Publication Data

Managers who lead : a handbook for improving health services.
     p.   cm.
   Includes bibliographical references and index.
   ISBN 0-913723-95-9 (alk. paper)
     1. Health facilities—Administration—Handbooks, manuals, etc.
2. Leadership—Handbooks, manuals, etc. 3. Health services administration—Handbooks, manuals, etc. I. Management Sciences for Health (Firm)

RA 971.M3463   2005
362.1'068—dc22   2005047959

1 2 3 4 5 6 7 8 9   05 06 07 08 09

AUTHORS

Joan Bragar Galer

Sylvia Vriesendorp

Alison Ellis

EDITORS

Janice Miller

Claire Bahamon

Barbara K. Timmons

CONTRIBUTORS

Ann S. Buxbaum

Lourdes De la Peza

Joseph Dwyer

Michael J. Hall

Sallie Craig Huber

Sarah Johnson

Riitta-Liisa Kolehmainen-Aitken

Nicole B. Lubitz

Cary Perry

Gregory Rodway

Steve Sapirie

Karen Sherk

Barry D. Smith

INTERNATIONAL REVIEW BOARD

Abdo Hassan Alswasy
Consultant for Obstetrics and Gynecology
Kom Ombo Central Hospital
Kom Ombo Aswan, Egypt

Timothee Gandaho
Executive Director
Partners in Population and Development
Dhaka, Bangladesh

Clare Gibson-Giraud
Leadership Coach and Facilitator
Performance Plus Coaching
Bordeaux, France

Atanu Majumdar
UNICEF Consultant
Kolkata, India

Morsy Mansour
Leadership Development Consultant
Cairo, Egypt

Luis Eduardo de Menezes Lima
Deputy Secretary for Education
State of Ceará
Fortaleza, Brazil

Zoonadi Joseph Ngwenya
Country Programme Manager
Southern African AIDS Trust
Lusaka, Zambia

Lourdes Quintanilla
Senior Consultant and Partner
Cali-Des
Saltillo, Mexico

Fenosoa Ratsimanetrimanana
Executive Secretary
National AIDS Council
Antananarivo, Madagascar

Irna Senekal
Health Diploma Coordinator
Fort Hare Institute for
Government
Bisho, South Africa

To the memory of

Dr. Pape Syr

the late Executive Director
of the Centre for African Family Studies
in Nairobi, Kenya

Dr. Pape Syr was a visionary and passionate leader
committed to improving reproductive health.
His greatest legacy is the young men and women
whom he inspired to follow in his footsteps.

Contents

FIGURES

TABLES

COUNTRY EXAMPLES

Foreword

Early in my career I provided primary health care in a village in Upper Egypt. My own family came from this area and I was deeply concerned about the health of the people there. Working in this remote area without support from anyone, I learned how hard it is for a young physician on his own to face the health challenges of an underdeveloped, underserved region.

This is the front line of health services around the developing world: health workers in rural as well as urban areas. They badly need good managers and supervisors who can enable them to succeed in protecting their communities from the dangers of poor health.

Years later, as Coordinator of Population Projects in Upper Egypt, I found myself responsible for these same rural health units. I struggled to give them the support I knew they so badly needed. The district team managers and supervisors tried to find a way to improve the quality of services and the service results. But no matter how much clinical training we provided for service providers, or training in planning and data analysis for central and local managers, there were only small improvements in service quality and results.

I began to feel that there was a missing piece in the health system. There was something that created a gap between knowledge and skills on one hand, and people's behaviors and attitudes on the other. Even when health workers knew what was right, they didn't practice it consistently. People knew about infection control, but they didn't practice it. People knew about the importance of counseling, but they didn't apply what they knew. What was missing was something inside their hearts, something that ignites the fire inside all who want to truly contribute or make a difference. What was missing was commitment.

The question became: "How can we inspire this commitment in every health service team and team member?" This is the question that health managers around the world are asking.

How can we take our limited resources and give the best of ourselves to ensure the quality we want our people to have? How can we not be stopped in the face of inadequate systems and limited resources? How can we motivate our staff to be creative in overcoming obstacles, when there are so many? I believe that when people are committed they can produce incredible results. Even if the systems are poor, with commitment they will find ways to continuously improve them.

Now you can see a change in Aswan in Upper Egypt. This week I visited a rural health unit, much like any in the developing world. I found the manager there, a young female physician, Iman. She is a quiet person, and before she was posted to this unit she was afraid that she would not be able to lead a health unit team. She said she thought that leaders had to have loud voices and yell at other people to make them afraid in order to get things done.

But Iman has developed her leadership skills with coaching from her district managers. With the support of her team and of managers in other health units, she is learning how to lead. She now knows that a good manager is successful not because people are afraid, but because she helps them find ways to overcome the obstacles. Her power as a leader comes from allowing her team to explore new ideas without fear. By trusting their ability, she is supporting them to produce results.

This book contains much of what these health workers in Aswan are learning. I recommend that you read and use the materials in it to develop yourself, your health team, and your organization to serve better those most in need. Whether you work in Haiti, South Africa, or India, you can focus on the missing piece in most health systems—how to lead—to change people's attitudes and behaviors. This book is written for those who dream of a better future.

Morsy Mansour, MD
Cairo, Egypt

Acknowledgments

This handbook is based on 20 years of experience in working with health professionals around the world in the public, private, and nonprofit sectors to strengthen the performance of health organizations and improve people's health. Initially the work focused on improving the management of health programs. Under the Management and Leadership (M&L) Program, funded by the US Agency for International Development (USAID), Management Sciences for Health has focused in recent years on developing the management and leadership capabilities of managers—at all levels of the health system—to achieve significant improvements in health services and health outcomes.

Building on our earlier work in management, the handbook crystallizes our collective experience with our partners in applying leadership and management concepts and best practices. The book provides a link between two bodies of experience. On the one side are the renowned leadership thinkers and researchers whose ideas and approaches inform our work. On the other are the managers on the front lines of health care who must use these approaches every day to achieve results. In this handbook, we have taken the best thinking in management and leadership and applied it to the challenges that health managers face.

This handbook was written by an interdependent team of authors and editors who worked together on all aspects of writing, editing, and producing the book. Each member brought a wealth of experience in management and leadership, and together the team members synthesized MSH's collective experience and that of our partners around the world. We are proud to have produced a result that no one person could have done alone and to have experienced the power of teamwork.

We have also benefited from the broad experience and critical thinking of health professionals around the world who work at different levels of the health system—in urban and rural settings and in the public and private sectors. We are indebted to the many health managers who imparted their experience and shared their challenges and successes with us. The country examples in this book are a testimony to their commitment to finding new ways to approach difficult challenges and to leading their health programs now and into the future.

We would particularly like to thank the members of the International Review Board for their detailed reviews and willingness to share their knowledge and experience in leading and managing health programs. We also extend our thanks to John Grove of the Centers for Disease Control and Prevention in Zambia, Benjamin Lozare of the Center for Communication Programs at Johns Hopkins University Bloomberg School of Public Health, and Marc Luoma of the Training Resources Group, Inc., for their technical reviews and insightful comments.

We are indebted to the many MSH staff who carefully reviewed and commented on early drafts of the handbook and to the staff of the M&L Program, who contributed to the handbook through their daily work with our partner organizations around the world. Their input based on real experience was invaluable and greatly improved and sharpened the content of this book. We would also like to thank Ceallaigh Reddy, Kristyn Stem, and Sherry Cotaco for their assistance in the production and distribution of this publication, and Ruby Thind and Alex Bermudez for producing the accompanying CD-ROM.

Joseph Dwyer, Director of the M&L Program at Management Sciences for Health, provided leadership, guidance, and steadfast support in the effort to distill the best of our experience for this handbook.

Finally, we thank Susan Wright, USAID Cognizant Technical Officer for the M&L Program, for her commitment to, and encouragement and support of, this handbook. We are also grateful to Barbara Addy of USAID for providing guidance and lending her experience to the handbook. We greatly appreciate the continued investment of USAID in improving the management and leadership capacity of health programs so that managers of public, private, and nonprofit organizations around the world can realize their vision of high-quality, accessible, and sustainable health services for all.

Introduction

"We aren't creating leaders—we are uncovering people's leadership capabilities and providing a path for them to put their capabilities into practice."

Managers Who Lead was inspired by the work of managers around the world who are on the front lines of health care—those who are making real improvements in health under the most difficult circumstances. This handbook is a tribute to their work. It could not have been written without the knowledge gained from their experience.

All over the world, health managers and providers face the challenges of producing results in an increasingly complex health care environment. Health sector reform, changing donor priorities, shifting client needs, and new technologies require that managers at all levels take on responsibilities previously held by people at higher levels.

Moreover, the drain on health systems due to the AIDS pandemic and new and emerging diseases has accelerated the need to learn new ways of leading and managing to achieve results. Through improved leadership, management, and teamwork, managers in public, private, and nongovernmental organizations can face these challenges with more confidence and lead their teams to effect significant changes in health.

Managers Who Lead is designed to help all managers tap into their natural abilities to lead others to reach for and achieve results. It is for managers who want to learn how to create a shared vision of a better future and mobilize individuals, teams, and entire organizations to make a difference. The handbook does not separate leaders from managers. It is for managers who lead, at any level. This approach is based on the belief that improvements in health care are made by managers who lead and manage well.

The approach in this handbook is based on these fundamental principles:

■ **Focus on health outcomes.** Good management and leadership result in measurable improvements in health services and outcomes.

Only by focusing on real organizational challenges can managers develop their ability to lead.

- **Practice leadership at all levels.** Good leadership and management can, and must, be practiced at every level of an organization. Working with their teams, managers at all levels—from health posts to national institutions—can confront challenges and achieve results.

- **You can learn to lead.** Leadership practices improve through a process of facing challenges and receiving feedback and support. By using this process, managers develop the leadership abilities of their staff.

- **Leadership is learned over time.** Becoming a manager who leads is a process that takes place over time. This process works best when it is owned by the organization and takes on critical organizational challenges.

- **Sustain progress through management systems.** Gains made in health outcomes can be sustained only by integrating leadership and management practices into an organization's routine systems and processes.

Now more than ever, effective leadership, with good management, is critical for health organizations. This handbook provides managers with practical guidelines and approaches for leading teams to identify and find solutions for their challenges. Staff at any level of the health system can use these concepts to improve their ability to lead and manage well. We invite you to invest in developing managers who lead at all levels of your organization.

HOW THIS HANDBOOK IS ORGANIZED

The handbook includes six chapters, a toolkit, an annotated bibliography, and a CD-ROM with additional resources. Each chapter presents key issues facing managers today, practical advice on applying leadership and management practices to address health care challenges, questions for reflection, and real-life examples that illustrate the role of leadership and management in improving health.

Chapter 1: Leading and managing to achieve results. Discusses the relationship between strong leadership and management, and the resulting improvements in health services and outcomes. It introduces the Leading and Managing Framework: the basic practices that enable work groups and organizations to face challenges and achieve results. Experience with applying this framework to develop managers who lead forms the backbone of this handbook. This chapter also discusses the "leader shifts," or changes in mindset, that managers need to make in order to learn and embrace new approaches to leading and managing their teams that will result in significant improvements in health.

Chapter 2: Leading teams to face challenges. Presents the Challenge Model, a process that helps managers work with their teams to deal with one challenge at a time to overcome obstacles in order to achieve results. The Challenge Model provides a systematic approach to creating a shared vision of the future and helping teams identify a challenge and a desired, measurable result. The process leads them to assess factors in the external and internal environments related to their desired result, and plan and implement priority actions to address the root causes of their obstacles. Teams can apply this process repeatedly to tackle each new challenge.

Chapter 3: Improving work climate to strengthen performance. Analyzes the critical factors in the work environment that support or detract from motivation and high performance. The chapter identifies the rewards of a positive work climate and helps managers recognize their role in influencing the work climate and, thus, the motivation and performance of their staff. The chapter also provides a tool for assessing the work climate of a work group and developing a plan for improving it.

Chapter 4: Moving up the leadership ladder. Looks at the four transitions that managers must make as they move into more senior positions. Each transition requires a shift in perspective, scope of responsibility, priorities, types of relationships, and time horizon. Being competent at one level doesn't mean one has the competence required for the next level. Rather, each higher level requires new skills and attitudes, and thus continuous learning. The chapter also presents the concept of creating a "pipeline" through which leaders keep flowing as long as managers at each level groom their successors, thereby ensuring successful leadership transitions throughout the organization.

Chapter 5: Reorienting roles in the health system. Discusses the challenges associated with decentralization and health reform with respect to new roles and responsibilities at the different levels of the health system. The chapter explains how these changes affect the roles of managers and the capabilities they need to perform effectively at the different levels of the health system. It highlights the necessary shift at the central level from a role of control to one of stewardship, the shift for the mid-level manager from implementer to planner, and the importance of becoming an empowered manager if you are working at the local level.

Chapter 6: Leading change for better health. Explores what is involved in leading successful change efforts—whether the change is related to clinical or management practices, changes in structure or systems, or changes in national or organizational policies or strategies. It outlines eight key factors of success in any change initiative and advises managers about how to work with people's responses to change. The chapter reinforces the importance of strong management systems and of adapting those systems to support new approaches and practices. It concludes with a discussion of how to coordinate with stakeholders to scale up successful practices within and outside an organization.

Toolkit: Resources to support managers who lead. Provides field-tested tools, exercises, and guidelines to support managers in developing their own and others' leadership and management skills. Each tool or exercise includes the instructions and handouts to make it immediately usable in small or large groups.

Annotated bibliography. Provides references to materials that shaped our thinking and were used in developing this handbook, as well as additional recommended resources on leadership and management.

Handbook CD-ROM. A comprehensive resource for managers and facilitators. It includes the entire handbook and toolkit, as well as numerous additional tools and previously published issues of MSH's quarterly on topics in international health management, *The Manager*. It also contains links to program guidelines, assessment manuals, and facilitator's notes. All these materials can be downloaded and printed for reading and use in staff development.

HOW TO USE THIS HANDBOOK

Whether you are supervising teams in rural clinics, working in the Ministry of Health, or working in a private organization, you can use this handbook to develop the leadership and management capabilities of your staff and become a better leader and manager. The handbook is designed so that you can use the sections that apply to your needs, without reading the book from cover to cover.

By applying the concepts and principles presented in this handbook you will see results. Your program and organization will be better able to adapt to change, managers will lead their teams more effectively and increase the productivity of their teams, and clients will benefit from higher-quality services and better health. Our hope is that by becoming a manager who leads, you will realize the rewards and accomplishments so aptly described in the "Tao of Leadership":

> Go to the people
> Live among them
> Learn from them
> Love them
> Start with what they know
> Build on what they have
>
> But of the best leaders
> When their task is accomplished
> Their work is done
> The people all remark
> We have done it ourselves.
> —Lao Tzu, *Tao Te Ching*

1 Leading and managing to achieve results

"The new leadership will not be provided by a 'take charge' elite but will emerge from the capacity that lies within each and every person. It will be a leadership that does not presume to have all the answers, but one that seeks to empower others."

—ANNABEL BEEREL
LEADERSHIP THROUGH STRATEGIC PLANNING

When you lead you take a stand to create a better future. Your actions demonstrate what you care about, who you are, and what you are committed to accomplishing. You need to be clear about what is important to you—what you are willing to risk to achieve lasting results.

The first question to answer is: What really matters to you? What do you want to create—for yourself, your family, community, organization, and country? As you imagine a better future, and begin to communicate that vision to others, you take the first step in a leadership journey.

To lead is to step forward, to move into often uncharted territory, and to take risks. There are no road maps for this journey, but there are tried and true values and practices that can guide you along the way. And while the path is challenging, there are many deep rewards and joys in creating a better future with others.

This chapter offers a starting point for becoming a manager who leads. Whether you are a senior manager or someone new to the management ranks, this chapter will provide you with an overview of the basics you will need for your journey by discussing the:

- mindset and values of someone who leads;

- leading and managing practices that produce results;

- leadership competencies that empower and inspire others to reach their potential and make an impact on health.

Looking at your mindset and values

"If you look to lead, invest at least 40 percent of your time managing your ethics, character, principles, purpose, motivation, and conduct."

—DEE HOCK
IN WALDROP, "DEE HOCK ON MANAGEMENT"

It takes dedication to a vision, and organization of motivated people, to achieve the results you envision for your community. It depends much less on authority than on a commitment to creating the future you dream of.

Leaders are committed to realizing a vision

To get a better picture of what leadership is, think of a leader you respect and know personally, someone who inspires you. The person may be a parent, teacher, political figure, religious leader, supervisor, or friend. What kind of person is she? How does she see the world, and what does she value? How does this leader treat other people?

People are drawn to leaders because of who they are and the way they relate to others. They help people to think bigger than they may have before. They encourage individuals to take on challenges that they may not have previously thought they could, and they support people in their efforts to forge ahead.

To explore your thoughts and generate discussion about leading, you can use the exercise "Understanding Leading and Managing Practices" in the handbook toolkit.

SHIFT YOUR MINDSET

To become a manager who leads, you need to gradually shift your mindset toward seeing yourself as someone who mobilizes and empowers others to create the future. To shift your mindset, it is critical to know your values, because they will influence the kind of future you can create and will guide and sustain you on your journey.

Examine your beliefs and assumptions

A mindset is a habitual way of interpreting and responding to situations. People's assumptions and beliefs about the world affect their actions. To take a stand and face a challenge, you may need to change how you see a situation, what you focus on and value, and then what you do.

How you think about the world determines how you act in it. If you believe deeply that people have something to contribute, then the tools and techniques in this book will help you encourage participation and shared learning. It is your belief in the value of others' contributions and participation that matters most; the tools and techniques build on and support this belief and your effort to produce better results.

With a shift in mindset, these tools and techniques can be applied with great results—motivating groups to think bigger than they have before,

From *Managers Who Lead: A Handbook for Improving Health Services* Cambridge, MA: Management Sciences for Health, 2005

TABLE 1   **Leader shifts**

Shift perspective from . . .	. . . to . . .
individual heroics	collaborative actions
despair and cynicism	hope and possibility
blaming others for problems	taking responsibility for challenges
scattered, disconnected activities	purposeful, interconnected actions
self-absorption	generosity and concern for the common good

encouraging them to take on challenges they might not previously have felt could be overcome, and thinking and working creatively together to achieve new goals. We call these shifts in mindset *leader shifts*. These leader shifts are fundamental to effective leadership (see Table 1).

Each of the five leader shifts represents a series of changes in perspective that occur when you deepen your understanding of yourself, others, and the environment. These shifts help you to gradually move from:

Moving toward a more collaborative way of working

- work based on the heroic actions that you take alone, to collaborative actions that build on the strength of groups to produce sustainable results;

- a state of despair or cynicism, where you see insurmountable problems and obstacles, to a place of hope and dreams, where you see possibilities to make things better;

- a tendency to blame others for problems or failures, instead of taking initiative, owning challenges, and working together to do something about them;

- frantic days filled with unrelated activities carried out for their own sake, to purposeful work directed toward achieving results that matter;

- preoccupation with yourself and ways to satisfy your needs, to a place where you can generously and compassionately serve a greater good and inspire others to do the same.

Seek support in making your own shifts

These shifts are not easy to make or sustain, because your own needs, habits, and worries can interfere at any time. But when you are mindful of these shifts, you can correct yourself when you notice that you are becoming busy but unproductive, or being drawn into a state of despair. You can stop yourself when you feel the urge to blame someone else, or when your own needs overshadow your concern for the greater good. When you have allies who are also making these shifts, they can remind you when you slip.

REFLECT ON PERSONAL VALUES

Personal values anchor your leadership. When you examine your values, you realize they guide your choices about how you serve your staff, clients, and partners. When you know what your values are, you can communicate them to others, and refer to them when you have to make difficult choices.

Your values influence how you lead. There is a strong ethical component to positive leadership that is absent from negative leadership. You can sustain yourself as a leader through concern for the common good, for example, whereas negative leadership draws on people's fears. It uses reward and punishment, and depends on including some people and excluding others.

Managers who demonstrate positive values gain the respect of their staff. You become credible to others when you match positive words with positive actions. You can more easily attract others to your dreams for the future if your actions fit with personal qualities that are universally valued:

Integrity and commitment. People respect leaders for their ethics and personal commitment. When you are honest and ethical, you are credible to others who value integrity. If you strongly believe in serving a greater good, you can avoid the temptations that often come with power. And when you dedicate yourself to achieving a goal, you attract others with similar commitment to work with you in creating a better future. For instance, when top leaders support national HIV/AIDS campaigns—as President Yoweri Museveni of Uganda did in 1990—others will follow their example.

Respect and trust. Respecting others means being willing to listen to their points of view and their needs. Respect builds trust over time, and trust is the foundation for developing productive relationships. When you lead, you nurture respectful work relationships with your subordinates, colleagues, and superiors. You create new connections to broaden your own network and mend existing relations that are problematic.

Courage to take calculated risks. One job of leaders is to set an example for taking calculated risks that do not endanger the organization, its mission, or individuals. People who lead do not give up if they fall down. They get up, dust themselves off, and find the courage to re-engage. In their persistence, they never lose sight of the positive future they are trying to create. When you create networks of trusting relationships, you find support and courage to take necessary chances, make tough decisions, and face criticism or personal failure. By example, you encourage others to take risks as well.

Openness to learning. Good leaders are open to learning and inspire others to do the same. When you have an open mind, you are eager for knowledge and information. You recognize new opportunities and find ways to deal with obstacles. You initiate approaches to learning with others. This openness to learning prepares you for ever-changing realities.

Positive
leadership
brings
credibility
and respect

Perserverance
is essential—
never give up

Your efforts to be a leader will require ongoing self-development over a lifetime. Yet the mindset and values you cultivate will sustain all you do to lead others. You can lead and manage better when you understand the power of good leadership and management.

Reflections on leadership values

The following reflections on key attributes of managers who lead are drawn from participants in MSH's leadership development programs and other discussions with managers of health programs in various countries around the world.

Integrity and commitment. "First, I have to be honest with the institution. I have to be very good, know all my limits, the abuses of authority.... It's also important to value what you have around you. The wealth you have around you is like gold, and it can be lost if you don't know how to handle it."

"Positive leadership...becomes negative when one lacks ethics and integrity. When leaders engage in nepotism, develop conflicting interests in management, procedures, and procurement systems, and practice unequal treatment of team members, this becomes negative leadership even when the other things are being done right."

Respect and trust. "I have learned to be a little warmer.... I have learned to be respectful. There's a very popular saying that goes 'Respect and you'll be respected.'... It has served me well in all I've done."

"I believe that adopting an attitude of openness and listening to others' points of view, while demonstrating a high level of professionalism, ultimately promote faith and trust in the service one provides, as well as in the professional herself."

Courage to take risks. "He helps them to push the envelope...not exactly according to the rules, but not wrong.... He understands where the line is and where it's stepping over that line. He encourages them to put one foot over, maybe two...."

Continuous learning. "She recognizes that she doesn't know it all, and often looks for information and advice."

"He is always finding out by chatting with people, informally networking, figuring out what's going on, calling people into the office, chatting with people one on one or in groups."

Applying leading and managing practices

"Leadership is different than management. . . . [They] are two distinctive and complementary systems of action. Each has its own function and characteristic activities. Both are necessary for success in an increasingly complex and volatile . . . environment."

—JOHN KOTTER
"WHAT LEADERS REALLY DO"

When you lead and manage well, you can achieve the healthy communities you dream of. What is the difference between leading and managing? When you *manage* well, you ensure that processes and procedures, staff, and other resources are used in an efficient and effective manner. Managing develops reliable operations that serve staff in their efforts to reach goals. As a result, your organization can consistently perform what it is trying to do.

When you *lead* well, you enable others to face challenges to creating the future that you all envision. You help them to overcome obstacles that stand in the way of desired results and encourage them to adapt to changing conditions. Leading is particularly important in times of crises, since it empowers and aligns people to move forward despite setbacks.

Leading and managing contribute different things

Leading means enabling others to face challenges and achieve results under complex conditions.

Managing means organizing the internal parts of the organization to implement systems and coordinate resources to produce reliable performance.

To improve your abilities to lead, as well as manage for results, you need to:

- empower yourself and others to face challenges;

- link leading and managing to positive outcomes;

- strengthen your leading and managing practices;

- become skilled in using the leading and managing practices in Figure 1 and integrating them into your daily work.

EMPOWER YOURSELF AND OTHERS

Building healthy communities calls for involving others: your staff, department, organization, and community and organizational partners. You can empower yourself and others to address many different kinds of challenges, including organizational, group, and personal obstacles. For example, you and your staff may need to improve services despite decreased donor funding, or increase clinic visits in the face of shortages and persistent rumors that keep patients away. You may need to get support from a supervisor who seems unapproachable. When you accept a challenge and inspire others to work on it with you, you all take responsibility for addressing it.

Through good leadership, you can find ways to release people's energy to reach results. When people get in touch with their aspirations, they find this source of energy. You can help them connect the hopes they hold for their families and communities with their work and the goals of the organization. When you inspire staff and partners to see how they contribute to a greater good, they will value their roles, find strength to overcome obstacles, and break through longstanding barriers to reach desired outcomes.

Nurturing people's dreams draws out their energy

> A clinic nurse who participated in a leadership program in Egypt had a dream that all of the women in her village had access to family planning. She cared deeply about this. She rallied her colleagues around this vision, and together, they were able to expand the quality and quantity of their family planning services.

Chapter 2 discusses how you can work with your team to create such a vision, face a challenge, and make a plan to achieve results.

LINK LEADING AND MANAGING TO POSITIVE OUTCOMES

Connect your activities to health priorities

You can start all your leadership and management activities with "the end in mind," that is, with results that justify your organization's existence (Covey 2004). No matter whether you are the Minister of Health or the manager of a rural health post, your job is to improve the health of the people your organization serves. If your country's national health strategy outlines strategic health priorities, you should link your vision to these strategic priorities. When you connect everything you do to these priorities, you don't waste time on activities that divert energy from end results. The Leading and Managing for Results Model shows the link between the leading and managing practices and improved health outcomes.

Leading and managing practices. Managers who lead well use all the leading and managing practices listed in Figure 1. Applying these eight practices consistently leads to strong organizational capacity, better health services and,

FIGURE 1   **Leading and Managing for Results Model**

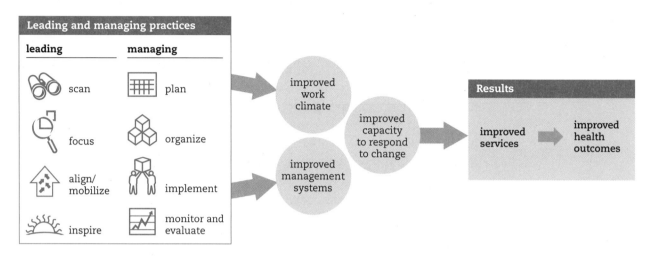

When applied consistently, good leading and managing practices strengthen organizational capacity and result in higher-quality services and sustained improvements in health.

From *Managers Who Lead: A Handbook for Improving Health Services* Cambridge, MA: Management Sciences for Health, 2005

ultimately, lasting improvements in people's health. For a detailed description of the leading and managing practices, see the Leading and Managing Framework (Figure 2).

In the center of the figure, three circles represent the core components of strong and well-functioning organizations. If you examine successful public health interventions and programs, you will find that the organizations have paid attention to the importance of having a positive work climate, sound management systems that were used consistently, and the ability to respond to change.

Results. Building an organization's capacity to address challenges contributes to achieving results—better services that enhance health outcomes. For example, a manager runs maternal health and family planning clinics. Infant mortality is high, and malaria is a major problem in her area. When you think about this situation, ask yourself:

> Choose services that will enhance health outcomes

- What are some health outcomes the work group or organization could influence? Examples include: infant mortality due to malaria is decreased, or all women who want no more children or want to space their children's births have access to and use high-quality family planning services. With some consultation, the manager determines that in her situation, she needs to focus on preventing infant deaths from malaria.

- What services could this team set up or improve that would contribute to this outcome? The manager and her team decide to provide vouchers that mothers can redeem at retail stores for insecticide-

> ## Core components of a well-functioning organization
>
> **Work climate.** Work climate refers to the prevailing mood of a workplace or what it feels like to work there. Climate is the array of conditions related to staff motivation. A positive work climate promotes staff motivation. In chapter 3, "Improving Work Climate to Strengthen Performance," you will learn how you can create a positive work climate that boosts staff morale and motivation.
>
> **Management systems.** Management systems are the structures, processes, and procedures that managers develop to facilitate work. These systems help staff to do their work. Managers use systems to organize tasks and track progress in performing these tasks. Your leading and managing practices can create these systems and encourage staff to commit themselves to using them. As your organization matures, you can improve these systems to strengthen the performance of your organization.
>
> **Capacity to respond to change.** Increasing your capacity to respond to change means that your organization or work group has increased its potential to anticipate and adapt to changing conditions in the internal or external environment. This capacity relies on staff resilience, empowerment, optimism, openness to learning, creativity, and the ability to communicate with partners from other ethnic, social, gender, and organizational groups. A positive work climate, strong management systems, and being open to new learning all foster an organization's capacity to respond to a changing world. Chapter 6 focuses on leading change and responding to change in a complex environment.

treated bed nets at a discounted price. Insecticide-treated nets can repel and kill mosquitoes.

- What changes in organizational capacity would lead to the selected outcome? The manager would have to amend her management system so that staff can provide the bed net vouchers to all pregnant women and mothers. After training her staff to inform clients about the advantages of using the nets and the need to replace the nets every six months, she would check to be sure that the management system can monitor this counseling and follow-up. She would need good relations with staff to encourage their commitment to this added work (positive work climate). She would establish a partnership (part of the capacity to change) with stores to sell the nets and develop a voucher form with shop owners that they would accept.

- What leading and managing practices would she need to improve? She would need to align the nursing staff with the opportunity to be trained about insecticide-treated nets, counseling clients in their use, and periodically following up with clients to replace their nets. She would need to consider how to align shopkeepers to stock and sell the nets to customers who use the vouchers.

There are many activities that promote health besides delivering services. For example, purifying water or training medical and nursing students in a new clinical area can affect health outcomes. The Results Model concentrates on implementing and supporting health services. By focusing your work group's attention on service improvements, you can make an important difference and also coordinate your actions with people working on other health-related challenges.

Promoting health is multisectoral

STRENGTHEN YOUR LEADING AND MANAGING PRACTICES

To lead and manage better, you need to apply the eight leading and managing practices consistently. The leading and managing practices described in the Leading and Managing Framework (Figure 2) offer specific behaviors you can use in many different situations to improve organizational performance and sustain performance over time. Here is how they work.

Managing practices. When managers use good management practices, they make sure that operational plans and reporting structures are clear and reflect organizational priorities. Because good managers reinforce the use of management systems and processes to make work easier, staff know what is expected of them and are able to carry out their activities. Staff receive feedback on their work through supportive supervision and monitoring and evaluation systems that provide timely, reliable information.

Pay attention to effectiveness, efficiency, and quality

To manage your organization well, you and other managers need to continuously pay attention to the health services that the organization provides to be sure that they are effective (the right services), efficient (services delivered in the right way), and of consistently high quality to meet clients' needs. Your performance as a manager rests on achieving these three goals.

When you manage well, you and other managers:

- plan how to achieve results by assigning resources, accountabilities, and timelines;

- organize people, structures, systems, and processes to carry out the plan;

- implement activities efficiently, effectively, and responsively to achieve defined results;

- monitor and evaluate achievements and results against plans, and continuously update information and use feedback to adjust plans, structures, systems, and processes for future results.

While management systems form the foundation for reliable processes, management alone does not guarantee results. Managers with new tools and systems often get the same outcomes as before, unless they lead others to use these systems well, periodically adapt them to meet client needs, and manage the organizational context in which they use them.

Leading practices. Managers who lead well can adapt to changing conditions in the environment and lead others to adapt as well. By using their adaptive skills, they are able to achieve results despite complex conditions and scarce resources. They are well informed about opportunities and threats. Their direction is clear to staff. People and resources are aligned around a common shared vision. And because of their commitment, work groups deliver the results that managers promised.

To lead well, you need to focus your work group's attention on achieving results that fulfill clients' needs and preferences, as well as respond to key stakeholders' interests. With your full support, the frontline staff who provide health services can learn to identify their own obstacles to service quality, initiate improvements, and serve their clients well. To sustain your support, you may also need to gain the commitment of senior managers.

When you lead well, you and other managers:

- scan for up-to-date knowledge about yourself (to be aware how your behavior and values affect others), your work group, your organization, and your environment;

- focus staff's work on achieving the organizational mission, strategy, and priorities;

- align and mobilize stakeholders' and staff's time and energies as well as the material and financial resources to support organizational goals and priorities;

- inspire your staff to be committed and to continuously learn how to adapt and do things better.

By applying these leadership practices, you and your team can face your main challenges and work together with your organization to address them.

The Leading and Managing Framework. The Leading and Managing Framework (Figure 2) presents activities and organizational outcomes associated with each leading and managing practice, so that you can see the value and expected result of integrating these practices into your daily work. By applying the eight practices consistently, work groups and organizations can systematically make improvements that will strengthen their services and improve health outcomes.

As you apply the leading and managing practices in your daily work, you can also help your staff develop and use these practices. With your work group, you can assess how well you apply them and identify those that you need to strengthen. To do this, ask members of your group to reflect individu-

Focus your work group on serving clients

Integrate the leading and managing practices into your daily work

FIGURE 2   **Leading and Managing Framework**

Practices that enable work groups and organizations to face challenges and achieve results

Leading	Managing
scanning ■ identify client and stakeholder needs and priorities ■ recognize trends, opportunities, and risks that affect the organization ■ look for best practices ■ identify staff capacities and constraints ■ know yourself, your staff, and your organization—values, strengths, and weaknesses ORGANIZATIONAL OUTCOME Managers have up-to-date, valid knowledge of their clients, the organization, and its context; they know how their behavior affects others	**planning** ■ set short-term organizational goals and performance objectives ■ develop multi-year and annual plans ■ allocate adequate resources (money, people, and materials) ■ anticipate and reduce risks ORGANIZATIONAL OUTCOME Organization has defined results, assigned resources, and an operational plan
focusing ■ articulate the organization's mission and stategy ■ identify critical challenges ■ link goals with the overall organizational strategy ■ determine key priorities for action ■ create a common picture of desired results ORGANIZATIONAL OUTCOME Organization's work is directed by well-defined mission, strategy, and priorities	**organizing** ■ ensure a structure that provides accountability and delineates authority ■ ensure that systems for human resource management, finance, logistics, quality assurance, operations, information, and marketing effectively support the plan ■ strengthen work processes to implement the plan ■ align staff capacities with planned activities ORGANIZATIONAL OUTCOME Organization has functional structures, systems, and processes for efficient operations; staff are organized and aware of job responsibilities and expectations
aligning/mobilizing ■ ensure congruence of values, mission, strategy, structure, systems, and daily actions ■ facilitate teamwork ■ unite key stakeholders around an inspiring vision ■ link goals with rewards and recognition ■ enlist stakeholders to commit resources ORGANIZATIONAL OUTCOME Internal and external stakeholders understand and support the organization' goals and have mobilized resources to reach these goals	**implementing** ■ integrate systems and coordinate work flow ■ balance competing demands ■ routinely use data for decision-making ■ coordinate activities with other programs and sectors ■ adjust plans and resources as circumstances change ORGANIZATIONAL OUTCOME Activities are carried out efficiently, effectively, and responsively
inspiring ■ match deeds to words ■ demonstrate honesty in interactions ■ show trust and confidence in staff; acknowledge the contributions of others ■ provide staff with challenges, feedback, and support ■ be a model of creativity, innovation, and learning ORGANIZATIONAL OUTCOME Organization displays a climate of continuous learning and staff show commitment, even when setbacks occur	**monitoring and evaluating** ■ monitor and reflect on progress against plans ■ provide feedback ■ identify needed changes ■ improve work processes, procedures, and tools ORGANIZATIONAL OUTCOME Organization continuously updates information about the status of achievements and results, and applies ongoing learning and knowledge

From Managers Who Lead: A Handbook for Improving Health Services
Cambridge, MA: Management Sciences for Health, 2005

Experiences in learning to use the leading practices

District teams, managers, and staff in Egypt learned to use the four leading practices as part of a leadership program to improve health services. Afterward, they reflected on the usefulness of these practices.

Scanning. "I think that scanning affected me the most. When I am facing a problem or a challenge, I have to look at the problem from all angles. I have to look deeply, not superficially, at the problem to find the root causes and the circumstances leading to the deterioration in the current situation in order to find a solution, because if I can't identify the root causes or the circumstances, I will not be able to find the solution." —District Manager

Focusing. "We met with the entire District Health Management Team and introduced the concept of focusing. We realized we were not able to sit down and prioritize, were fire fighting a lot, spending so much time in seminars [we could not] implement. We need[ed] to refocus our attention so as not to be taken away from our objective. We redid our workplan, realizing it was not focused, and picked the priority issues." —District Health Team

Aligning/mobilizing. "Before this program, we were distracted, not only myself, but all of my district work group; we were all going in a different direction. Each person worked according to his personal concept, but we are now one team. There is no difference between family planning, primary health care, or immunizations. We all have the same target, which is to improve the level of performance in the district." —District Manager

Inspiring. "After everyone accepted the [leadership] concept, there was a new belief.... Because this belief was in each individual, all were competing to bring out what was inside them, doing their utmost, even if their role was small. They came to understand that the size of their role is unimportant, because no matter what their role is, it is essential to achieve the desired results. There was a team spirit and everyone was cooperative. I now feel, thank God, that I have several arms, I don't have to do everything myself anymore." —District Family Planning Director

"To solve any problem, the answer has to come from within. If we wait for the solution from outside, then it will not be solved. This is an obvious change and a result which we noticed and achieved." —Health Unit Doctor

---

ally on the one practice in the framework that is their strongest and the one that is their weakest. Then you can tally the strong and weak practices in your group. You may find that your team needs to improve its ability to scan so that you can be more successful in identifying new funding sources. Or you may decide to focus your team on priorities, identify your key challenges, and direct your scarce resources to fewer, more well-defined results.

To learn more about leading and managing and to assess your own capabilities, please refer to the exercise "Understanding Leading and Managing Practices" in the handbook toolkit.

INTEGRATE LEADING AND MANAGING PRACTICES

Lead and
manage
simultaneously

Leading and managing do not form distinct, sequential processes that you complete separately. The leading practices are not independent of the managing practices. Accomplished managers move fluidly between leading and managing to support their teams to face challenges and achieve results.

As Figure 3 shows, facing challenges requires you to scan, focus, and plan. After scanning your environment to identify your challenges, you focus on a few priority challenges and make a plan to address them. Once you have a plan that addresses your challenges, you need to align and mobilize your stakeholders, staff, and resources, organize your team and the work, and implement the plan. Throughout this process, you inspire your group by enabling your staff to act on their commitment, creativity, and learning. You also monitor and evaluate progress by setting baseline measurements and collecting and using data to track improvements.

The example from Guinea illustrates the challenge that one regional health director identified and how he and others integrated leading and managing to address a serious public health situation.

FIGURE 3   **Integrated leading and managing process**

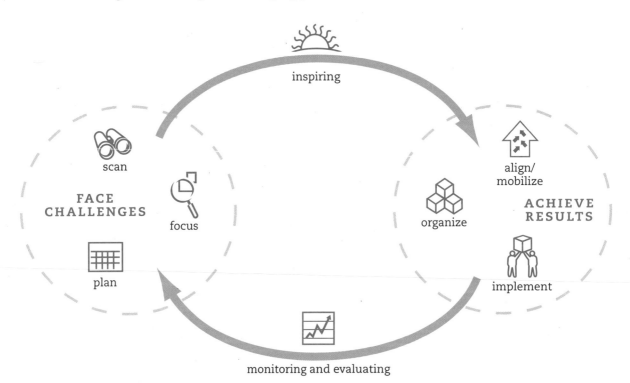

From *Managers Who Lead: A Handbook for Improving Health Services*
Cambridge, MA: Management Sciences for Health, 2005

**Improving capacity to respond to a challenge—
Example from Guinea**

In Guinea, a regional health director led communities in his region to respond to the needs of his poorest subdistrict, Boké. Geographically isolated, Boké had a population of less than 55,000, suffered from a lack of resources, and had a coverage rate of 0% for fully immunized children.

Boké's challenge. The regional health director scanned the health data from all his subdistricts, and noticed the dangerous situation in Boké. He decided to focus efforts on this subdistrict and articulated the challenge with his team: "How can we improve vaccination coverage in this subdistrict in the face of a chronic lack of resources and other obstacles?" Together they planned how they would address this situation.

Increasing coverage. The regional health director then encouraged other people to align themselves with this challenge. He mobilized communities in Boké to donate resources to local health centers. He also negotiated with more affluent surrounding subdistricts, which were at first reluctant to share their resources, to make available to Boké the needed staff, transportation, and materials for a period of six months. He and his team organized the flow of resources from these subdistricts and implemented a vaccination campaign. Through their efforts, the vaccination coverage rate for fully immunized children in the Boké subdistrict increased from 0% in December 2001 to 62% in December 2003.

Inspiring other groups. The regional health director was able to inspire others to assist in improving vaccination coverage through his commitment. He persuasively showed the other subdistricts that their support was in their self-interest, since a disease outbreak in Boké would likely spread to their communities.

Monitoring and sustaining progress. Through monthly community meetings, the people involved continue to monitor progress and sustain their good work. They have improved their capacity to respond to challenges as a team.

Building leadership competencies

"This is leadership—that our health personnel do not wait for instructions from the highest levels, but rather make decisions that enable them to do what they need to do to serve their communities."

—MARGARITA GURDIAN
MINISTER OF HEALTH, NICARAGUA

Leadership competencies are the specific mindset, skills, and knowledge that help managers lead more effectively. We have looked at the shifts in mindsets (leader shifts), but having the right mindset alone is not enough. You also need to expand your knowledge and strengthen particular skills so that you are better able to empower others to achieve results. The eight competencies shown in Table 2 are the ones we have observed in people whom their peers considered to be effective leaders of public or private health programs.

There are many ways to improve these competencies. Attend workshops, read, and ask for feedback from someone else—your supervisor, your best

TABLE 2   **Leadership competencies**

Competency	Application
Master yourself	Reflect on yourself and be aware of your impact on others, manage your emotions effectively, use your strengths, and work on your shortcomings
See the big picture	Look beyond a narrow focus to take into account conditions outside your immediate area of work
Create a shared vision	Work with others to envision a better future and use this vision to focus all your efforts
Clarify purpose and priorities	Know your own values and what is most important to accomplish
Communicate effectively	Hold conversations focused on outcomes; balance advocacy with inquiry; and clarify assumptions, beliefs, and feelings within yourself and others
Motivate committed teams	Create the clarity, trust, and recognition necessary to lead teams to high performance that can be sustained over time
Negotiate conflict	Reach agreements from which both sides can benefit
Lead change	Enable your work group to own challenges, enlist stakeholders, and navigate through unstable conditions

friend, your spouse, or a coach—to strengthen your weakest areas. Look for opportunities to apply these competencies. Consider developing a self-improvement plan; if you keep a journal, you can reflect on how you are progressing in your efforts to improve. By mastering these eight competencies, you will be able to lead with more confidence.

> The handbook toolkit offers exercises for developing these competencies in yourself and others.

Starting your journey

"No person can be a great leader unless he takes genuine joy in the successes of those under him."

—SAMSONRAJ PANDIAN
WORLD VISION INDIA

Taking a stand to lead others to a healthier world takes hope and courage. While you may hesitate, wondering how you can accept this role, the question is really how can you not? When you make the choice to create a better future, you empower others to step forward as well.

This chapter offers a starting place for your journey toward becoming a manager who leads. Table 3 offers steps to organize your journey and concepts to use along the way. These will contribute to your effectiveness as you

TABLE 3   **Becoming a manager who leads**

Steps to take	Concepts to use
Examine your mindset and values	Mindset ■ leader shifts Values ■ integrity and commitment ■ respect and trust ■ courage to take risks ■ openness to learning
Improve your abilities to lead and manage	■ Leading and Managing for Results Model ■ Leading and Managing Framework ■ Integrated Leading and Managing Process
Build leadership competencies	■ master yourself ■ see the big picture ■ create a shared vision ■ clarify purpose and priorities ■ communicate effectively ■ motivate committed teams ■ negotiate conflict ■ lead change

strive to make a positive difference in the lives of others. And they may help you handle whatever obstacles you encounter on your path.

By becoming a manager who leads, you can build the leadership competencies of your staff and foster changes that will reshape your organization's health services. In the following chapters, you will learn how to frame your challenges and gain commitment from others to achieve desired results. These changes in yourself, your staff, and your services will have a powerful impact on the health of the people you serve.

Questions to consider on . . .

Leading and managing to achieve results

Taking a stand

- Have you ever hesitated and then declined to take a leading role when it was open to you? What held you back? What would have helped you to step forward?

- Have you ever wished that you had led an initiative or a group after you saw disappointing results? What would you have done differently?

- What are the risks of taking a leading role in your organization? How can you minimize these risks?

Mindset and values

- What are your dreams for yourself, your family, your community, and your country?

- Examine your mindset and values. What shifts do you need to make, so you can contribute to a healthier future?

- How can you enlist others to work with you?

Leading and managing practices

- Reflect on the Leading and Managing Framework. Which of the leading and managing practices are most and least used in your work group or organization?

- Which practices are generally strong? Which practices need improvement?

- How could changes in leading and managing practices help you address your challenges?

- Where will you start to improve your practices?

Leadership competencies

- Assess your competencies to lead. Which are you strong in and which do you need to work on?

- What methods will you use to improve your competencies?

2 Leading teams to face challenges

"Never doubt that a small group of thoughtful, committed citizens can change the world. Indeed, it is the only thing that ever has."

—MARGARET MEAD

As a manager who leads, you face challenges every day. You have to respond to the needs of your staff and your superiors, deal with supply crises, and respond to outbreaks of contagious diseases, and there is always the worry about money.

But managers who focus only on the immediate issues are unable to put their energy toward their most important responsibility—leading their work groups to face their challenges and create better services for the future.

This chapter focuses on helping your group face challenges in ways that will result in better health care. It is organized around the "Challenge Model," which provides a systematic way for groups to experience the direct impact of applying management and leadership practices to achieve results.

It helps you work together with your team to:

- create a shared vision and define one measurable result;

- assess the current situation and identify opportunities and obstacles;

- define your challenge and select priority actions;

- develop an action plan;

- implement your plan and monitor and evaluate progress toward achieving your desired result.

The chapter concludes with a section on the importance of supporting, inspiring, and motivating your team members to take on new challenges and work together to make lasting improvements in the health of your clients.

Working as a team

". . . leadership is about giving a team or organization the courage to truly commit to extraordinary goals. Well-managed teams understand their capability extremely well and set commitments they know they can meet."

—TIMM ESQUE
"MANAGING TO LEAD"

As a manager who leads, you are responsible for keeping your team focused on results and finding new ways to address challenges so you can achieve results. By working with a team of people who are committed to achieving the same results, you have more power to change your situation.

THE IMPORTANCE OF TEAMS

A team works
toward a
common goal

A team is a group of people who work together cooperatively to achieve a common goal. In health care settings, clinic staff form a group of health care providers, but they don't necessarily work as a team. As a manager, it is your job to form, support, and inspire your team, so that together you can achieve more than you ever thought possible.

> Picture a clinic that has chronic problems with long client waiting times. Each service provider and administrator will have his own understanding of the problem and could respond individually to improve the process. But only when these people form a shared understanding of the causes of the problem and work together in a unified and coordinated way, can they begin to really improve the situation. Then change would happen and clients would see the difference. If they work as a team to put new procedures in place, it is likely that the change will be sustained.

FACING CHALLENGES AS A TEAM

Stretch
capabilities to
face challenges

Leading means helping people identify and face challenges. Facing a challenge is fundamentally different than solving problems. A challenge is stated in terms of a question that asks, "How can we achieve the result we want to achieve in the face of the obstacles we have to overcome?" Taking on a challenge requires that you are committed to working together—as a team—and that you stretch to use all your capabilities to reach the result you want to achieve.

Framing a challenge is one of the leadership tasks you will learn about in this chapter. It requires you to scan your environment to understand all the factors that will impact the results. It helps you align and mobilize your stakeholders to achieve those results. It gives you a broader understanding of what you are up against and what you need to learn and change. Facing a challenge compels you to reflect on your attitudes and behaviors to discover which ones you need to change in order to achieve significantly better results.

The Challenge Model (Figure 4) offers a systematic approach for working together—as a team—to identify and face one challenge at a time and achieve results. The model leads you through a process of forming commitment to a shared vision that contributes to realizing your organization's mission, defining and owning a challenge, prioritizing actions for implementation, and carrying out the work plan to achieve results.

The Challenge Model helps you create the path to the result by focusing on one challenge at a time: if this is our organization's mission and this is our vision, then this is one result that will get us closer to the vision. Next, given the current reality, these are the obstacles we need to overcome, and here is how we plan to go about it. Your success in facing each challenge inspires your team to apply the process repeatedly with new challenges to keep moving toward the vision. The process and the experience of applying the Challenge Model strengthen the team and build confidence among its members that they can effect real change in the health care of their clients.

FIGURE 4   **The Challenge Model**

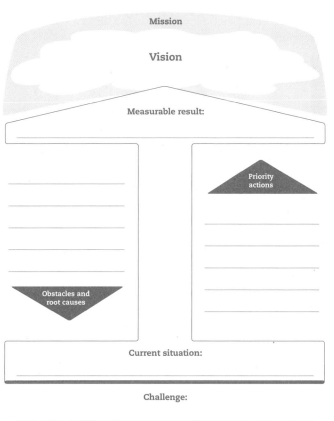

[How will we achieve our desired result in light of the obstacles we need to overcome?]

Face one
challenge
at a time

From Managers Who Lead: A Handbook for Improving Health Services
Cambridge, MA.: Management Sciences for Health, 2005

How to . . .

Use the Challenge Model

Step 1. Review your organizational mission and strategic priorities
With your team, form a common understanding of your organization's mission and strategic priorities. This understanding will help you shape your vision and make sure that it contributes to the larger organizational priorities.

Step 2. Create a shared vision
Work with your team to create a shared vision of the future you want and that contributes to accomplishing the organization's mission and priorities. This shared vision serves to inspire the team to face each new challenge.

Step 3. Agree on one measurable result
Pick an aspect of your shared vision and create one measurable result that you all want to achieve. This measurable result is what will drive your work. Because it is measurable, it allows you to monitor and evaluate your progress toward achieving it.

Note that *finalizing* the result is an iterative process. As you learn more about the current situation and obstacles you need to overcome, you may need to adjust your stated result so that it is appropriate and realistic.

Step 4. Assess the current situation
Scan your internal and external environments to form an accurate baseline of the realities or conditions that describe the current situation in relation to your stated result.

Step 5. Identify the obstacles and their root causes
Make a list of obstacles that you and your team will have to overcome to reach your stated result. Use root cause analysis tools to analyze the underlying causes of these obstacles to make sure you are addressing the causes and not just the symptoms.

Step 6. Define your key challenge and select priority actions
State what you plan to achieve in light of the root causes of the obstacles you have identified. (It helps to begin your challenge statement with "How will we…?") Then select priority actions that you will implement to address the root causes of the obstacles.

Step 7. Develop an action plan
Develop an action plan that estimates the human, material, and financial resources needed and the timeline for implementing your actions.

Step 8. Implement your plan and monitor and evaluate your progress
Provide support to your team in implementing the plan, and monitor and evaluate your progress toward achieving your result.

A full-size diagram with these instructions for using the Challenge Model can be found in the handbook toolkit.

From *Managers Who Lead: A Handbook for Improving Health Services* Cambridge, MA: Management Sciences for Health, 2005

Creating your vision and defining a measurable result

"Martin Luther King did not say, 'I have a strategic plan.' Instead, he shouted, 'I have a DREAM!' and he created a crusade."

—ANONYMOUS

Leading a team at any level means you need to create a vision together of where you want to go and what you want your team or program to become, or achieve, over the long term. A vision is important not only because it inspires and motivates, but also because leading with a vision helps to remind you why you are doing what you are doing. It provides the big picture and the inspiration to keep a team going in the face of obstacles as it strives to achieve its stated results.

Vision is different from mission

Unlike the mission or purpose of the organization, which states why the organization exists, the *vision provides a picture of a desired future*. It describes where the group or the organization wants to be in the future and creates the field for working toward that vision of the future.

Example of a vision

"Our health center is known for consistently producing excellent service results and people come from all around to receive our high-quality services. We have reduced the spread of communicable diseases, and the people in our area are healthier and happier."

CREATING A SHARED VISION

Shared vision has power

Some think that vision should come from the top level of an organization or program, that the new minister, executive director, or management team establishes it. Experience has shown, however, that a vision is more powerful when more people share it. Thus, a vision created by others for a team to endorse is not very compelling for those who were not part of the effort. Since people usually support what they help create, try to create a shared vision that is developed and owned by those who will need to carry it out.

A team can develop a vision of how it wants to work together to produce products or services or of the role it wants to have in the organization in the future. Depending on the level at which your team operates in the organization or program, you may want to include key stakeholders in developing or

How to . . .

Create a shared vision

Step 1. Imagine the future

- Ask the participants to think about a time in the future.

- Say "Imagine it is two years from now and we are looking back. We have accomplished all that is important to us. What picture do you see in your mind that represents that accomplishment?"

- Ask each participant to write a newspaper headline reporting on your accomplishments in the year 20_ _ (two or more years from now). Each individual writes a few words to describe what has been accomplished.

Step 2. Integrate your vision with another one

- Have the participants divide into pairs and ask them to share their visions with each other.

- Ask each pair of participants to create one shared vision combining the best aspects of both visions.

- In groups of four (composed of two pairs), discuss the combined visions, and further consolidate these visions to arrive at one shared vision for each group of four people.

Step 3. Record the key elements of all the vision statements

- In plenary, ask each group of four to present its combined vision.

- Record the key elements or phrases of each vision statement on a flipchart.

- Review the elements and consolidate them to eliminate overlaps.

Step 4. Prioritize the elements

- If the list is long, ask each participant to choose the three elements that are most critical. Record them on a flipchart.

- For each element, ask how many others listed it as one of their top three elements.

- Choose the three elements of the vision that were listed most often.

- Check with the entire group to see if these three elements or phrases correspond to their vision.

Step 5. Present the shared vision statement

- Combine the elements and phrases into one vision statement and write it on a clean flipchart. Put it in the front of the room to guide further discussions.

For other visioning exercises, including an adaptation of this exercise for use with a large group, please refer to the handbook toolkit.

From Managers Who Lead: A Handbook for Improving Health Services Cambridge, MA: Management Sciences for Health, 2005

reviewing the vision. Stakeholders may include existing and potential clients, community representatives, board members, or other partners.

Start with the end in mind. To lead your team to achieve results, start with creating the vision and identifying a future measurable result, then assess the current situation, and develop the priority actions and an action plan. This process helps to link the present to the future. Leading your team with a shared vision provides the power to pull the current situation closer to your vision and desired results, rather than pulling the vision back to the current reality. To prepare for a visioning exercise, you may want to explore a number of questions:

- What are we committed to doing? Who do we serve now and who do we want to serve?

- What kind of work climate do we want, and what values do we want to practice?

- What sort of future do we want to create for our community?

DEFINING A MEASURABLE RESULT

Once you have crafted your vision, identify one measurable result you want to achieve. The result you define needs to come from your vision and relate to the priority health care needs in your area. It may concern just one element of your vision, but if you can achieve that one element, you will move closer to your vision.

To make sure your desired result is clearly defined, follow the SMART rule:

Specific. Clearly written to avoid different interpretations;
Measurable. To allow you to monitor and evaluate progress toward achieving the result;
Appropriate. To the scope of your program or work activities, so that you can influence or make changes;
Realistic. Achievable within the time allowed;
Time bound. With a specific time period for completion.

In considering the SMART criteria and whether your desired result is "appropriate," think about whether the issues and obstacles that you will need to address are sufficiently under your control to allow you to influence changes.

You can explore your team's sphere of influence by using the exercise "Recognizing Your Sphere of Influence" in the handbook toolkit.

The vision pulls the current situation to the desired result

Clearly define your desired result

> ### Examples of measurable results
>
> The following measurable results relate to two aspects of the vision (to reduce or eliminate communicable diseases and to provide high-quality services).
>
> - To increase use of voluntary counseling and testing (VCT) services in one district by 50% (to an average of 80 clients per month) by the end of the year.
>
> - To streamline the intake process for new clients in our clinic so that, by the end of the year, the prescreening process takes an average of 10 minutes.
>
> For more detailed guidelines on developing measurable results, please refer to the exercise "Developing Measurable Results" in the handbook toolkit.

Keep in mind that *finalizing* your desired result is an iterative process. You should adjust the definition of the result after assessing the current situation and identifying your obstacles and root causes, so it takes these factors into account and is a result for which you are willing to be held accountable. The examples shown here reflect the result of this iterative process.

Gain commitment from senior levels

Once you have defined your measurable result, consult with senior management so that they can see how your intended results are aligned with larger program priorities or organizational goals. Communicating your intentions will also help senior managers understand the need for resources when and if you request them, and determine whether the change in client health care warrants the resources needed. This stage also serves to garner commitment to the result by a more senior level, if not the top level.

You will also need to determine what the current situation is with respect to the result you identified. Doing so requires having accurate data and information about key health indicators and national health priorities and objectives as well as baseline information against which you will measure your results. Understanding the current situation will clarify your challenge, help you fine-tune your measurable result, and allow you to develop priority actions for addressing the challenge. The following section guides you through a process of scanning the external and internal environments so that you can understand your situation better.

Assessing the current situation and identifying opportunities and obstacles

"We must accept life for what it actually is—a challenge to our quality without which we should never know of what stuff we are made, or grow to our full stature."

—ROBERT LOUIS STEVENSON

With a vision of where you want to be in the future, and a measurable result defined, you are ready to look at the current conditions in your external and internal environments in relation to that result. Being aware of the environment in which you work (external) and looking objectively at your capabilities and operational systems (internal) will help your team identify the obstacles and opportunities that will affect your ability to move toward your vision.

Scanning current conditions is an important leadership practice. You and you team need to find out what is going on, look for opportunities that will help you move closer to your desired result, and identify current and potential future obstacles. Think creatively about how to overcome the obstacles and how to capitalize on the opportunities.

There are various factors to consider when scanning your internal and external environments. If you intend to increase the number of clients seeking voluntary counseling and testing (VCT) services, find out what the situation is now, and why it is like that. If potential clients are not seeking services when they need them, find out why. Possible reasons might be that:

■ services are not accessible or are not easily accessed by public transportation;

■ clients are not aware of your clinic or range of services;

■ there are not enough trained providers;

■ lack of supplies causes clients to seek services elsewhere;

■ so much stigma is attached to HIV/AIDS that many clients are afraid to seek VCT services.

Figure 5 illustrates factors to consider in scanning the current situation and indicates the role each plays in the larger environment. Scan only those aspects that are *directly related* to your stated result and could either pose significant obstacles to (or open new opportunities for) achieving it.

Scan the internal and external environments

FIGURE 5   **Factors to consider in scanning the environment**

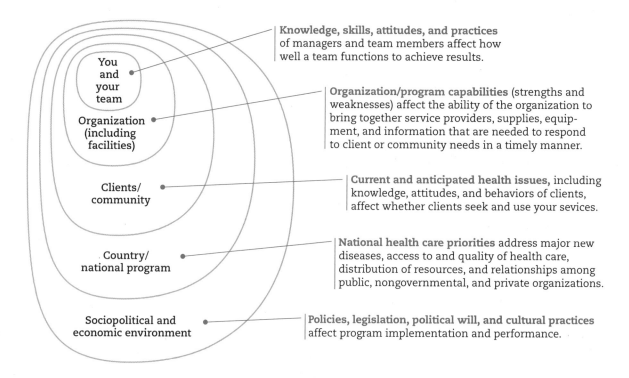

Knowledge, skills, attitudes, and practices of managers and team members affect how well a team functions to achieve results.

Organization/program capabilities (strengths and weaknesses) affect the ability of the organization to bring together service providers, supplies, equipment, and information that are needed to respond to client or community needs in a timely manner.

Current and anticipated health issues, including knowledge, attitudes, and behaviors of clients, affect whether clients seek and use your sevices.

National health care priorities address major new diseases, access to and quality of health care, distribution of resources, and relationships among public, nongovernmental, and private organizations.

Policies, legislation, political will, and cultural practices affect program implementation and performance.

Consider how the realities that exist in your internal and external environments will contribute or pose obstacles to achieving the result.

SCANNING THE EXTERNAL ENVIRONMENT

If your team works at the national or organizational level, your scan will be broader than if it works at the local level or is a unit in a larger organization. At any level, be sure to look up and around you, as we all work in interrelated systems.

Think about when your program has set out to do something new, such as coordinating with a local community group or providing a health service that you haven't provided before. What happens if you move toward a new endeavor without your eyes fully open? By analyzing factors in your external environment, you can be better prepared to respond to identified health and client needs and accomplish what you set out to achieve.

For assistance in understanding the interests of others in the environment, refer to "Analyzing Stakeholder Interests and Concerns" in the handbook toolkit.

When scanning the external environment in relation to a specific service delivery result, you need to find out:

Look for trends when scanning the environment

Sources of data

You will need to decide which sources of data are relevant to what you want to accomplish and will adequately inform the scope of issues and questions related to your result. The data sources you need to consult also depend on the level at which you are operating, but they should always include a review of national and local health plans and priorities.

If you are focusing on one particular service-related result, you should review data that you routinely collect, such as service statistics and financial data. In some instances, the data you need will not be readily available and you will need to collect them. This work could include collecting information on client satisfaction with your services through client exit interviews or focus groups. You can also convene community meetings to learn more about how people perceive your services and why they may not be coming to your clinic for services. Gathering this kind of qualitative and quantitative data is critical to a good scan of the external environment because you gain firsthand knowledge of the issues that are important to clients.

For a more comprehensive effort, you may need to access census data; data from the Demographic and Reproductive Health Survey; National Health Accounts; Ministry of Health statistics; data from household surveys; seroprevalence studies; Ministry of Finance data; economic trends data; and knowledge, attitudes, and practices (KAP) studies.

For more information on accessing and using national and local data, please refer to these issues of *The Manager*: "Using National and Local Data to Guide Reproductive Health Programs" (MSH 1997) and its supplement, "Guide to National and Local Reproductive Health Indicators," and "Exercising Leadership to Make Decentralization Work" (MSH 2002).

- why the current service is not up to standards;

- how people in the external environment view the services;

- how the service has operated in the past;

- who is being served, which other groups ought to be served, and how clients feel about the services;

- what kinds of services are in greatest demand and in least demand;

- whether the types and quantity of services you offer suit those demands.

What else do you see when you scan? Think about the trends you see and their underlying causes. Look below the surface, below the "tip of the iceberg."

SCANNING THE INTERNAL ENVIRONMENT

In your external scan you may have begun to identify some opportunities. For example, there may be an opportunity for your organization to expand services to underserved areas. If you work in a nongovernmental organization, perhaps there are opportunities to form partnerships with the public sector to deliver services. You may have identified threats as well, such as reduced client purchasing power due to difficult economic times, greater competition among service providers, or changing donor priorities.

Assess factors directly related to the desired result

Can your unit, division, or program perform effectively in the external environment? If you have competition, can you stay ahead of the others? Scanning the internal environment will help you answer these questions. Assess those factors that are *directly related* to your desired result and that may enhance or hinder your ability to achieve it. Factors to examine might include the aspects listed on page 33 as related to your unit, division, or program.

When you have scanned the external and internal factors related to your desired result, summarize your findings to form a set of statements that describe the current situation. The current situation sets a baseline for measuring progress when you begin to implement your plan.

Example of statements about your current situation

- Only 40 clients use our VCT services each month.
- Many more people need VCT services, but they are either afraid to seek the services or do not have easy access to a clinic.

IDENTIFYING OPPORTUNITIES AND OBSTACLES

Look for opportunities and take note of obstacles

In your scan of the current situation, you may discover opportunities that you had not seen before that will help you to achieve your result. It is important to be clear about which opportunities you can reasonably take advantage of, given available resources and your team's role or mandate.

Your scan will also reveal problems or obstacles that currently impede your ability to achieve the result. Be sure to talk to key stakeholders outside the organization about their perspectives on the trends that you see. Does what you see happening around you represent an opportunity? Are there trends that represent threats or potential threats?

It is useful to document the opportunities and obstacles (or threats) along with the strengths and weaknesses you have identified in your internal scan. This process is called a SWOT analysis (strengths, weaknesses, opportunities, and threats). A SWOT analysis helps to organize the information so that

---

Factors to consider in scanning the internal environment

Performance/results. These include client satisfaction with your services; client access to, and utilization of, the various health services that you provide (number and types of people served across regions, facilities, and services); and your financial situation. Look at current data and at performance three and five years ago.

- Are the program results better or worse than last year?

- Are more or fewer clients using your services?

- Has their health status improved or declined?

- Has the client mix changed?

- Are your donors or other stakeholders satisfied with the program's performance?

- Is your financial situation stable? Has it improved?

Staffing. Questions to consider include:

- Are staff working at full capacity?

- Are they appropriately trained for the jobs they do?

- Are staff distributed appropriately across activities for which your team is responsible?

- Do staff understand what constitutes good performance?

- Is there a system for developing new managers who lead and strengthening existing leaders?

Management capacity: Planning, organizing, implementing, monitoring, and evaluating. Whether you are leading a team at a lower level within a program or organization, or leading a senior team, how well you and your team manage your work is critical to achieving results and the sustainability of the whole program. Analyzing current management capacity is particularly important if you are working at the organizational level. It is an essential part of a wider organizational scan.

The Management and Organizational Sustainability Tool (MOST), available on the handbook CD-ROM, is one tool you can use to assess the management capacity of your organization.

---

you can use it to inform decisions about programs, activities, and areas for improvement. (For instructions on conducting a SWOT analysis, please refer to *The Family Planning Manager's Handbook,* Wolff et al. 1991.)

ANALYZING ROOT CAUSES

Determine
underlying
causes of
obstacles

Once you have identified the obstacles, you and your team need to determine the main cause(s) of the obstacles in order to know how to address them. This process is called root cause analysis. By examining the root causes of the obstacles, you will not only understand the obstacles better but also be able to formulate solutions that address the underlying problem, not just its visible symptoms.

What is root cause analysis?

The goal of root cause analysis is to identify and remove the causes of problems or obstacles by asking why the obstacles are occurring. It is based on the principle that only a few primary factors are responsible for producing most of a problem, and it provides a systematic method for gathering and analyzing evidence about a problem so that you can address it effectively.

In the health care setting, there are often many contributing factors to a problem or obstacle. Analyzing root causes helps to determine the primary underlying causes that are most responsible for creating the problem, so you can focus your efforts (priority actions) on the causes that are most critical to resolving the problem.

Examples of root causes

- People don't know what VCT is and why it is important.
- People have fears, beliefs, and superstitions about HIV and AIDS.
- Some staff are not adequately trained to provide follow-up counseling to clients who test positive for HIV.
- Clients are not being referred to clinics that provide VCT services.
- The layout of the VCT clinic makes privacy impossible.
- The delivery of test kits is erratic.

There are many methods and tools for determining root causes. Choose which ones to use by considering the nature of the problem or obstacle, the skills of the person leading the analysis, and the people involved in the analysis. Two techniques are the Fishbone Diagram and the Five Whys.

> ### Root cause analysis using the Fishbone and the Five Whys techniques
>
> The Fishbone technique, which was created by Kaoru Ishikawa of Tokyo University, helps you look for the causes that are most responsible for a particular obstacle. The technique derives its name from its shape: the obstacle is at the head and a set of bones (usually four) are used to identify the primary causes of the obstacle. The causes are grouped under four categories: people, procedures, policies, and environment (or you can develop your own categories).
>
> You can identify secondary or tertiary causes by using the Five Whys technique (Imai 1986). Take one of your problems and ask why it is that way or why the problem is happening. Keep asking why after each answer until you get to the underlying cause. (It doesn't have to be five times.)
>
> The Fishbone and Five Whys techniques, with complete instructions on how to apply them, can be found in the handbook toolkit.

Defining your challenge and selecting priority actions

"You have to teach managers to focus or they will be called away for everything. Managers often get lost in trying to control things that don't produce results."

—HUMBERTO DANTAS
CEARÁ, BRAZIL

Once you have assessed the current situation and identified obstacles (and their underlying causes), and made any needed adjustments to your intended result, you are ready to state your specific challenge and develop priority actions to address that challenge.

DEFINING YOUR KEY CHALLENGE

Your main challenge should state what you want to achieve in light of the obstacles you have identified. By clearly identifying both the results you want to achieve and the obstacles you need to overcome, you will lead your team to shift from focusing on problems to focusing on the challenge and the stated result.

For a helpful group exercise, see "Distinguishing Challenges from Problems" in the handbook toolkit.

Criteria for defining a challenge

A well-defined challenge should meet the following criteria.

- Addressing the challenge will contribute to achieving critical organizational objectives.

- The challenge focuses on accomplishing extraordinary results that are measurable and within the scope of the team's mandate.

- Addressing the challenge requires leadership and new team behaviors.

- The challenge mobilizes the team to stretch its capabilities and find new ways to work together.

Example of a challenge

"How will we increase the use of our VCT services when clients who need these services are not coming to our clinics?"

Shift focus from problems to challenges

Let's suppose that you and your team work in a public-sector program that provides integrated health services through several clinics in your district. As in many areas, the HIV/AIDS pandemic is responsible for an increasing number of deaths and new infections. Your scan of the current situation shows that many more people should be receiving VCT services, and you have the capacity to provide those services to many more people than you do currently.

Based on your desired result—to increase the use of VCT services in your district by 50% by the end of the year (to an average of 80 clients per month)—and considering the obstacles and root causes that have influenced your current situation (only 40 clients per month use VCT services), you can now define your main challenge. If you and your team don't address this challenge, you will not be able to achieve your intended result and move toward your vision.

SELECTING PRIORITY ACTIONS

Priority actions are activities or interventions that directly target the root causes of the obstacles you identified and, when implemented, will result in achieving your result. Prioritizing your actions will help focus staff and others on actions that will lead to results. When you work on your priority actions, try to keep the number of actions to a manageable level. Three to five actions are often enough to focus your efforts on a single challenge and on the underlying root causes of the obstacles.

To address your main challenge of increasing the use of VCT services, actions might include:

How to...

Set priorities using the Priority Matrix

The Priority Matrix helps rank actions based on the time it takes to complete them, cost, potential for improving quality, and availability of resources. This tool can be used for prioritizing strategies and actions as part of developing an action plan.

Step 1. List priority actions
Choose three actions that address the obstacles that are preventing you from reaching your result. List them in the boxes under "Priority actions."

(It is important to complete a root cause analysis first, so the actions you choose will address the root causes of the problem and not just the symptoms.)

Step 2. Rank each priority action on a scale of 1 to 3
On a scale of 1 to 3 (with 1 providing the least benefit and 3 the most benefit), rank each priority action according to the time needed, cost to implement, potential for improving quality, and availability of resources.

Step 3. Calculate the total points for each priority action
Add the numbers in each column to see the total score for each action. The higher the score, the higher the priority of the action based on the criteria listed. You may choose to change the criteria depending on the type of challenge you are working on.

Sample completed Priority Matrix

	Priority actions		
Criteria *rank from 1 to 3*	**Train counselors**	**Conduct community education seminars**	**Renovate clinics**
Time to implement 1= *the most time* 3= *the least time*	2	2	1
Cost to implement 1= *the highest cost* 3= *the lowest cost*	2	3	1
Potential for improving quality in the long term 1= *the least potential* 3= *the most potential*	3	2	2
Availability of resources 1= *the least available* 3= *the most available*	1	3	1
Total	8	10	5

This example illustrates that conducting community education seminars should be a priority. It doesn't mean that you don't carry out the other actions, but you should focus on those that will have the most impact on achieving your result, taking into account time and money.

The complete Priority Matrix tool with a blank worksheet can be found in the handbook toolkit.

- educating the community about VCT and HIV/AIDS;

- renovating or relocating clinics so there is privacy for counseling;

- training more counselors to provide VCT services;

- creating formal links with other area clinics that do not provide VCT services so they can refer clients to the VCT clinic;

- improving the supply of test kits.

Using the example of VCT in this chapter, the box on the next page provides an overview of how all the parts fit together and lead to a clear plan of action.

Developing your action plan

"To achieve greatness, start where you are, use what you have, do what you can."

—ARTHUR ASHE

Before you can begin to implement your priority actions, you need to develop an action plan. Developing an action plan is one of the managing practices. The action plan provides you and your team with a clear path for taking action, monitoring progress, and measuring results. At a minimum, an action plan should identify:

- the *actions or activities* that will be implemented;

- *who will be responsible* for carrying out each action;

- the *human, financial, and material resources* needed to implement the actions;

- *a timeline* showing when the actions will be carried out.

Plans are much more likely to be implemented and bring results when they:

- are created and owned by the team and reflect the shared vision of the team;

- address a well-defined challenge that is based on an observable gap between desired and actual performance;

- contain measurable indicators that allow you to see that the performance gap is closing;

Putting it all together: Vision, measurable result, current situation, obstacles and root causes, challenge, priority actions

Vision

Our health center is known for consistently producing excellent service results and people come from all around to receive our high-quality services. We have reduced the spread of communicable diseases, and the people in our area are healthier and happier.

Measurable result

Increase the use of VCT services in one district by 50% (to an average of 80 clients per month) by the end of the year.

Current situation

- Only 40 clients use our VCT services each month.
- Many more people need VCT services, but either are afraid to seek the services or do not have easy access to a clinic.

Obstacles and root causes

- People don't know what VCT is and why it is important.
- People have fears, beliefs, and superstitions about HIV and AIDS.
- Some staff are not adequately trained to provide follow-up counseling to clients who test positive for HIV.
- Clients are not being referred to clinics that provide VCT services.
- The layout of the VCT clinic makes privacy impossible.
- The delivery of test kits is erratic.

Challenge

How will we increase the use of our VCT services when clients who need these services are not coming to our clinics?

Priority actions to address the challenge

- Sensitize the community about VCT and other HIV/AIDS issues to encourage clients to seek and use VCT services.
- Train counselors in providing high-quality VCT services.
- Create a referral system with other area clinics.
- Renovate clinics that do not allow for adequate privacy.
- Improve the routine supply of test kits.

- focus on prioritized actions that were selected after a thorough analysis of root causes;

- contain a clear timeframe for implementing each action and designate specific individuals to carry out each action and be held accountable for results.

The action plan provides a clear path to results

The action plan worksheet (Figure 6) will help you organize the components of your action plan and make sure that your priority actions directly address the root causes you have identified.

The next step is to list all your priority actions on a timeline showing when each action and sub-action will be carried out, who is responsible, and what resources are required. Depending on the requirements of your program, you may also need to submit a separate budget that provides more detail on the costs of the resources required. Table 4 is a sample format for developing a timeline for your action plan.

> For complete instructions and handouts for group work, see "Developing an Action Plan That Leads to Results" in the handbook toolkit. For assistance in defining resources needed from external sources, see "Mobilizing Stakeholders to Commit Resources," also in the toolkit.

Implementing your plan and monitoring and evaluating progress

"If you keep on doing what you have always been doing, you will keep on getting what you have always gotten."

—ANONYMOUS

Great ideas to make improvements and bring about change often come to a halt during implementation. In many cases, the real problem is not inappropriate activities but poor execution. Here again leadership and management are critical. You can't always use the same old systems and processes when you are approaching your challenges in new ways.

IMPLEMENTING YOUR ACTION PLAN

Apply leading and managing practices to stay on course

Planning is one of the four key managing practices presented in chapter 1. Implementing a plan is another. The other six leading and managing practices will help you stay on course:

- Scan continuously so that you can anticipate potential problems or changes in the environment that could impact your work;

FIGURE 6   Sample action plan worksheet

Challenge	Current situation (baseline data)	Measurable result
Root causes	Priority actions	

TABLE 4   Sample action plan format

Actions	Person(s) responsible	Resources needed (human, financial, material)	Timeline																
			1st month				2nd month				3rd month				4th month				

- Focus on specific challenges and set new priorities as needed;

- Align your team members to work together to deal with problems as they arise, mobilize new resources, and align new stakeholders as needed;

- Organize people to do the work in the most efficient and effective way, and re-assign duties or redistribute work or resources as needed;

- Monitor progress along the way and make sure you have a feasible evaluation plan;

- Inspire and motivate people to stay engaged.

Often during implementation, the priorities you have set compete with other urgent work that arises. These competing priorities can divert you and your team from what is most important.

The exercise "Putting First Things First: The Important and Urgent Matrix" in the handbook toolkit can help you focus on the right activities to stay on track and achieve your results.

MONITORING AND EVALUATING YOUR PROGRESS

Meaure progress against a baseline

Make sure that you are clear at the outset about what success will look like and how you plan to measure it. If you have formulated your result using the SMART rule and established clear baseline data, you will be able to monitor and evaluate your progress toward achieving the result. The mechanisms to use for monitoring and evaluating your progress will depend on the level at which you are working, the complexity of your stated result, and the resources available. Be sure to budget for the cost of monitoring and evaluation.

If you focus on one particular service delivery result, then routinely collecting and analyzing monthly or quarterly service statistics will allow you to see whether you are making progress. The bottom line is that you will never know whether you've arrived at where you want to be if you don't measure where you were in the beginning and where you are now. And remember to talk with your staff about the changes you see resulting from your work, because seeing real change is more inspiring than motivational speeches.

The following example shows how one health team increased the use of family planning by applying the Challenge Model.

Use the Challenge Model to strengthen leadership capabilities

As this example from Egypt illustrates, MSH's Leadership Development Program is a simple process that organizations can implement with their own resources to build leadership capabilities at all levels of an organization. Based on the Challenge Model process and the practices of the Leading and Managing Framework, participants work together in teams to learn how to face their challenges and achieve organizational results.

Leading with a vision to achieve results—Example from Egypt

In 2002, Aswan Governorate, a rural area in the underdeveloped region of Upper Egypt, launched a process to improve the quality and accessibility of health services in three districts. The health units in this area were faced with a considerable challenge: how could they improve health indicators for their population? To face this challenge, they would have to increase client use of and satisfaction with their services, and make a commitment to serve their clients better. Staff from six health facilities and three districts participated in the year-long Leadership Development Program sponsored by the Ministry of Health and Population and MSH. The program focused on increasing the capacity of managers to lead others to achieve results.

The teams and process. Forty-one doctors, nurses, and midwives from five health centers, one rural hospital, and three districts were grouped into ten working teams. Through a series of one-day workshops held every two months, participants learned the leading and managing practices and worked in their teams to create a shared vision. They used the Challenge Model to frame their specific challenges and develop and implement action plans. Between workshops they continued their work together in district and team meetings in their health centers. Many of these teams also continued on their own to expand the program to other health units in their areas.

El Khor Health Unit challenge. The experience of the rural health unit El Khor, which was trained by the teams in the original program, illustrates the application of the Challenge Model. Faced with low use of family planning in the village, the team first created a shared vision: that all the women in their area could have access to family planning services. When the team scanned the current situation, they learned that current use of family planning by women of reproductive age was 21.5%. They agreed to focus on achieving a measurable result, increasing use of family planning to 25% within six months, from January 2004 to June 2004.

The team members' analysis of the obstacles they needed to overcome to reach this result focused on several root causes that were preventing more women from seeking services and practicing family planning. Many people had misconceptions about injections, oral contraceptives, and especially IUDs. There were widespread rumors that their religion prohibited practicing family planning. The team then identified its challenge as how to raise the use rate for different family planning methods for women of reproductive age in the face of public misinformation.

(cont. next page)

Leading with a vision to achieve results—Example from Egypt *(cont.)*

The action plan. The El Khor Health Unit's action plan focused on creating an alliance between the clinic and the community to address rumors and misunderstandings about family planning. Staff made it a priority to work with local religious leaders and hold seminars on religious views about family planning. They also trained two women volunteers from the village to help the team communicate correct information about the use and benefits of different family planning methods through public meetings and other events. Small teams went door to door, offering information, resupplying users, and encouraging nonusers to visit the health unit.

Results. At the end of the six months, family planning use among married women of reproductive age in El Khor Health Unit had increased to 34.3%. The total number of new family planning clients had more than doubled, from 96 clients during the six-month period before the Leadership Development Program to 222 clients during the period January through June 2004. Other teams in the leadership program increased the number of new family planning clients, doubled the number of postpartum visits per client, and improved vaccination rates and infection control.

Transfer of approach. Using this simple process, doctors and nurses in Aswan Governorate now know that they can make significant improvements in the health of their people by facing their challenges and working together as a team. They have become deeply committed to producing their intended results, and their approach to their work is now centered on the needs of their clients. The Aswan teams continue to expand the program by training new teams and including new districts. Other governorates across Egypt have recognized Aswan's improvements in health indicators and have invited facilitators from the Leadership Development Program to transfer the Challenge Model and leadership approach to support health unit teams in improving their service results.

For more information on how these teams are scaling up this program, please see the country example in chapter 6.

Implementing a leadership development program

The Leadership Development Program follows the principles of developing managers who lead. It takes place over several months; participants work in teams on real organizational challenges; they develop leadership competencies through a process of facing challenges and receiving feedback and support. The participating organization owns the process and takes responsibility for championing its success.

The process. Designed to be adapted to fit local organizational needs, the Leadership Development Program includes a series of one- to two-day workshops spaced over several months, during which local facilitators introduce the Challenge Model and leading and managing practices and competencies. Between workshops, local work teams apply what they have learned. They scan their environment to understand their challenges and the root causes of their obstacles. They focus on priority actions and plan for implementing their actions. They align people and mobilize resources to support their efforts, and monitor and evaluate their progress. They apply the leadership competencies to inspire others to achieve results.

Challenge, feedback, and support. When the teams implement their action plans they achieve measurable results, which, in turn, motivate them to take on a new challenge. Managers in the organization serve as facilitators and coaches to provide support and feedback during planning and implementation. In addition to providing an effective way to improve organizational performance and health outcomes, the program enables shared learning of best practices across units and regions.

Sustained improvements. The program requires an organization's commitment over time and is intended to become part of an organization's ongoing management and supervision system. The Leadership Development Program builds confidence in the organization's abilities to make continuous and sustained improvements in health.

For an introduction to the Leadership Development Program, please refer to the handbook CD-ROM.

Supporting your team

"The morale of team members plays a crucial role in any program's success. If the self-confidence of the team members is low and the leader does nothing to build it up, the team is very sure to break down."

—SAMSONRAJ PANDIAN
WORLD VISION INDIA

In implementing a new action plan, particularly when it involves changing how things have been done before, you should expect to encounter obstacles. Even though you and your team are fully committed to the plan, you are still learning as you go and finding out what you need to achieve your results.

Sometimes people outside the team (and maybe even some of your team members) may need explanations to understand the reasons for doing things differently and encouragement to try the new way. Other times you may need to work harder on aligning your outside stakeholders around the challenge so you can get their cooperation. When you run into a sizable issue, it can lead to a breakdown. How you handle the breakdown is what matters.

LEADING YOUR TEAM THROUGH BREAKDOWNS

Use
breakdowns
as catalysts
for learning

One of the differences between a group of individuals and a high-performing team is that, in a team approach, difficulties and breakdowns are expected and embraced, and the team addresses the breakdowns together. Help your team identify breakdowns and see them as catalysts for understanding what is missing or what stands in the way of achieving the results you desire.

What is a breakdown?

A breakdown is any situation that:

- threatens progress toward a commitment
- violates an explicit agreement
- presents uncertainty or difficulty
- stops effective action
- presents obstacles to fulfilling your commitments.

When they are not handled well, breakdowns lead to minimizing or ignoring problems, blaming each other, or eroding teamwork, trust, and effectiveness. When handled well, breakdowns can be a major source of *breakthroughs* or finding new ways to approach your work and achieve results. To change how you think about and approach breakdowns, remember that:

- all large commitments will have breakdowns;

- the greater your commitment, the more and greater the breakdowns will be;

- when there is no commitment, there will be no breakdowns.

It is your job to help your team's members understand how to respond to breakdowns and to work with them to approach problems together and find a way through that will result in new and better ways of doing things.

For ways to lead your team through breakdowns, see the exercise in the handbook toolkit called "Coaching Your Team through Breakdowns."

Use breakdowns to find better ways of doing things

ACKNOWLEDGING YOUR TEAM

To keep the members of your team inspired and motivated, point out and celebrate incremental results, and link those results to specific actions they have taken. Above all, acknowledge and praise both individuals and the team on a regular basis, and be there to support them.

Acknowledge people's efforts

As you team works to face its challenges and implement the action plan, be sure to:

- show appreciation regularly to individuals and the team for their work;

- acknowledge the challenges they are facing;

- praise them whenever their work is well done, even if it is not at a major milestone;

- thank them for their commitment and their daily efforts;

- recognize them for their accomplishments and show how their work has made a difference.

Face challenges together and share ownership of results

"The adaptive demands of our time require leaders who take responsibility without waiting for revelation or request. One can lead with no more than a question in hand."

—RONALD HEIFETZ AND DONALD LAURIE
"THE WORK OF LEADERSHIP"

Challenges and change are two constants in life. They are part of nature and part of our work life. This chapter has pointed out the critical role that managers have in leading their teams to face important challenges in complex situations.

By applying the Challenge Model and working with your team to follow the process, one step at a time, you will give your team direct experience in applying the leading and managing practices and see the results. At the same time, the members of the group will gain the confidence to tackle problems in the future, the skills to inspire mutual commitment, experience in practicing effective teamwork, and above all, an opportunity to see how they can make a difference in people's lives.

Face challenges
one at a time to
realize results

Questions to consider on . . .

Leading your team to face challenges

Vision. What is it that your team would like to create in the future?

Results. What specific result will move you closer to your vision within the next year?

Current situation. What is the current situation with respect to this result?

Root causes. Why are things this way? Ask why, why, and why.

Challenge. What is the main obstacle you need to overcome to achieve your stated result? (How do we...?)

Priority actions. What are the key approaches you should take to address this challenge? What should you be focusing on right now?

Monitoring and evaluation. How will you know if you have been successful?

Supporting your team. How will you use breakdowns to improve how you face your challenges? How will you acknowledge people for their efforts?

3 Improving work climate to strengthen performance

"The essential task of management is creating opportunities, releasing potential, removing obstacles, encouraging growth, and providing guidance."
—DOUGLAS MCGREGOR
LEADERSHIP AND MOTIVATION

When people work in a supportive environment, they strive to produce results. Such an environment is called a positive work climate. What exactly is work climate, and how is it important for improving performance?

Work climate is the "weather of the workplace." Just as weather conditions can affect your daily activities, work climate influences your behavior at work. A good work climate can improve an individual's work habits, while a poor climate can erode good work habits. Most importantly, a positive work climate leads to and sustains staff motivation and high performance (Litwin and Stringer 1968, Stringer 2002).

This chapter discusses what contributes to and results from a positive work climate. It focuses on what managers at all levels can do to create and sustain a positive work climate for work groups by helping you:

- understand what makes a positive work climate and how it affects performance;

- improve work climate by motivating staff and providing challenge, clarity, and support;

- strengthen communication by listening, understanding, and responding constructively;

- sustain your group's commitment through your own commitment and supportive techniques;

- set the tone for the organization at the senior level.

Recognizing a positive work climate

*"A positive work climate is conducive to creative, productive work; it is
a cooperative, civil workplace that is relatively free from bad mouthing,
backstabbing, or petty bickering."*

—PAUL WONG
"THE POSITIVE PSYCHOLOGY OF 'CLIMATE MANAGEMENT'"

Every office and health facility has a work climate. Some climates are positive
and productive, while others tend to demotivate staff. Although the type of
climate may be easy to recognize in some workplaces, it may be more subtle
in others. To understand the climate of your workplace, begin by asking yourself what it feels like to work with your colleagues, including your manager
and your staff.

> **Work climate**
>
> Work climate is the prevailing workplace atmosphere as experienced by
> employees. It is what it *feels* like to work in a group.

Think back over all your experiences as a member of a team, whether at
work, in school, or in sports. Is there a team in which you shared a sense of
excitement in working together? Reflecting on your experiences can help you
recognize a positive work climate (see the box on the next page).

REWARDS OF A POSITIVE WORK CLIMATE

A positive
climate
stimulates
motivation and
performance

To improve a work climate, it helps to understand how climate affects people and how it develops. A positive work climate stimulates staff motivation
because it provides conditions under which people can pursue their own
goals while striving toward organizational objectives (Bennis and Schein
1966). Everyone has motivators—impulses, needs, and energy reserves—that
can drive him or her to work more effectively. When staff feel motivated, they
want to put their capabilities to work. They may even make efforts that exceed
job expectations. Quite simply, they try harder with all their potential, and
doing so improves their performance on the job, as Figure 7 shows.

FIGURE 7   **Rewards of a positive work climate**

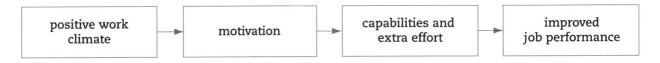

Recognizing a positive work climate

Think of a time when you were a member of a great team. How did you feel? Were you:

- energized?

- empowered?

- excited?

- looking forward to the next day at work?

- impatient to get started?

- motivated?

All these experiences indicate a positive work climate.

Now think about how all of you interacted. What did your supervisor, teacher, or coach do to encourage your team's efforts? What did you do to contribute to the team effort? What was your team able to accomplish? Once you identify elements of this team's climate, you can begin to grasp the kind of positive work climate you can create.

Research demonstrates the effects of positive work climate

The relationship between work climate and performance is not just intuitive; it has been demonstrated in fields as diverse as health, education, and business. Canadian staff nurses found that a positive work climate increased their sense of empowerment and job commitment, which, in turn, improved their care of patients. A positive work climate was also responsible for students' and teachers' success in British schools. And in a study of corporations, climate accounted for nearly a third of strong financial results—profits, efficiency, and revenue growth (Laschinger et al. 2001, Hay Group 2000, Goleman 2000). When you pay attention to the work climate, you too can improve your staff's performance.

FACTORS THAT CREATE A WORK CLIMATE

The climate of a work group develops through the influence of an organization's:

- history—its founding, successes, setbacks, and reputation;

- culture—shared work values, beliefs, assumptions, and traditions;

- management strategy and structure—growth and job opportunities, definition of roles and responsibilities, policies regarding promotion and rewards;

- external environment—the broader context of politics, regulation, workforce skills, and social barriers;

- managers' practices and competencies in leading a team.

It is important to know how you can influence work climate and distinguish between factors that are within your control and those that are not. On one hand, you can change a climate that undermines staff commitment and performance by managing and leading your team better. On the other hand, factors such as organizational history, culture, and management strategy and structure may be beyond your influence unless you hold a powerful position in your organization. Figure 8 summarizes the causes of work climate and its effects on performance. It highlights the importance of leading and managing practices and competencies in influencing work climate.

Leading and managing practices and competencies. The leading practices—scanning, focusing, aligning and mobilizing, and inspiring—all contribute to the creation of a positive work climate. Aligning and inspiring are especially useful in facilitating teamwork by building strong work relationships among group members. When you forge connections between each member's special skills and interests and their work, they willingly commit their time and efforts. You also inspire staff by demonstrating honesty, creativity, and personal commitment in your work. At the same time, you show trust and confidence in what they can do and acknowledge their contributions.

Supportive
supervision
fosters a
positive climate

FIGURE 8 **Causes and effects of work climate**

Of all organizational factors, managers' practices and competencies have the greatest influence on their groups' work climate, and through climate, managers can sustain staff motivation and performance.

From Managers Who Lead: A Handbook for Improving Health Services Cambridge MA: Management Sciences for Health 2005

Practicing good management also helps you to build and sustain your group's enthusiasm for its work. Supportive supervisory practices empower your staff to learn through addressing challenges. Good management systems also make it easier for staff to do their work, stay informed, and monitor their progress in addressing challenges. All these practices create a positive work climate.

Leadership competencies enable you to clarify your purpose and priorities, communicate effectively, handle conflict, and motivate committed teams. When you develop or refine your leadership abilities, you can apply the leading and managing practices more effectively.

What about the effect of organizational culture? How will it affect the climate you try to create for your work group?

Organizational culture is different from climate

While climate is the way it feels to work in a group, culture is the pattern of shared values and assumptions that organizational members share. Assumptions that have worked well in the past are taught to new members as "the way we do things here."

A manager may develop a climate that differs from the prevailing cultural norms. She may encourage participation and a sense of collective responsibility in her work group while the organization is characterized by strict definition of roles, authoritarian decision-making, and an attitude of "that's not my job." In such cases, the manager can expect pressure from the rest of the organization to conform and will have to handle the tension between culture and climate. When she eventually produces results that please senior managers, she may feel less pressure.

Improving work climate and staff motivation

"What the boss of a work group does is the most important determinant of climate. The boss's behavior drives climate, which arouses motivation. And aroused motivation is a major driver of bottom-line performance."

—ROBERT STRINGER
LEADERSHIP AND ORGANIZATIONAL CLIMATE

As a manager who leads a work group, you influence the climate of your work group more than any other factor. This finding is based on a survey of 2,500 organizational units in 24 organizations. It found that the unit manager (not pay, benefits, or the organizational leader) is the most critical player in building a strong workplace (Buckingham and Coffman 1999).

Your behavior and leading and managing practices can create a positive work climate and strong results within your group, even if your organization's climate isn't optimal. How successful you are will depend on how well you:

- know your staff, their motivations, work styles, and interests;

- know what motivates you, what you value, and what rouses your emotions;

- focus on providing challenge, clarity, and support to your group.

KNOW YOUR STAFF

Be the "human connector" who makes things happen

The most important things you can do to develop a positive work climate are to know your staff and establish a good work relationship with them. Managers are the "human connectors" who make things happen (Kouzes and Posner 1999). If you have a good work relationship with the individuals in your group, it will be much easier for you to align their efforts with yours and mobilize their energies to face a challenge. If you are a caring and supportive supervisor, your staff will also be more likely to stay with the organization, instead of looking for work elsewhere.

You can ask your team members, individually or together, to talk about their hopes and dreams for their communities and country (see Table 5).

TABLE 5 **Learning about your staff**

Learn about the ideas, past experiences, goals, and behavior of your staff to understand what makes each person want to do his or her best.

Staff characteristics	Examples (interests, experience, temperament)
Dreams	For the community or the country
Motivation	Power: visibility and prestige Affiliation: having good relations Achievement: pride in a job well done and greater responsibility Job security
Life situation	Past jobs Transportation to and from work
Work style	Abstract thinker or practical See the big picture or very detail-oriented Eager to act or reflective Aware of others or concerned only about self
Preferred team roles	Initiator Follower or supporter Observer Opposer

Sources: McClelland 1985; Kantor 1999

Gathering this information will help generate ideas about how your work group might be able to effect some changes to improve health. Talking with your staff and observing them as they interact will give you a good idea of what motivates your colleagues in their work.

> The handbook toolkit offers an exercise, "Creating a Climate of Hope and Possibility," you can use to help a group that needs encouragement and self-confidence to embrace a positive vision of the future.

Three big motivators: power, affiliation, and achievement

In the workplace, internal sources of motivation energize staff as they work. People often feel motivated for high performance by one of three primary motivators (or a mix of them): power, affiliation, or achievement (McClelland 1985). For example, people motivated by power want positions of visible responsibility. People motivated by affiliation want to work in a group where the interpersonal relations are pleasant and supportive. People motivated by achievement want to see results and to know that their efforts contributed to those results. You can create a climate that addresses such motivators and allows productivity, results, and sustained performance to flourish.

Do job-related factors such as money, safety, or training opportunities also motivate performance? You may hear complaints about these job-related factors. While (as much as possible) you need to ensure that pay and other external factors are acceptable to staff, increasing them above an acceptable level does not increase staff's motivation for performance. For example, when people receive pay they consider adequate, additional money does not improve their job performance (Buckingham and Coffman 1999, p. 29).

KNOW YOURSELF

As you become more aware of your staff's internal dynamics, reflect on your own behavior and how staff may perceive you. How you behave and respond to stress, or experience strong emotions in the workplace, affects your team and coworkers. Sometimes people fool themselves into thinking that they are in control of their strong emotions and that no one notices. Feelings, especially strong ones, have a way of filtering into conversations, however. They show through your tone, choice of words, and behavior. Staff perceive these cues and adjust their behavior to you accordingly.

Reflecting on personal motivators and emotions

The more you model supportive, enthusiastic behavior, the better you help others manage themselves. You can explore what energizes you and discover whether you are motivated more by power, achievement, or affiliation. How much do you also seek to serve your community? Your actions will reflect what motivates you, and your motivation and actions will affect how your staff see you. Also become more aware of things that drain your motivation or make you angry, disappointed, frustrated, or afraid. When you reflect on these, you can usually find ways to do something constructive that will lessen these feelings and help you feel more in control again.

Watch your health and level of distress. If you feel continually overwhelmed by all the things you need to pay attention to, be mindful of your own physical and psychological well-being. "How can I worry about my own health if I have the responsibility for the health of eight million people?" said one senior health official from South Africa. While it may seem selfish to be concerned about your own health, if you no longer have the physical energy to lead and have not built the leadership capacity of those around you, you may significantly compromise all your efforts.

As a leader, you have a responsibility for individual and organizational health. While everyone's different demands may produce distress, you can begin to cope with it by making individual and organizational changes to manage perceptions of stress. Manage the work environment and manage your lifestyle (Quick et al. 1997).

PROVIDE CHALLENGE, CLARITY, AND SUPPORT

Besides knowing your staff and yourself, you can positively influence work climate by changing the way you assign and manage the workload. Look for ways to:

- *challenge* your staff to help them grow;

- *ensure clarity* about work roles and responsibilities;

- *support* staff by providing resources, making connections, and understanding their needs.

Make work assignments that stretch staff

Challenge staff. You can challenge staff by offering assignments that stretch them beyond their current level of competence and confidence. Such assignments offer the possibility of doing something in a new way or starting something new. They are opportunities for staff to show leadership potential. When staff members are not challenged, they do not grow or learn from mistakes, and they become bored. As one staff member commented, his supervisor knew the right way to challenge his team:

> He knows how to ask people to do things well, even things we don't know we can do, and gives us support to do it. He throws people into something they think they cannot do, but he never throws people into something they would fail at. He gives us the confidence to try.

Clarify roles and responsibilities. When each group member understands the roles and responsibilities of everyone in the group, then all members see how their roles contribute to the desired results of their group and ultimately of the organization. They know who their internal and external clients are and what their clients need from them.

To clarify responsibilities with your staff, talk about your expectations as well as clients' expectations and make sure to point out the consequences of not meeting these expectations. Inquire to see whether staff understand them and follow up with written documentation, so they can easily access this information. This kind of clarity exists when staff can say what this person said about her supervisor.

> I know where I stand with him. He clearly expresses his intentions and personally upholds high standards of performance. We're all treated fairly. I know that I'll be letting my manager and my team down if I fail to complete this challenge.

Support comes in many forms

Support staff. Supporting your group means advocating for its work and its needs. Make the services your group performs and what it accomplishes visible to the wider organization. Once you've established a good reputation for the group, you can follow up by securing or providing the resources it needs to do its job. These include not only time, materials, and money, but also political and emotional support. Offer political support by making connections, paving the way, and getting necessary approvals to proceed. Help your staff to deal with organizational politics. Also consider whether particular individuals in your group could benefit from a mentor and look for

---

Use leading and managing practices to improve work climate

Leading practices. As you design strategies for improving your work group's climate:

- scan to get to know your staff better;
- focus by clarifying expectations and identifying challenges;
- align and mobilize the entire team around shared goals and aspirations;
- mobilize individuals by addressing their needs for power, affiliation, or achievement;
- inspire team members by recognizing their accomplishments and modeling the kind of behavior you seek in others.

Managing practices. You will also improve work climate when you and your staff:

- plan regular meetings to exchange information on progress and share learning;
- organize management systems, especially systems that promote work efficiency and information flow;
- implement activities that move your group toward your shared goals;
- monitor progress and use mistakes as sources for learning.

trusted colleagues in other parts of the organization who could guide their professional development.

It is important to be aware of different work styles and needs that people have for your support. Some may want a sympathetic ear, others want to explain themselves, and some just need help in setting limits or structuring their work. Men and women may have different needs when it comes to support. In the following staff descriptions of supervisors, the supervisors have different ways of supporting their staff. The staff who are quoted also appear to be differently motivated. The first staff member appreciates support for achieving results, while the second appreciates opportunities to affiliate:

> He holds people responsible. When they take on initiatives, they have [the] means, time, and money to help them get things done.

> One of the things that she changed is the attention to personal relationships with people at all levels in the department, using first names and inviting people into her office. She always tries to involve people by making personal connections.

Balance challenge, clarity, and support. To help your work group respond productively to changing circumstances, you may need to adjust the balance of challenge, clarity, and support. Staff who face challenges but lack support or clarity can experience stress and frustration. They may feel set up to fail. Without challenge or support, however, staff who are clear about expectations may find little intellectual and professional stimulation at work. When you find the right balance for your group's climate, you are on the way to helping your staff improve their performance.

Strengthening communication

"Have you ever thought you failed to communicate what you intended? Putting yourself on the receiver's end is one way of putting things right."

—LYDIA MUNGHERERA
NATIONAL FORUM OF PEOPLE LIVING WITH HIV/AIDS, UGANDA

To build the strong work relationships and balance of challenge, clarity, and support you need for a good work climate, it is critical to communicate in ways that encourage understanding and learning. Communicating effectively is a key leadership competency for developing a motivating work climate. When you communicate well, you help to create a work climate that encourages the flow of ideas and conversations where people learn from one another. In a learning conversation, people can ask questions in a sincerely curious, non-

Understand
others' work
styles and
needs

critical way. They seek to understand before being understood. They also feel free to discuss their own ideas and share their assumptions. Learning conversations help people reflect and be creative as they address their challenges.

To have meaningful communication, you absorb and reflect on what others are saying and then respond constructively in a way that others will find helpful. Small changes in the way you communicate can make a big difference in your work climate. In Nicaragua, municipal teams from the Ministry of Health built skills in interpersonal communication, coaching, and negotiation as a way to address poor morale. As a result, working relationships between supervisors and staff, coordination among departments, and work climate all improved.

Good communication improves morale

HEAR WHAT OTHERS HAVE TO SAY

As simple as it sounds, many people fail to thoughtfully hear and reflect on other people's comments. In a busy day, it can be hard to focus on something that does not seem immediately related to the task you are involved in. But people who are open to learning from each other know when to listen carefully and ask questions, and when to propose ideas. They deal with differing opinions and negative feelings before they cause conflict.

Listen carefully. A good place to start is with listening skills. Not listening when another person speaks indicates disinterest and lack of courtesy. When a coworker seeks your advice and you promise to give him time, it is important to listen fully to what he has to say and respond appropriately to his concerns. That means ignoring outside interruptions, such as phone calls. It means not reading unrelated materials or bringing up unrelated topics. If you cannot be fully present, propose a more convenient time and place for the conversation.

Be attentive to others

If people in your group have poor listening habits, you can address these through role plays of poor and good listening. You can also remind staff that it is particularly important to pay good attention to their clients, coworkers, and stakeholders. This simple skill can be powerful, as a colleague in Uganda noted:

> Effective listening encourages interpersonal relationships. Good listening improves morale. When leaders listen effectively (with full attention), they receive respect. This helps satisfy others' needs for self-esteem. As a result, the morale of the group improves.

Balance advocacy and inquiry. For lively discussions about work issues, encourage verbal give-and-take. Sometimes we promote our own view, hoping others will accept it and change their minds. This is called *advocacy*. At other times we are curious and try to understand the other's thinking and reasoning. This is called *inquiry*.

Encourage verbal give-and-take

Pay attention
to how you
communicate

To create a space where everyone learns from everyone else, first try reflecting on your pattern of communication. Do you tend to tell people what to do or think, or do you ask questions to learn where others are coming from? In your interactions with others, how do you balance these forms of communication? If you use only advocacy, you will not learn how others think and will limit your outlook. If you use only inquiry, you do not make your own voice heard and may have difficulty reaching consensus.

By observing your group over time you can determine how advocacy and inquiry are used, and whether there is a good balance or whether one is too dominant. If some people frequently advocate, do others stop listening to them? Do they feel ignored or overwhelmed with information? If some always inquire, do others see them as indecisive? Achieving balance between advocacy and inquiry in your group will improve the quality of the discussions and provide opportunities for staff to learn from each other.

Identify assumptions. When you promote the exchange of ideas, conflicting opinions will inevitably emerge. These are good, since better solutions often come from wrestling with differences. Identifying each person's assumptions will help in sorting out disagreements.

Different
assumptions
yield different
conclusions

From the massive amount of information that comes your way, you filter what is useful to you by making assumptions and interpretations, and then you draw conclusions. Your coworkers do the same, except the subset of data they pay attention to, and the assumptions and interpretations they use as a filter, can lead to very different conclusions. It is no surprise then that people can disagree strongly with others in the workplace.

When you ask each other questions, you can uncover people's assumptions and the reasons behind their initial conclusions. The Ladder of Inference is a useful model for understanding the assumptions that led to your conclusions.

The following scenario illustrates how people can apply the Ladder of Inference.

Roberto Suarez assigns Marina Costas to a task force for developing a clinic strategy to reach male clients. You disagree with Roberto's decision because you think Marina lacks good ideas, never having heard her speak in meetings. Your assumption is that staff with ideas share them in staff meetings. Roberto stubbornly defends his assignment. So far you have just advocated your point of view.

Then you shift your approach by inquiring into Roberto's reasoning. You ask him what he has observed about Marina that supports his decision. Roberto says that when he walks to the bus with Marina, she often suggests ways to help the clinic attract other kinds of clients. As Roberto expands the data you have about Marina, you change your interpretation and conclude the assignment makes sense. Over the next few months, Marina comes up with a number of creative approaches to reach male clients.

Climbing the Ladder of Inference

People base their conclusions on their interpretations of selected data and on what they observe other people saying and doing. When you and another person disagree, you can go back to the reasoning behind your conclusions. You can each disclose the data (the words or actions) you observed and your interpretations of them. Then *slowly* you can move up the Ladder of Inference, explaining to the other person, "This is what I am thinking and this is how I reached these conclusions." Together, you can find flaws in your selected data, interpretations, or conclusions, which will enrich your communication.

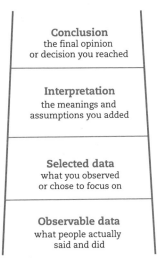

Conclusion
the final opinion
or decision you reached

Interpretation
the meanings and
assumptions you added

Selected data
what you observed
or chose to focus on

Observable data
what people actually
said and did

Source: Adapted from Argyris 1982 in THE FIFTH DISCIPLINE FIELDBOOK by Peter M. Senge, Charlotte Roberts, et al., copyright © 1994 by Peter M. Senge, Charlotte Roberts, Richard B. Ross, Bryan J. Smith, and Art Kleiner. Used by permission of Doubleday, a division of Random House, Inc.

If you and your group are able to question your assumptions and learn together, you are more likely to discover new ways to address your challenges.

Seek to understand diverse viewpoints. To introduce interesting viewpoints into your team, seek to hire capable people from diverse groups, especially those who represent your client population or skilled workers of the opposite gender. When you do this, you may need to help everyone on your team understand each other's way of communicating.

The same words and gestures can mean different things to different groups. They may also approach challenges differently. For example, one person may want to go straight to the point and make decisions quickly, and become annoyed with someone who wants to hear everyone's opinion first. This style of decision-making may irritate others. To keep diverse styles, temperaments, cultural norms, and gender dynamics from derailing conversations, patiently check assumptions about the meaning of words before reaching conclusions.

End conflict before it spreads. When you sense yourself entering into conflict with another person, step back and ask yourself "What brought me to this situation? What is happening?" Then put yourself in the other person's shoes and ask, "What would you do in his situation?" If at all possible, check your conclusions with the other person, revealing your reasoning (how you went up the Ladder of Inference). You can have more meaningful conversations when you clarify your thoughts, feelings, and beliefs and when you try to see things from the other person's perspective.

RESPOND CONSTRUCTIVELY

Once you clearly hear and understand what staff are saying, you are in a better position to respond in ways that help them. How they receive your feedback depends partly on how you deliver it. Simple changes in your style of communicating can clarify expectations, lift morale, and give people ways to deal with situations they complain about.

Think about how you give feedback

Give specific feedback. Providing helpful feedback is a great motivator of performance. You can reinforce a person's constructive action by letting the person know what you specifically appreciated about their action. For instance, you might comment, "I liked the way you organized the meeting agenda and kept time. We accomplished all we needed to and even finished early."

On the other hand, poorly delivered, critical feedback can make people feel resentful or helpless. In giving staff constructive feedback, you should avoid saying "You always . . . ." Rather, identify the specific action that bothers you

TABLE 6   **Shift from reactive to proactive language**

Reactive language	Proactive language
There's nothing I can do	Let's look at what we can do
That's just the way I am	How can I be more effective?
She makes me so mad	I can control how I feel
They won't allow that	Maybe we can negotiate
I have to do that	I choose to do what is appropriate
I must	I prefer
Should I?	I will
No one will help me	Will you?

Source: Stephen R. Covey, *The 7 Habits of Highly Effective People: Restoring the Character Ethic*, p. 78, text adapted (Fireside edition, 2004).

and indicate how it affects you and the group's work. Then you can request a different action from the person.

Balance the negative with the positive. When you find yourself giving critical comments about poor performance, you can balance these with positive comments. In meetings and informal conversations, pay attention to how often you share the things you like about your staff's work and how often you focus on what you want them to improve. A study of successful teams found that their conversations included, on average, five positive comments for every negative comment (Gottman 1994).

This balance is especially important if your group suffers from low morale and you tend to criticize. Consider decreasing your critical comments and increasing positive feedback to your staff. In discussions about performance, if you start off with genuinely positive comments, your staff are less likely to grow defensive and more likely to accept your suggestions. Also encourage staff members to give positive feedback to each other when their work deserves praise. However, positive feedback for mediocre work is dishonest and can encourage persistently mediocre work or even arouse cynicism.

Use proactive language. The language you use can be a self-fulfilling prophecy that helps to determine your and others' actions. To lead, it is important to use "proactive" language that enables you and others to face challenges

Be genuine with positive comments and constructive with criticism

---

Exercises to improve communication

The following exercises, found in the handbook toolkit, offer an opportunity to learn more about and practice communication skills.

Listening. To practice listening skills, you can refer to "The Art of Listening."

Balancing advocacy and inquiry. When there is no or little balance in your group's modes of communication, consider using the exercise "Balancing Advocacy and Inquiry: Changing the Pattern of Conversation."

Identifying assumptions. You will find a detailed process for using the Ladder of Inference in the exercise "Exploring Each Other's Thinking: The Ladder of Inference."

Ending conflict. If you are already involved in a conflict, you can use "Reflecting on Communication: The ORID Method" to carefully review what happened, separate your feelings and thoughts from what you observed, and make a fair decision or reach agreement with the person. ORID stands for: be Objective, Reflective, Interpretative, and Decisional.

Giving feedback. "Giving Useful Feedback" offers a way to practice constructive feedback.

Convert complaints into requests. You and your group can practice requesting help by using "Making Effective Requests and Reducing Complaints."

and create the future. Reactive language does not offer space for creating new possibilities. Think about the language you use when you encounter obstacles. How can you shift from words that close off options to language for overcoming obstacles? See Table 6 for examples.

Convert complaints into requests. You can shift the language that staff use as well, by encouraging them to convert the complaints they make when they feel discouraged into requests. Ask them to identify the person(s) they think can help remedy the situation. Then support them in asking that person to take a specific action and to act by a specific time. Remind them that if they get a negative answer to the request, they can always ask, "Then what *can* you do that would help?"

Your staff will sense your interest and support for their work when you listen, understand assumptions, and balance your responses with inquiry and positive, proactive comments. As you give staff specific feedback and suggestions for acting on their complaints, they will hear clear expectations and begin to feel empowered to seek assistance in facing their obstacles. All these communication strategies will help you achieve and maintain a positive work climate.

Sustaining your group's commitment

"True leaders are merchants of hope, speaking to the collective imagination of their followers, co-opting them to join them in a great adventure. Leaders inspire people to move beyond personal, egoistic motives—to transcend themselves, as it were—and as a result they get the best out of their people."
—MANFRED KETS DE VRIES
"ORGANIZATIONS ON THE COUCH"

Your ability to sustain a positive work climate also depends on your ability to inspire commitment in your team. Creating an initial vision with your team will go a long way toward engaging the team's commitment to addressing challenges. You can reinforce this commitment through conversation and actions that encourage individual staff to connect their own goals to this group effort. Over the long term, you can maintain your team's motivation if you keep an eye on your own behavior and apply techniques to sustain your staff's performance. You can:

- rekindle your commitment if it begins to fade;

- remain worthy of people's trust;

- balance commitment and compliance;

- acknowledge others' contributions;

- encourage your staff's performance through supportive techniques;

- foster learning that will encourage creative group solutions.

When you do these things continually, they become part of the prevailing work conditions that staff experience as a positive work climate. All contribute to an atmosphere in which your group's members feel inspired, clear about what they are doing, and supported in facing every challenge.

REKINDLE YOUR COMMITMENT

A support
network that
reinforces
hopes and
dreams

Leading any group requires hard work at a personal level, the courage to take significant risks, and the constant need to manage expectations of stakeholders and those who rely on you for direction. From time to time, when you find your commitment fading, you can take important steps to rekindle it. Remind yourself of your dreams for your community. Ask whether you are achieving personal growth and what you can do now to better satisfy your source of motivation. One way to do this is to form a support network of peers.

Developing a good support network involves selecting a group of people whom you know and trust to have your best interests at heart. It can help you learn how others handle similar work challenges, how others respond to your work style, and what changes you need to make in yourself and your work style to influence your group's commitment to good performance. These people can be honest, remind you of your direction, and tell you when you fall into old habits. This kind of support can go a long way toward rekindling your commitment.

REMAIN WORTHY OF PEOPLE'S TRUST

Mutual trust
through
integrity

Trust underlies everything that successful managers do with their work groups. Trust is essential for information exchange, problem solving, success of teams, enjoyment, and productivity. Being trustworthy means that others willingly rely on you because of your integrity, ability, and character. Team performance depends on mutual trust between you and the individuals in your team.

But trust takes time to build and maintain. If you didn't already know this intuitively, think of someone you trust. What have they done to earn your trust? There are things you can do to build trust and maintain it during times that test your resolve (see the box on the next page).

To reflect on your trustworthiness or to identify features that gain your colleagues' trust, refer to the exercise "Inspire through Building Trust at Work" in the handbook toolkit.

Building and maintaining trust

A study of managers (Bragar 1991) who were able to influence their colleagues effectively showed that they used the following practices to build and maintain trust.

Practices that build trust:

- agree on a code of conduct for your team
- keep your promises
- be clear about your intentions
- avoid gossip
- consider alternative viewpoints
- draw on the expertise and abilities of others
- be open to others' influence in making your decisions
- be fair in your treatment of others
- support staff in meeting standards and expectations
- look for causes of problems in work processes, not individuals
- increase your competence
- trust others and accept the vulnerability that comes from relying on them
- humbly and wisely admit mistakes, doubt, and uncertainty

Practices that maintain trust:

- consistent messages
- consistent standards and expectations
- strong group performance
- information for understanding organizational incidents
- availability to staff
- open discussion of large, disturbing issues

BALANCE COMMITMENT AND COMPLIANCE

As your commitment and communications inspire your staff to move ahead, you may still need to set some standards so their performance yields the desired results. First, it is important to understand the difference between commitment and compliance.

To continuously innovate, improve, and achieve sustainable results in health services, you need people who are committed to achieving those results. In many organizations it is also important to have compliance. To ensure the

TABLE 7   **Distinguishing commitment from compliance**

Commitment comes from inside a person. You do something because you care about the results. Compliance, on the other hand, is motivated by something outside you: the need to meet external requirements. You do it because you *must*.

Source of motivation	Outcome
Commitment (internally driven) You want to do something extraordinary You believe in it	Good results that you are proud of and care about
Compliance (externally driven) You have to do something	Obedience to orders and working according to a plan
Formal compliance You do just what is required and no more	Results that are expected
Noncompliance You don't do what is required	No results
Malicious noncompliance You purposely do the wrong thing, although you may not object openly	Negative or sabotaged results

Commitment unleashes energy to overcome obstacles

quality of health care, organizational or national standards or guidelines must be adhered to. You may choose to set a few performance standards for your group that relate to the results to which they have committed themselves. And sometimes people need to comply with new ways, before they can understand the changes well enough to be committed. Table 7 summarizes this difference.

It is important to balance mobilizing people for commitment and setting standards for compliance so your staff not only own their challenges, but are also aware of the standards they are expected to follow. Formal compliance produces many results. Commitment, however, is a key to encouraging staff to face obstacles, overcome resistance, and realize sustainable results. It unleashes the extra effort often needed to develop and implement creative, effective approaches.

> To explore the differences between commitment and compliance with a group, you can refer to "Gaining Commitment, Not Just Compliance" in the handbook toolkit.

ACKNOWLEDGE OTHERS' CONTRIBUTIONS

Praise and recognition bolster team spirit

As you balance commitment and compliance, make sure that you develop processes for acknowledging individuals' accomplishments. Recognizing others for positive contributions is a powerful motivator because it shows that someone is making a difference and her contributions are noticed. You can acknowledge another's efforts by thanking her directly, writing a personal note, and emphasizing her contribution in a formal work review. When you *publicly* congratulate individuals and teams, however, you foster a climate where all staff can say "Look what we can accomplish."

> ## Seven essentials of encouraging the heart
>
> **To start—**
>
> - Set clear standards. Clearly link specific goals and principles with rewards and recognition (for example, with an annual merit increase or bonus, or with opportunities for attendance at conferences).
>
> - Expect the best. Express confidence in your staff's good intentions and competence (for example, "You can do this. I know it.").
>
> - Pay attention. Look for positive examples of staff as they meet the standards. (For example, walk around, read, and notice good work practices and accomplishments.)
>
> **When you find a good example—**
>
> - Personalize recognition. Become familiar with the individual's preferences before you reward her good work. (For example, recognize the person with a carefully worded award that speaks to the interests of the individual.)
>
> - Tell the story. Describe the individual's efforts in a memorable and inspiring way. (For example, "I noticed that she observed the pharmacy serving long lines of clients and then figured out a way to speed service for medication refills.")
>
> - Celebrate together. Hold a party to show support for the whole group.
>
> - Set the example. Personally follow through on this process to show you mean these standards.
>
> Source: Adapted from Kouzes and Posner 1999

Acknowledge people's contributions to boost cooperation

A caveat about acknowledgment: Think carefully before singling out one person or one group. Word your recognition in such a way that everyone can feel proud about the accomplishment.

To encourage staff members to strive together for results and recognition, you can follow the "seven essentials of encouraging the heart." The essentials presented in the box above will make clear to everyone what kind of performance you are looking for.

You can also strengthen the group's team spirit by asking people to recognize each other's contributions. At any time, you can call a meeting and ask people to write a sentence on a piece of paper for every member of their team, beginning with the phrase "I acknowledge you for . . ." These acknowledgments can include what the other member has contributed to the team, to clients, or to the community. Have each person read his acknowledgement to the other members of the team. Through this process, your group members will grow more appreciative of each other's efforts and commit to producing desired results for each other.

ENCOURAGE PERFORMANCE THROUGH SUPPORTIVE TECHNIQUES

Besides public acknowledgments, you can adopt techniques to support your staff's performance. Some techniques can help you coach good performance, while others can help you manage performance issues if they arise.

Apply coaching techniques. Coaching is a conversation in which the manager is committed to the development and success of the person he is guiding. An effective coach cares about the person being coached. He builds a relationship of trust and listens well.

When you meet with a staff member as a coach, take time to observe and relate to the other person. Sense how things are going for the person and set a supportive tone. Then you can ask about her issues and point of view. Listen to her response, give her specific feedback, and repeat the process until you both agree on a course of action that she will take. This process is known as OALFA, for Observe, Ask, Listen, give Feedback, and Agree.

Coaching to encourage new behaviors

The questions you ask can help the person think through her commitments, results achieved, and obstacles that still need addressing. Through a guided inquiry, the staff member may see new possibilities and come up with new actions to strengthen her performance.

To learn more about coaching staff, refer to the exercises "Coaching to Support Others" and "Improving Coaching Skills: The OALFA Checklist," in the handbook toolkit.

Manage performance issues. Sometimes a staff member repeatedly falls short of meeting the standards you communicated. Keeping a record of occa-

---

Guided inquiry for coaching a staff member

A good coach asks questions and works with staff to find solutions. In this way, staff become more thoughtful about their performance and more skilled at solving problems independently. Some of the questions a coach can ask are:

- What are you committed to achieving?
- What have you achieved so far?
- What obstacles are you facing?
- Why do you think you are stuck?
- If it could turn out exactly as you dreamed, how would it turn out?
- What actions could you take to overcome your obstacles?
- What support do you need from others?
- How can I support you?

sions of poor performance can help you see patterns in performance, so that you have some objective information in considering possible causes of the inadequate performance. Your main source for this information is the staff member, but you may also want to look at what systems are in place to help staff work well. Find out if staff understand your performance expectations and if they have received feedback on their performance. Do current policies, procedures, and resource flows support and reward good performance? Do staff have the skills and training needed to perform well?

> Please refer to "Diagnosing Performance Problems" and "Giving Useful Feedback" in the handbook toolkit to pinpoint issues affecting staff's performance.

In discussing
poor
performance,
separate
feelings from
observations

It is important for you to give the person a warning and a chance to improve. Meet with a staff member who has performed poorly or been involved in an incident such as theft or disrespectful or dishonest interactions with others. To protect yourself from being overwhelmed by strong emotions, you can prepare for the conversation using the ORID method (be Objective, Reflective, Interpretative, and Decisional). With ORID, you can carefully review what happened, separating your feelings and thoughts from what you observed, and then reach a decision with the person that re-engages him in the task at hand. During the meeting you can also apply techniques already mentioned in this chapter: the OALFA process, specific feedback, and positive comments on things that the person has done well.

> For more information on ORID, please see the exercise "Reflecting on Communication: The ORID Method" in the handbook toolkit.

ENCOURAGE SHARED LEARNING

Learning new things on the job can inspire staff members' enthusiasm, creativity, and commitment. Here, we refer to learning as *expanding the ability to produce intended results.*

Create
opportunities
for learning
that promote
growth

One way for you to encourage continuous learning is to create opportunities for staff to share their knowledge and best practices. Collecting and sharing information contributes to achieving a positive work climate and helps produce the desired results. Not only does the group gain information about its progress toward results, it also learns what has worked and what has not. It can then apply these lessons to its ongoing work.

Be humble and manage expectations. To learn from one another over the long term involves a group commitment to learning. Becoming conscious of what you do not know requires humility on everyone's part. Then you can all seek out new skills and information, and change your attitudes, so that everyone becomes more competent. This continuous motion from unawareness to awareness is what drives learning.

Show that you don't know it all

- When people look at you for an answer, turn the question back to them.

- Listen to others first when you have an urge to pronounce your opinion.

- Wait until someone else says what you want to say (and then if no one does, you can say it).

- Ask people: What would you do if you were me? What should we do?

- Acknowledge the authors of successful ideas and suggestions.

- Learn to say "I don't know."

- Ask for help from your staff and peers.

- Inform your staff about the complexities of the work (make connections visible).

- Explore the consequences of decisions.

- Involve your staff in "what if" thinking.

- Admit mistakes promptly and apologize if necessary.

Improve team learning. In groups that learn well together, people generally assume different team roles. Some common roles in teams are that of initiator, follower, opposer, or observer. When faced with a difficulty, someone initiates an idea or action to address the situation. Another follows or accepts the idea so it gains momentum. A third person opposes or questions the idea, which encourages the group to refine the idea by exploring its drawbacks. Finally, someone observes and gives feedback on the group's progress.

Balance team members' roles

Groups can become stuck on less-than-optimal solutions when one or more persons dominate the discussion while others tend to follow, or when someone constantly disagrees. In such a climate, much of the team's creative talent remains untapped. To function well, a group needs to find a balance for all four roles.

To help your group apply these roles, you can use the exercise "Understanding Roles in Teamwork" in the handbook toolkit.

By continually modeling commitment, maintaining trust, acknowledging accomplishments, developing support processes, and learning with your staff, you create a climate that maintains group dedication to results. Before you begin your effort to build a more positive work climate, you may want to assess the climate of your group. This assessment will give you a basis for determining the effects of the changes you introduce.

Applying the Work Climate Assessment

The Work Climate Assessment, developed by MSH's Management and Leadership Program, is designed to measure work climate in work groups at all organizational levels. Assessing work climate provides insight into group members' perceptions of what it feels like to work in their team. You can discuss the results with your group and use insights gained from this discussion to direct your change effort. You can also use the assessment as a monitoring tool by applying it as a baseline survey and then repeating it later to assess progress.

The tool is designed to be completed by all members of a work group. It consists of 10 items. Eight items, validated through an evaluation, measure elements of work group climate. The last 2 items assess work group perceptions of quality and productivity. Each group member rates the 10 items on a scale of 1 to 5. The items are:

Climate items

1. We feel our work is important.

2. We strive to achieve successful outcomes.

3. We have a plan that guides our activities.

4. We pay attention to how well we are working together.

5. We understand each other's capabilities.

6. We seek to understand the needs of our clients.

7. We understand the relevance of the job of each member in our group.

8. We take pride in our work.

Perceptions of productivity and quality

9. Our work group is known for its quality work.

10. Our work group is productive.

An independent facilitator guides the process of collecting and analyzing the data to maintain the confidentiality of group members' responses. In discussing the overall results, your group may articulate how it wants to work together in the future. Or individual members may voice their opinions to the facilitator. As the group's manager, your role is to support your staff in making a commitment to a new work climate and to provide the clarity needed.

For the complete assessment tool and instructions on how to use it, please refer to the handbook CD-ROM.

Setting the tone at the senior level

"Daily one gets carried away by the power that one has to change the quality of our people's lives, simply by creating space for initiatives and innovations. What inspires me is the level of commitment and resolve my team has, and their enthusiasm to add value to what we are doing in South Africa."

—DR. SIPHIWO STAMPER
DEPARTMENT OF HEALTH
EASTERN CAPE PROVINCE, SOUTH AFRICA

Choose allies carefully to initiate change

If you are a senior manager, you have a critical role to play in setting the tone for the organization by articulating and living the values that you want the organization to embody. You can make far-reaching changes simply by starting to operate in a different way. For example, if you want transparency and honesty, you must be transparent and honest. If you want a focus on clients and results, show it in all your conversations about work. Setting the tone at the senior level requires discipline and humility, each and every day.

To set a new tone, you need allies. Make sure you have the support of important peers and superiors, for example, the board or the minister, and secure their full commitment before you go ahead. Be sure to engage your peers in the senior management team in this change initiative.

ENGAGE YOUR MANAGEMENT TEAM

Reconnect your staff to field realities

It is important to anchor the work climate you want to create in a shared vision for your organization or ministry. (See chapter 2 and the handbook toolkit for visioning exercises.) Before creating such a vision, however, you may need to prepare your management team. At times, senior managers lose track of the program's purpose because they are far removed from the program's ultimate beneficiaries. They sometimes become immersed in the complexities of the political or economic environment; unclear, shifting donor priorities; or their reputation and opportunities for securing more attractive positions. If so, reconnect your team with service providers or people politically committed to improving health services.

> As part of a strategic planning exercise, senior managers from various agencies and divisions involved in Zimbabwe's National Family Planning Program fanned out over the city of Mutari and into the countryside to visit clinics and youth centers, and follow community-based distribution agents and their supervisors over difficult terrain. They returned with a vivid picture of the challenges that they faced and took these field realities into account in their subsequent strategic planning.

Improve factors that undermine work climate. Once you have a vision, you can begin reflecting with other senior managers on the organization's culture and ways you could go about changing it to move toward the vision. Perhaps your organization's history and culture may once have inspired people but are currently crippling the organization's momentum because times have changed. Examine the factors related to work climate that undermine performance or productivity throughout the organization. And cultivate a positive work climate in your own senior management team.

ORGANIZE A SUPPORT NETWORK

A good support network is especially important for senior managers. With such a network, you will be able to influence your organization's work climate and much more. When senior managers form networks of peers, they come to realize that in banding together, they can "move mountains." They can publicly question unmentionable practices, such as siphoning off resources,

A strong support network can move mountains

> **Improving work relationships, group climate, and performance—Example from Senegal**
>
> Concerned about the underperformance of its districts, the Ministry of Health of Senegal initiated a Leadership Development Program in two regions for teams from 14 districts. The district teams identified a challenge in maternal and child health or family planning and learned how to improve their leading and managing practices and competencies so that they could face their challenge. In the first of four bimonthly meetings, each team assessed its work group climate. The teams also discussed motivation and relations with internal and external clients. In subsequent meetings, they built their leadership competencies through exercises to improve team communication, emotional intelligence, and commitment. Working on their challenge also provided ample opportunity for them to consciously adjust the ways in which they worked together.
>
> **Better communication among team members.** At the end of the four-month program, participants said they were able to listen better and put themselves "in other people's shoes." They experienced better control over their emotions, especially anger, so that when faced with a conflict, they remained calm. They could successfully mediate to prevent the conflict from growing. Participants shared much more information with their team than in the past. As one participant summed up, "We have become more receptive, tolerant, and open."
>
> **Staff committed to teamwork and results.** Teamwork has become the norm. Rather than seeing each other as superiors or subordinates, staff now see themselves as colleagues working together toward a common goal. Senior members of the team stopped giving orders. People who tended to work

that severely hamper the delivery of health services in the field. Feeling safe about questioning such practices is possible if you can count on support in high places.

> In their discussions, senior managers in a West African Ministry of Health began to realize that their behavior had something to do with how their subordinates reacted to them. Some team leaders recognized that they created passivity and dependence among their staff, even as they complained about how passive and dependent their staff were. The leaders also realized that they often triggered their own crises and sometimes blamed these crises on someone else. By reflecting together on their own experiences with motivation, delegation, and communication, they discovered that what motivates them can often motivate others. This was a starting point for significant change.

By engaging your management team and organizing a support network of senior managers, you can create the kind of work climate in which managers at all levels can lead. Do not leave this important task to someone else.

Improving work relationships, group climate, and performance— Example from Senegal *(cont.)*

alone or were seen as "difficult" are now working with others, allowing team members to learn from one another for the first time. Most importantly, all are committed to producing intended results. They used to drop their plans or get discouraged when they encountered obstacles. As one participant says, "Now we count on our own strength" and find almost all solutions rest "on our doorstep."

Improved work climate. Work climate assessment scores before and after the program also indicated that the teams perceived an improved work climate. Among other things, the changes signaled an increase in mutual trust.

Service results. A positive work climate and motivated staff have contributed to improved services and produced measurable results. Four of the eight teams that had collected data at the end of the program met or surpassed their performance objectives. Depending on the challenge they had chosen, different districts reported that the majority of births were now assisted (67%, up from 35%) or were assisted by qualified personnel (100%, up from 75%); postpartum visits (two) were completed (more than 50%, up from 37%); or prenatal visits (three) were completed (17%, up from 9%; and 59%, up from 12%).

By addressing service delivery challenges and building leadership competencies simultaneously, district teams in Senegal have created a work climate in which all team members feel encouraged to work through barriers to strengthening services.

In a number of countries, district teams have improved their work climate as they have applied leading and managing practices to strengthen health care services. The day-to-day struggle to achieve a desired result, if approached from a leadership perspective, can change how staff members interact and how they feel about working with their peers.

Achieving a positive work climate

"The best thing we gained is that we perform our work as a team, not as individuals. If something affects one person, it affects the whole team. If we are faced with a constraint, we take a poll of each other's opinions to try to overcome it."

—SUHEIR SABRY SIAM
ASWAN HEALTH DISTRICT, EGYPT

When staff feel they are engaged in meaningful work and belong to a good team led by an inspiring manager, they experience a positive work climate. They also contribute to creating and maintaining this positive climate. In this atmosphere, everyone strives to learn, do what she needs to do, and avoid disappointing her colleagues. You often see this kind of cooperation in sports events, where the players count on each other to perform well and cover for each other when needed. Behind every great team is a committed coach who encourages this behavior. The coach understands the players' motivations and capabilities. He organizes their positions, builds their skills, and channels their energy into coordinated actions that produce results.

Build a climate
of teamwork
and support

Similarly, your style of communicating, coaching, and acknowledging individuals can continually mobilize your team to put forth its best, for each other and for clients. Working and learning well together, staff will overcome obstacles to produce remarkable results. These prevailing work conditions will sustain group commitment over the years, as current challenges are addressed and new challenges emerge. As you move up the leadership ladder in your organization, you can create a work climate in each of your work groups that keeps you and your group energized, enthusiastic, and motivated to move mountains.

Questions to consider on . . .

Improving work climate to strengthen performance

Current work climate and organizational culture

- How would you characterize the current work climate of your group?

- What aspects of the current work climate are undermining your group's efforts to address key challenges and achieve results?

- What elements from the broader organizational culture are influencing the current work climate of your group? Which ones can you do something about, and which are outside your control?

The best work climate for your group

- What sort of work climate would motivate your work group?

- What are the easiest things you can do to improve the group's work climate? The most challenging? Which areas require support from higher levels? Which can you do on your own?

Leadership competencies to improve the climate

- How does your behavior influence the work climate? What do you think you need to change in yourself to improve the work climate?

- What sort of communication breakdowns are most common in your team? What can you do about these?

- What is the most important thing you can do to gain your group's commitment to achieving results?

4 Moving up the leadership ladder

"We turn out . . . to realize our greater potentialities . . . by viewing our own individual crises as opportunities to let go of who we have been, and to set forth on the journey toward becoming something more."
—WILLIAM BRIDGES
THE WAY OF TRANSITION

When someone moves to a higher position in an organization, this progression is called a leadership transition. People tend to think of leadership transitions as those that occur at the top level of an organization when the head of the organization leaves and a new person steps in. But leadership transitions take place at all levels of an organization, every time people move from one level to the next. These transitions increase the person's scope of responsibility and accountability for the performance of increasingly larger parts of the organization.

This chapter explores the ways in which your role changes as you move up the organizational hierarchy. It builds on the skills needed to develop a positive work climate and encourage strong team performance, and shows how these skills should be applied at each management level. We explore four typical levels of transition:

- becoming a first-time manager who leads: Level One;

- moving from managing a team to managing other managers: Level Two;

- becoming a senior manager: Level Three;

- leading and managing at the top: Level Four.

This chapter also discusses the important role that managers at all levels have in grooming those below them to become competent managers who lead, so that there is a constant flow of qualified people in the pipeline to take on increasingly more complex and senior roles in the organization.

Building a pipeline of managers who lead

"The major job of leaders is to develop other leaders."

—NOEL TICHY
THE LEADERSHIP ENGINE

Leadership transitions, except those at the very top, are often not very visible in an organization. Part of the reason for this is that when people move from one level of responsibility to a higher one, we rarely refer to those changes as leadership transitions. More commonly, we call these transitions *promotions*.

Technical expertise is not enough

In many cases, when people are promoted or move into new positions, they are not prepared to take on new management and leadership roles and responsibilities. Outstanding technical expertise is often considered a sufficient qualification for moving someone into a managerial or leadership position. For example, good doctors and nurses are frequently promoted with little consideration of their management or leadership capabilities. When someone from the outside is hired, you may not realize that he is making a significant transition in taking a position with management and leadership responsibilities. This may be a role that he is not fully prepared to handle, in spite of having excellent technical qualifications.

Researchers who have studied the progressions of managers in organizations have observed that job requirements are qualitatively different from one level to another (Jaques and Cason 1994). At each level, the time horizon (or scope of time that relates to the position's role in planning for the future) and the complexity of the job expand. These changes require increasingly complex mental processing abilities.

Each transition requires expanding one's time horizon

When people work at levels that are above what they can handle (a time horizon and level of complexity that they cannot quite grasp), they are unable to focus on their leadership and management tasks, and often do the work they are most comfortable doing, which tends to be the work of a lower level. As a supervisor, it is the manager's job to groom lower-level staff for taking on new management and leadership responsibilities, and when they are promoted, to support them so that they can perform well in their new role.

GROOMING MANAGERS FOR LEADERSHIP TRANSITIONS

Ram Charan introduced the image of a leadership "pipeline" and asserts that, if whatever is flowing through it gets stuck, the pipeline will not deliver the resource it contains (Charan et al. 2001). Where the pipeline shifts direction, things can easily get stuck. It is the task of managers who lead to help those who get stuck to move on (up or out), and make room for others.

Organizations that recognize that people do not become great leaders overnight have instituted organizational practices that develop staff to take on increasingly complex leading and managing roles. In this way, organizations effectively build a pipeline of leadership talent and support their staff in making these important leadership transitions.

To keep the pipeline full with qualified staff, it is critical that managers understand that at each level there are significant changes in the time horizon, priorities, relationships, and tasks people must deal with and differences in the skills and management and leadership practices they need. How successfully people adjust to these changes and differences will determine how well they and others flow through the pipeline.

In his book *Leadership without Easy Answers,* Ronald Heifetz urges leaders to "get off the dance floor and onto the balcony," where they can get a broader view of the scene below. At each subsequent transition, the manager moves up to the next "balcony" (see Figure 9). As the manager moves up in the hierarchy of the organization, the details of the people on the dance floor begin to recede, while the overall setting in which the dance takes place becomes more and more visible. This metaphor illustrates the challenge of managing leadership transitions: to make sure that the balconies (levels), the rhythm of the people who dance, and the beat of the music are all in harmony with one another.

Through the four levels of leadership transition presented in this chapter, we discuss the changes that are inherent in moving up to the next "balcony." The tasks, capabilities, and shifts in mindset that are required to perform effectively at each level are grouped into five key areas, each of which becomes more complex as you move up the hierarchy:

FIGURE 9   **From stage to balcony: A change in perspective**

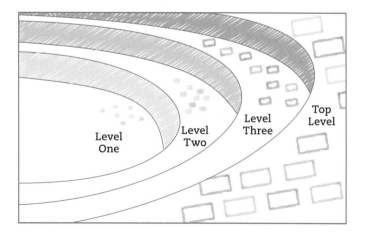

Being at a higher level provides a different perspective and
helps you see patterns that are not obvious at the ground level

- *Time horizon* or time frame for which you need to plan and achieve results;

- *Priorities* for your attention;

- *Types of relationships* that you need to cultivate and manage;

- *Tasks* or core responsibilities;

- *Leading and managing skills and practices* that support high performance.

Watch for signs of derailment

Signs of derailment (presented in boxes in this chapter) indicate that the manager is not adequately performing at the requisite level and needs to improve his skills and practices before being considered for a higher-level position. It is the responsibility of the supervisor to see these signs and provide support and coaching so that a manager can be competent and effective.

Since the transitions described in this chapter are generic, they might not quite fit your specific situation. Sometimes people move back and forth between being an individual contributor and member of a team, to managing a team and being responsible for its overall performance. The challenges involved in these roles are different. This chapter is about the challenge of rising up the managerial ladder and helping others to do the same. The ability to adjust to new priorities and acquire the appropriate competencies at each level is essential to successfully making these transitions.

Becoming a first-time manager who leads: Level One

"I didn't set out to be a leader; I set out to be a good worker. I set out to learn and be led by people who knew better than me so that I could learn from them."

—DR. PETER MUGYENYI, EXECUTIVE DIRECTOR
JOINT CLINICAL RESEARCH CENTRE, UGANDA

Consider this story of Maria de Souza, a successful nurse who has been promoted to be the manager of a unit in which she used to work. No matter how well respected she is as an excellent nurse or how good her clinical skills are, if one member of her unit is not productive or provides care below quality standards, it becomes her problem. She is responsible for the results of the whole unit, not just for her own work or that of a few star performers. When her staff lack needed resources, Maria is now responsible for solving the problem.

For Sonny Gonzales, who is a physician, the situation is even more challenging, since he went directly from being a medical student—with all the attention on developing clinical skills—to being the head of a small rural health center. In many countries, these first postings are in remote areas, with a supervisor who is not on site. Even when the supervisor comes for a supervisory visit, the focus is most likely on clinical skills, not how to manage or lead a team. Sonny was seriously challenged in managing the dynamics between the staff in his health center and felt he was "being thrown into the deep water to sink or swim."

The first transition entails new priorities

These examples illustrate that the first transition, from being an individual contributor as a clinical service provider to being a manager of others, is challenging. This may be the first time in your professional career that you cannot let a conflict go unaddressed, even if it does not directly affect your own performance as a service provider. At each leadership transition, there will be less time to provide services to clients yourself and more demands on your time to be a manager who *enables* the work of others.

As a manager who leads, any problem affecting your staff is also *your* problem. Thus, as a manager at this first transition, not only do you have to learn a new set of skills, but you also have to pay attention to new priorities, cultivate new relationships, and practice new behaviors that reflect that your work now includes the work of those who report to you.

A SHIFT IN TIME HORIZON

Anticipate changes in the health environment

A significant shift in the first transition is a change in your time horizon. Before, you were responsible only for your own timeliness—arriving at work on time and completing assigned tasks and duties on time. The time span you were responsible for ranged from one day to a few weeks, or at most one month. Now you are responsible for the accomplishments of your unit's tasks over a longer period of time as measured by, for example, quarterly service delivery results. You also have to anticipate changes such as seasonal fluctuations in disease patterns and the corresponding resource requirements, and develop plans to make sure your team is prepared. You have to anticipate things you never had to think about before. Your time horizon has shifted from a day or a week to several months or may be even a year. You are no longer only on the dance floor; you also need to go up periodically to the next balcony to survey the scene.

NEW PRIORITIES

To be successful in this new role, you will also need to make a shift in how to direct your energy and spend your time. You now have to pay attention to and value the success of others, and put it ahead of your own need to be seen

Broaden your perspective

as a successful service provider. You have to be available and accessible to your staff, listen to their needs, give them feedback on their performance, and coach them to become more successful.

If you lead a team with people representing various specialties or functions (maternal and child health, family planning, child survival, infectious diseases, nutrition, and others), you also need to give each of those as much attention as you used to give to your own specialty. This shift is not easy, especially if you always believed that your specialty or your skills were more important than those of others.

NEW RELATIONSHIPS

As a newly promoted manager you need to build and maintain a network of relationships that will help your team be effective. This network of relationships may be different from the one you had before your promotion. Consider the following example.

> Pauline Ntumba used to work as a family planning nurse in a health center. Although she knew about some of the resistance in the religious community about family planning, she did not have to deal with the problem directly. When she was promoted to be the head of the family planning clinic in the district hospital, she had to pay more attention to the community leaders and try to turn her opponents into supporters. To do this, she initiated a dialogue with the religious leaders in the district and engaged them in finding common ground, such as a concern for the health and well-being of their people. In this way, Pauline learned to strategize to get support from people whom she had never had to deal with when she was primarily a service provider.

Talk with influential people outside and inside your organization

In this new position you have to learn many new things as you establish relationships with people other than your patients or clients. You will need to learn:

- whom to talk with in the community, government, and private sector;

- what influence these people have on others, particularly on your clients;

- what the various political agendas are, and how to reconcile those agendas with your organization's or program's goals.

Within your organization, you will need to know:

- how to redefine your relationship with those who were formerly your peers and who now report to you;

- who can help you get access to which resources;

- who the power brokers are so that you can get things done and get the resources your staff need;

- how to redefine your relationships with those who were formerly your peers and who now report to you.

If you live in a remote rural area, you will spend much of your waking hours with your staff. If they were formerly your peers, you will need to create new relationships with them that are both collegial and supportive, without denying that you are now also their supervisor. This change will be particularly difficult if there was any jealousy about your promotion or if your promotion was contested.

TASKS OF THE FIRST-LEVEL MANAGER

The success of your whole team is what matters

If this is your first transition into a position of leadership, you will need to make a number of significant shifts. Before this transition to leading teams, your success was measured by the quality and timeliness of your work, being punctual, and having positive interactions with patients and colleagues. Now, as a team leader, your success is measured by the success of your entire team.

At this level, you are responsible for helping each person on your team to perform his job well, and for supporting good relationships among the team members so you can reach your goals. Even if you complete all your assignments in a timely way and they are of high quality, if the rest of your team (or even one person on the team) is not performing well, then it is your job to work with individual members of the team to build their strengths and to make sure that the team performs well as a whole.

At this stage of transition you will usually continue to carry out your old job of working directly with patients and perform additional tasks. But now you also need to:

- make sure that the work of your team is clearly defined;

- make sure that tasks are assigned to the right person;

- spot new tasks and distribute them among the team;

- make sure that each team member has the resources and support needed to do her job well.

CRITICAL SKILLS FOR LEVEL ONE

To help you successfully navigate the transition, you will need to learn and be comfortable with using the following skills:

Designing and
assigning tasks

Organizing work. Often called work design, organizing work is the ability to match a (new) piece of work with the strengths of individual team members. Doing so requires understanding the particular tasks and the skills needed to do the work and deciding who is most likely to succeed in doing those tasks. For example, if you find that a rumor is circulating that puts your clinic in an unfavorable light, you need to find the source of the rumor, then rebuild trust within the community. If you think that you are not in the best position to resolve the issue, then you need to design a task and find the right person to accomplish it.

Delegating. Delegating is the ability to hand over the information, authority, and resources to someone on your staff while retaining full accountability for results. Delegation is not the same as abdicating, or handing over work to your staff and then withdrawing your attention. By having regular meetings and discussions in which you review progress and address challenges, you can build your team's confidence and problem-solving skills. This follow-up will also increase your confidence in their ability to make good decisions.

Recruiting staff. This ability refers to selecting or hiring the right people for a job. You need to pay attention to such issues as fit with the culture of your unit ("how we do things here") and that of the larger organization. If you have the authority to hire new staff, you will need to resist the urge to hire people who are most like you and the temptation to hire friends, relatives, or people with similar backgrounds or political leanings. Hiring people from different backgrounds makes workplaces richer, as long as everyone is competent to do his job and you are able to handle the dynamics. Be clear about the job requirements and skills you are looking for. Hiring people who are not up to the task will harm them, you, your team's performance, and possibly your reputation.

Network with
others to gain
support

Networking. The ability to find and nurture relationships with people and groups inside and outside the immediate workplace, including people higher up in the organizational hierarchy, is networking. Effective networking requires that you understand your organization, program, or division's management structure and that you know how to connect yourself and your team to those in power. Being connected enables you to get the information and resources that you need. If you are far away from the center, you have to work hard at staying connected by communicating regularly with others outside your immediate workplace.

Networking can also be useful for psychological support. In a place where women are rarely in positions of authority, it may be useful to seek out other women in similar positions so you can support each other. In some places, it may be useful to network with the business community or such groups as the Rotary Club. Your relationships are often as important as the authority of your position when it comes to getting things done.

LEADING AND MANAGING PRACTICES AT LEVEL ONE

To be successful as a first-level manager you will need to incorporate the leading and managing practices that address the elements of time horizon, priorities, relationships, tasks, and skills. These can be organized according to the key practices of the Leading and Managing for Results Model presented in chapter 1. Table 8 lists leading and managing practices that are useful for the first-level transition. Ask your supervisor to give you feedback and support so that you can perform these practices well at this stage before moving on to the next. And remember, once you are promoted to the next level, you will need to do the same with your new supervisees!

TABLE 8 **Key leading and managing practices for the first-level manager**

Practice	What to do
Scanning Focusing Planning	■ Pay attention to what is going on inside and outside your team. ■ See the relationship between yourself and your team as part of the larger management structure. ■ Observe and talk with patients and community members to identify health needs, and gauge your team's performance in addressing those needs. ■ Help your team identify their challenges and their responsibilities in meeting those challenges as a team. ■ Be able to describe the team's challenges within the context of the organization's mission. ■ Help people prioritize their tasks.
Aligning Mobilizing Organizing Implementing	■ Provide opportunities for the members of your team to see how their work fits together and serves the organization's goals through exchanges, visits, reading, new assignments, and partnering with other teams. ■ Hold discussions to align with others outside your team about desired goals or vision, gaps, priorities, expectations, and deadlines. ■ Match staff skills and motivation to jobs. ■ Facilitate the work of your staff by removing obstacles to performance.
Inspiring Monitoring Evaluating	■ Model a trusting attitude, respect, and integrity in all your interactions inside and outside the team. ■ Conduct performance evaluations and give people feedback on how they are doing. ■ Track the measurable progress of the team and share your findings. ■ Recognize individual and collective contributions to organizational goals.

SIGNS OF DERAILMENT

This first transition is difficult and the shifts are more fundamental than most managers realize. Not surprisingly, there are quite a few derailments at this stage. These derailments are serious if they are not spotted and corrected, because they will cause trouble later when the manager is promoted to the next managerial level. Therefore, it is important for the manager's supervisor to pay attention to potential derailments and provide support, so that the manager can overcome them. As Charan and his coauthors note, when derailments happen, the pipeline becomes clogged with people who have been promoted but who cannot manage and lead at the higher levels. Such bottlenecks become increasingly difficult to clear.

Signs of derailment at the first level

- Inability to delegate work to team members
- Competition with or micromanaging team members who work in the area of one's expertise
- Tendency to consider time spent coaching or supporting team members as wasteful or unproductive
- Considering questions or requests for help from supervisees as if they were interruptions
- Recurrent urge to fix supervisees' mistakes, rather than teaching them how to prevent them in the future
- Tendency to maintain distance from team members' mistakes and successes
- Tendency to treat patients, communities, and government officials as outsiders

---

Moving from managing a team to managing other managers: Level Two

"Inexperienced managers are tremendously impressionable, and they naturally model the actions and attitudes of bosses. If their bosses are either unwilling to set a proper example and help them develop in the right direction, the leadership pipeline is clogged at its source."

—RAM CHARAN ET AL.
THE LEADERSHIP PIPELINE

At this level you become a manager of other managers. You might think that the second transition would not be as significant as the first, since you already have a managerial mindset. But this transition represents the first time that you need to develop and support other managers as they go through their first transition. If you do not support the new first-level manager and you overlook signs of derailment, you will compromise the entire pipeline.

At this level, there is a new series of shifts in time horizon, relationships, and tasks that requires the application of new skills and leading and managing practices.

A SHIFT IN TIME HORIZON

You may have been promoted to this management level because you are a superb clinician: you have a good track record for delivering quality services. You have strong clinical skills and are seen as an example of the kind of service providers the organization or program needs. Unfortunately, service delivery no longer represents the majority of your work.

Strategic planning at Level Two

At this level, anticipating the needs of other levels requires expanding your time horizon to approximately three years. Planning and predicting the activities for just one year is very different from planning and predicting the activities and requirements for the next three years. To plan this far ahead, you need to know more about the larger strategic context within which your program operates, spot trends farther away, and look for synergies and opportunities. That is precisely why you need to get off the dance floor, so you can expand your view and see more of the bigger picture!

NEW PRIORITIES AND RELATIONSHIPS

With an extended time horizon you will be planning with your team for activities and results farther into the future. You will be concerned not only

Developing
a network of
relationships
to support
your goals

with collaboration among your team members, but also with establishing collaborative relationships with groups outside your immediate work setting. You will look for and build collaboration across functional areas within your program or organization, among the programs and organizations in the public and private sectors, and even with ministries or organizations whose focus is not health.

You will also be seeking to establish supportive relationships with district authorities and politicians and with local organizations and leaders in the community in which your organization works. Among your new priorities will be the need to establish and nurture these relationships and garner commitment in your mutual goals to serve the health needs of the population.

Provide support appropriate to people's skills and interests

Sometimes health professionals switch back and forth between management and clinical positions during their careers. You may discover that some people feel more useful or productive as individual contributors and that others are thriving as managers. It is important to acknowledge those strengths and preferences and support people's ability to perform well at the appropriate levels. After all, management and leadership may not be the right fit for some people. In that case, it is better to use their skills as individual contributors, for example, as an advisor (consultant) or senior-level service provider.

Another type of transition is the shift from a field-based position to a headquarters position. This change poses a new set of challenges requiring the ability to scan broadly and take responsibility for a wider horizon of projects and programs while not being based in the field. Ideally, people will move back and forth between headquarters and the field to allow for a cross-fertilization of perspectives from these different vantage points.

TASKS OF THE SECOND-LEVEL MANAGER

The transition
from service
provider to
manager

As a manager of managers, your time spent managing will increase. This new role is especially hard for professionals who were trained to do clinical work, such as doctors, nurses, and midwives. As a manager of managers, you are now responsible for the performance of a small facility or a department that comprises several functions, some of which will be completely new to you (for example, human resource management, pharmaceutical and commodity management, financial management, and public relations).

To make sure that the managers who report to you receive the necessary support so that each of their units can fulfill its mandate, your job is to take care that:

- there are sufficient supplies of pharmaceuticals and commodities;

- the premises are clean and safe;

- the finances are in good shape and can pass an audit;

- service statistics are reliable and up-to-date;

- reports are submitted on time;

- the facility and its services comply with government standards and regulations.

You are also responsible for the facility's reputation in the community, good relationships with authorities and community leaders, and producing the results that are spelled out in the annual and three-year plans.

> Consider Fatma Mahmoudi, a newly appointed head of a department. Having made the shift from unit leader of prenatal care to department head at the provincial level, she is no longer responsible for the performance of individual service providers. She is now more than one level removed from "where the action is" and instead needs to support the various unit leaders. Fatma was used to having contact with clients and finds it hard to get used to this distance.

You may be like Fatma and need to resist the temptation of returning to the dance floor to help those individuals whose dancing needs to be improved. When you see a performance problem with a staff member, you may want to intervene directly with that person. But your responsibility now lies in helping the first-level managers improve the performance of their staff. If you bypass a manager, you will usurp her authority and undermine her credibility and success as a manager.

Help first-level managers to support their staff

Standing on the balcony rather than on the dance floor means that you need to watch how people dance together. If someone is out of pace or needs assistance, make a mental note of it and talk with the team leader who is responsible for that person's performance. In the end, this approach will be more helpful, and you will be teaching the team leader to be more proactive when there are performance problems at the service level.

In organizations where managerial work is not valued, or worse, seen as a waste of time, managers may feel ineffective. The irony is that by being a good manager and exercising managerial leadership you contribute directly to the performance of your department and to the organization as a whole by increasing efficiency, reducing duplication of effort, and having staff carry out work that is well matched to their skills and interests.

CRITICAL SKILLS FOR LEVEL TWO

To help you successfully navigate the transition to this level, you will need to learn and be comfortable with using the following skills:

Spotting leadership talent. One of the most important responsibilities at this level is to identify leadership potential among individual providers who are capable of becoming first-time managers who lead. People often look at the quality of providers' clinical services, but that is no guarantee of future leadership success. As a second-level manager, you need to sharpen your observation skills and identify people who have good communication and interpersonal skills, can make good decisions under pressure, can manage their own stress levels, are eager to learn, and have an interest in managerial work.

Giving constructive feedback and support. Once new first-level managers have been identified, you need to work with their supervisors to identify ways to groom them for managerial leadership. This preparation may include giving a person specific assignments, such as leading a task force or a committee. But that is not enough. The unit leader needs to closely supervise these new experiences. As the supervisor of the unit leader, you need to provide constructive feedback and support to the unit leader, who, in turn, provides feedback to the individual being groomed. All parties need to apply good judgment and have a good sense of timing in providing such feedback.

Holding first-level managers accountable for results and managerial work. Your challenge is not to go over the head of the unit leader and pressure individuals to produce results, but rather to hold the unit leader accountable and offer feedback and support when needed. Meeting this challenge requires meeting regularly with each of your staff and keeping a watchful eye on what happens in the facility or department (this has been called management by walking around).

Deploying and redeploying resources among units or teams. Assigning human resources requires close contact with each of your staff members and knowing whether or not they are on track, and if they are not, why not. It may be that the team needs a specific type of expertise or an extra pair of hands. In such cases, you need to make arrangements to (temporarily) deploy the needed expertise from one team to another. Similarly, material or financial resources may be in short supply in one team and not well used in another. You need to rise above organizational politics and preferential treatment of one team over another, to make sure that *all* the teams that report to you can be successful. Remember, for you to be successful, *all* the teams need to be successful!

Managing competing priorities. As a second-level manager, you need to balance the interests of individual contributors and their team leaders, on one hand, and the rest of the organization, on the other. This is a difficult job because the realities, pressures, needs, and perspectives of each of these

---

Identify people
with potential
and groom
new leaders

Balance
individual and
organizational
needs

Become skilled
in managing
conflict

groups are very different. Political considerations on one side may override technical considerations on the other. Much organizational conflict arises when managers choose sides instead of listening to and looking for ways to mitigate the impact of opposing perspectives.

To manage conflicts well, you have to rise above an allegiance to one side or the other and find ways to bridge the two points of view. Managing conflicts requires skill in understanding others' perspectives and "fluency" in using the language of each side. It helps to be curious, ask questions, and try to understand what is behind the positions that people take on an issue. When people use a word that has a specific connotation in your work, find out if it has the same meaning to the others. Simplify your own use of language and make sure that you explain what you mean.

LEADING AND MANAGING PRACTICES AT LEVEL TWO

Table 9 presents an illustrative list of leading and managing practices for the second-level transition. They focus on your ability to oversee the work of a team and help guide you away from the tendency to take care of details yourself. These practices are intended to be instructive to you, as a manager who

TABLE 9 **Key leading and managing practices for the second-level manager**

Practice	What to do
Scanning Focusing Planning	■ Look for signs of success or failure in first-level managers' ability to exercise management functions. ■ Help them set priorities. ■ Educate yourself about the larger strategic context within which the program operates. ■ Identify teams that are not performing well and look into the causes. ■ Guide teams in their performance in relation to program strategies and priorities.
Aligning Mobilizing Organizing Implementing	■ Ensure that the teams' work contributes to the larger program strategies. ■ Mobilize resources and make sure that they are aligned with needs. ■ Align goals and create team spirit across unit boundaries. ■ Provide challenging assignments to help first-level managers develop their managerial skills.
Inspiring Monitoring Evaluating	■ Coach team leaders on effective managerial behavior. ■ Provide appropriate feedback and support. ■ Serve as an example to team leaders. ■ Check regularly on progress against stated objectives and work plans. ■ Share results of evaluations, and celebrate successes. ■ Recognize and reward managerial talent.

leads, and to your supervisor, who needs to support you in learning how to step back from the details and guide and support a team toward achieving results.

SIGNS OF DERAILMENT

When a newly appointed second-level manager continues to operate as a first-level manager, or worse, as an individual contributor, the development of the next generation of leaders is seriously compromised. In addition, when a manager derails at the second level without anyone's noticing and is then promoted to become a senior manager (the third level), the whole process of on-the-job leadership development is jeopardized.

Signs of derailment at the second level

- Interfering with the job of immediate staff (the unit managers) by managing the performance of people in those units

- Bypassing or usurping the unit leader's authority

- Missing cues that show a unit leader is sliding back to being solely a service provider

- Failure to delegate tasks

- Inability of reporting units to deliver results or to implement plans

- Sabotage or competition among the manager's supervisees

- Overemphasis on doing "the real work" at the expense of important organizational culture, work climate, and strategic issues

- A tendency to rewrite memos, letters, and reports that were delegated to other staff

- Selecting service providers as future team managers who are most like oneself or who are related or connected (for example, through family, political connections, or ethnic or tribal links)

Becoming a senior manager: Level Three

"Developing people for important leadership positions requires work on the part of senior executives, often over a long period of time. That work begins with efforts to spot people with great leadership potential early in their careers and to identify what will be needed to stretch and develop them."

—JOHN KOTTER
"WHAT LEADERS REALLY DO"

Often the transition to this level of leadership means that you are transitioning into being a member of the senior team of your workplace or the organization. As a senior manager or program director, you are no longer responsible for a small or specialized part of the organization's work; you are now one of the organizational decision-makers. Strategic thinking is imperative, requiring that you rise beyond professional or functional allegiances and produce results that directly promote the organization's reputation, financial performance, and sustainability.

Be comfortable making decisions

One of the major shifts at this level is that you have to make decisions with less-than-perfect information. Not only do you have to gauge whether the information you have is correct or reliable, but you also need to know where to find additional information and how to interpret the information you find. As evaluators know so well, information can be shaped to serve the particular needs and motives of the one who provides it. None of the divisions or departments under you will want to look bad, and data can be presented in such a way that they illuminate the good news and hide the bad.

To deal with the challenge of making decisions with inconsistent or incomplete data, you need to demonstrate a high degree of maturity and good judgment. You need to be humble and acknowledge that you don't have all the answers, find objective information, and be comfortable making decisions based on partial information.

A SHIFT IN TIME HORIZON

Focus on sustainability

With this transition you move up to another balcony, allowing you to see more of the surroundings and less of the specific activities on the dance floor. As a program director or senior manager, your time horizon expands to five years. This is the planning range that the senior management team has to consider for securing a healthy future for the organization.

With such a long timeline, the complexity of your task increases exponentially. You will need to take even more variables into consideration than before. The complex issue of organizational, programmatic, and financial sustainability is, or should be, on the forefront, especially for managers in nongovernmental organizations. Once the organizational strategy has been mapped out, make sure that your program's strategies support the overall organizational strategies and goals for the next five years.

NEW PRIORITIES AND RELATIONSHIPS

See beyond
your own
specialty

Regardless of your particular field of technical expertise, your charge now is to look out for the good of the whole program, the whole region, or, if you are in charge of medical facilities, all of them, not just those in one region or of one particular type. All the subspecialties and institutions included in your program or division's area will claim your attention. Focusing on your new priorities may not be easy if you have strong opinions about particular functions or elements of a health program. Whatever the program's particular function or performance, your contributions are now directed toward supporting the broader organizational goals. Consider the following scenario.

> Lorenzo de la Peza was recently promoted to Director of Hospital Administration. He is now in charge of all hospitals in the country. As a surgeon, Lorenzo has always focused on doing an excellent job in curative services at a fairly well-equipped referral hospital, both as an individual service provider and, later, as the administrator. In his new role, he has to pay attention to all hospitals, not just the ones he is most familiar with.

> In paying attention to larger strategic and public health issues (a function that is new to him), Lorenzo has to resist the temptation to focus only on providing the best possible curative services at a few well-equipped hospital. He has to shift his attention to looking at the role of all hospitals, their distribution across the country, the ways in which they are being used or not, and how to enlist hospitals to pay attention to public health concerns as well as to the health of individuals.

> He also needs to look at ways in which he could contribute to the success of the other divisions, such as laboratories and pharmaceuticals. This job is very different than the one he had before as a hospital director, in which the success of his hospital took precedence over anything else.

Model
constructive
behavior

People who lead at this level can bring about significant change by changing the way people work together and by supporting systems and processes that contribute to the success of the whole program or system. They can model humility and show an open mind as they focus conversations on the good of the whole, rather than on the interests of one group or another. In looking at the whole, they can see where there are blockages or competition for resources, address the obstacles, and allocate resources appropriately.

At this level, we often see people appointed to high-ranking leadership positions who have spent much of their professional life as individual contributors. Such appointments are not uncommon, either as part of the political process

Put the organization's goals first

Peter Senge (1990) describes one of the seven learning disabilities of organizations as the "Myth of the Management Team." This myth, applicable to most organizations, tells us that the high-level managers that meet periodically and form the senior team carry out their responsibilities for ensuring the well-being of the entire organization, each contributing her special expertise to advise and guide the organization into the future.

In his work with countless organizations around the world, Senge found, unfortunately, that this ideal of what the senior management team does is often a myth. Instead, he found that it is common for division or department heads to compete with each other for resources and for ownership of success. This situation does not foster collective learning and good organizational performance.

Foster collective success

or because the internal pipeline did not produce enough candidates. Taking on this role can be particularly challenging for such a high-ranking manager if he is not practiced at fostering collective success and mutual support, doesn't place a high value on the importance of the team effort, and doesn't recognize the importance of good processes in producing good results.

TASKS OF THE THIRD-LEVEL MANAGER

Your attention to strategic issues now has to exceed your area of technical expertise. You need to educate yourself quickly about issues that other people took care of before. For example, if your focus had been on clinical or public health issues, you now also need to be knowledgeable about the strategic dimensions of financial or human resources management.

As you interact more with the external world than you had to do before, you will also become more visible. People will watch how you conduct yourself during crises and how you handle criticism.

Develop other leaders

Within your organization or program, you will have to continue facilitating the development of managerial and leadership talent. You should start looking for a successor the moment you take office, then help that person (or persons if the size of your organization requires that you groom a pool of people) develop her confidence and skills to take over when you move on.

CRITICAL SKILLS FOR LEVEL THREE

To help you successfully navigate this transition, you will need to learn and be comfortable with using the following skills.

Strategic thinking. *Strategic thinking* is a way of interacting with the larger environment and interpreting events that help you and your colleagues envision what the future might be like and how you might prepare your organization to be ready for it. *Strategic planning* involves applying the insights about trends and patterns to the planning process, and translating them into choices about where to put organizational resources. The more developed the strategic thinking, the more robust the strategic planning.

You will have to learn to think strategically about the skills, processes, and knowledge that provide significant value to your clients and that no one else can provide. (These unique capabilities are sometimes referred to as strategic competencies.) For example, your organization may be the best place to provide services to young adults and it may be a need that no other service provider is filling. Or you may decide that too many organizations are providing too many of the same types of services, resulting in unnecessary competition and duplication of services.

In such instances, you may decide to pull out of one service area and concentrate on another that adds value to those provided by others. In either case, it is important to look several years ahead and think about potential positive and negative consequences that may result from adding or removing a service. This kind of strategic thinking will help you shape your program, maximize your opportunities, and minimize any potential threats to your plan.

> An exercise that can help you set priorities, "Putting First Things First: The Important and Urgent Matrix," is included in the handbook toolkit.

Coaching. Being a coach is important from the very first transition, but the stakes are higher as you move up. How well you coach affects the success of other managers and team leaders all the way down the hierarchy. Coaching helps establish a culture of accountability and performance at the operational levels and provide appropriate support to other managers.

Managing consultants. As a senior manager, you need to learn to rely on both internal and external consultants to do specific technical pieces of work, even when you think you could do them yourself. You need to know how to contract with consultants and develop confidence in monitoring their performance even if they have more expertise and experience. You also need to become an intelligent consumer of the approaches that consultants use to guide their interventions and be willing to ask difficult questions.

Managing conflict. Conflict management skills are important at any level, but neglecting to manage conflict at this level has much more serious and widespread consequences than at lower levels. Whether you can tolerate conflict or not, you will have to manage conflict situations, keep small conflicts from escalating, and model effective conflict management for your staff. To carry out these tasks, you need to know your preferred style of managing conflict, your weaknesses, and specific techniques for dealing with conflict.

> Exercises in the handbook toolkit that can help managers and their teams learn together and practice how to manage conflict are:

Think strategically

Support others' performance

- "Balancing Advocacy and Inquiry: Changing the Pattern of Conversation"
- "Exploring Each Other's Thinking: The Ladder of Inference"
- "Coaching Your Team through Breakdowns"
- "The Art of Listening"
- "Negotiating to Achieve Intended Results"

Using reflective skills. The higher you rise on the organizational ladder, the less likely it is that you will get honest feedback about the impact of your behavior and decisions on others lower down. This limitation means that it is even more important to be self-reflective. Develop a habit of periodically stepping back to reflect on data and decisions and the impact they have on others (clients and employees) and on the organization as a whole. If staff are reluctant to give you constructive feedback, work hard to cultivate the kind of relationship that builds trust and show people that you actually use their feedback to change your ways. Help your team become more reflective as well, so that you can learn from your experiences and do things better in the future.

> In addition to the exercises noted above, the handbook toolkit offers several exercises that help to improve communication and have productive conversations. These include "Giving Useful Feedback," "Reflecting on Communication: The ORID Method," and "Coaching to Support Others."

Seek honest feedback

LEADING AND MANAGING PRACTICES AT LEVEL THREE

Essential skills for third-level managers

With the third-level transition, your ability to look far beyond your immediate context is important. You will need to rely on your second-level managers to directly lead and manage teams so that you can focus your energy on the larger issues in the internal and external environments. Just as your supervisor will need to support you in learning how to function effectively in this larger context, you will need to support managers at the level below you to help them provide leadership and support to their teams. Table 10 presents practices that will help you succeed in this role.

SIGNS OF DERAILMENT

At each higher level, derailment has more profound influences on the organization as a whole. Dealing with management and leadership shortcomings at higher levels becomes increasingly difficult and political agendas are more likely to interfere. If people find it difficult to confront managers who derail at lower levels, the fact that they have moved up over the years has given the wrong signals, making it much more difficult to face these challenges later. Yet the stakes are much higher.

TABLE 10   **Key leading and managing practices for the third-level manager**

Practice	What to do
Scanning Focusing Planning	■ Take a broad view of the all the developments (political, technical/technological, socioeconomic) that positively or negatively affect the services you are providing and the health of the population. ■ Immerse yourself in new areas of responsibility that are unfamiliar or not in your field of expertise. ■ Know the needs and concerns of key stakeholders who influence, receive, or affect your services. ■ Identify overall strategic priorities for the program, leaving adaptation to local conditions to be decided by the appropriate level. ■ Use data to identify challenges, and identify resources and actions to address them.
Aligning Mobilizing Organizing Implementing	■ Work on interorganizational or national task forces and committees to expand your knowledge of other groups' perspectives and your network of relationships. ■ Meet periodically with peers to see the totality of the organization's efforts and to exchange information and receive feedback. ■ Look for new funding sources. ■ Shift resources as priorities change or new opportunities arise. ■ Intervene when program implementation appears to be blocked.
Inspiring Monitoring Evaluating	■ Support lower-level managers by helping them see the cultural and business contexts in which initiatives for change take place. ■ Recommend promotions for lower-level managers or provide other rewards for good leadership and sound management. ■ Show leadership maturity in interactions. ■ Show humility. (Acknowledge when you don't know, and invite and accept feedback from staff.) ■ Track program progress and reflect on progress and setbacks with others. ■ Share successes and failures with affected parties and learn from the experience.

Signs of derailment at the third level

- An obsession with showing that one's program (district, region) is responsible for improved health indicators (rather than sharing the credit)

- The tendency to point the finger at others for mistakes, absolving oneself and one's team from blame

- Favoritism toward a particular unit in one's program

- Signs of short-term thinking and an operational rather than strategic mindset

- The tendency to ignore or ridicule organizational policies, compliance requirements, programs, needs, and procedures

- A tendency to isolate oneself from contact with the people who do the work (in the field)

- Significant turnover of staff and low morale

- Poor communication with stakeholders

- Lack of trust in others, leading to doing work oneself, and maintenance of strict control

- A tendency to overdelegate, combined with poor control systems

- Satisfaction with or use of superficial or self-serving assessments and analyses to guide the team's work

- Unwillingness to acknowledge personal weaknesses and accept coaching or support

- Inability to see one's role in causing serious organizational problems

Leading and managing at the top: Level Four

"I am conscious that being a leader is not an end in itself, but a role whose purpose is to transform society."

—EDUARDO JAVIER BALDOMAR
CONSEJO DE SALUD RURAL ANDINO, BOLIVIA

In this transition, you become the head of the organization or of the permanent staff of the ministry. You now carry the ultimate accountability and responsibility for the current reputation and ongoing success (or failure) of the organization, and, in the public sector, for progress toward fulfilling your country's health agenda. This is a very visible position. People look to you for answers, even if you don't have them. The lives of many people depend on you, either for their health care needs or for employment, or both.

A DISTANT TIME HORIZON

Responsibilities
of fourth-
level leaders

You are now responsible for the organization's success well into the future. In the public sector, you carry the heavy responsibility for ensuring that your country's population is healthy—that adults can actively engage in economic production; that children can fully engage in education; and that the old, poor, and infirm are properly cared for. If you manage an HIV/AIDS program, you need to be able to think 20 years ahead and do this thinking together with other ministries, organizations, and groups that have a stake in battling the pandemic.

If in your previous position your time horizon was five years, this perspective represents a significant jump. It is one that is hard to operationalize, because few people think this far into the future, so there are few models. In the public sector, such a long-term view stands in stark contrast to the usual four- or five-year election cycles and the short-term mindset of political parties. This sort of expansive and long-term thinking in the public sector exemplifies a rare act of leadership. Those who manage to transcend narrow party politics and short-term interests are truly top-level leaders, who tend to attract a broad constellation of followers that often reaches beyond the boundaries of their country.

A SHIFT IN PRIORITIES

You now have to pay attention to the success of *all* the different divisions and programs that comprise your organization or ministry and do everything you can to help them be successful. This does not mean insisting on results from

Keep the
pipeline filled
with new
leaders

the work groups that these managers lead, because that is *their* responsibility. For some people this shift is difficult, because they are so used to holding groups accountable for results. Instead, you have to make sure that the senior managers who report to you are all first-class managers who lead and that, when they are ready to move on or up, there are good replacements waiting in the pipeline. The success of those managers will largely make or break your organization and, therefore, should be of great concern to you.

RELATIONSHIPS AND THE PRECARIOUSNESS OF TRUST

Engage with
the board of
directors

Leaders at the top are responsible for cultivating and maintaining good working relationships with key stakeholders. In the private sector, as the chief executive your relationship with the board of directors is of critical importance. The board is there both to look after the well-being of the organization and to help you do well, by giving you advice and feedback, and opening doors to opportunities that you could not tap into on your own. If you have chosen your board members well and established a relationship with them that is marked by respect, honesty, and a commitment to the mission of the organization, the entire organization will benefit from the combined expertise of its members. Cultivate such a relationship; it will be one of your greatest assets.

In the public sector, as the most senior civil servant in your ministry, you are the bridge between the people appointed to lead your ministry and the ministry's permanent staff. Political appointees come with political agendas, which may or may not match the objectives that you and your staff have been

---

Trust-breakers

Leaders can lose others' trust by:

- sending inconsistent messages;
- applying inconsistent standards;
- not intervening when there are problems with particular managers;
- providing false feedback;
- not trusting others;
- ignoring elephants in the parlor (issues that everyone knows about but that cannot be discussed openly);
- accepting rumors as fact and allowing rumors to thrive without getting enough objective information to straighten out the facts;
- not being concerned about consistent underperformance by the organization.

Source: Based on "The Enemies of Trust" by Robert M. Galford and Anne Seibold Drapeau, *Harvard Business Review,* Feb. 2003.

pursuing for the last few years. Your job is to manage the relationship between these two major constituencies and set the tone for constructive dialogue and productive outcomes. You need to watch out for the effects of politically motivated criticism and at the same time use the change at the top as an opportunity to improve performance. You have to know how to translate public health realities into politically acceptable strategies and translate politically motivated changes into actions that contribute to, rather than distract from, delivering better health care to the people.

Leaders in both sectors are highly visible at this level. Everything you say and do will be scrutinized and possibly given more meaning than you intended. You will find that the trust you painstakingly built while working at lower levels can be shattered in an instant and that rebuilding that trust is as hard as putting a broken egg back together. But preserving trust is actually not that difficult if you pay attention to how trust can be broken.

TASKS OF THE TOP-LEVEL MANAGER

If you have been responsible until now for one particular function, such as hospital administration, district health management, preventive services, laboratories, or a particular geographical region, you now have to consider all regions, all specialties, and all functions. In short, you are responsible for the entire organization, ministry, or government agency. This means that you have to learn about everything that affects the business you are in, namely that of delivering on promises about health and access to services. You also need to have some understanding of all the support functions that have a bearing on your mandate, such as marketing, public relations, finance, and human resource management.

Anticipating changes and trends becomes one of your key responsibilities. You need to prepare the organization for the future so that it can keep pace with the trends, and change organizational strategies if they are heading the organization in the wrong direction. Your thinking has to become truly multidimensional, not focusing on any one strategy but on a portfolio of strategies that, together, fulfill all aspects of the organization's mission. Although strategic thinking should not be new to you at this stage, it is more complex than thinking through strategies for a particular program or a particular region or area of expertise.

CRITICAL SKILLS AT THE TOP LEVEL

The skills needed at the senior level include all the skills of the other levels, as well as skills in modeling a healthy work climate and encouraging productivity and excellence.

Demonstrating belief in self and others. This is the fundamental belief in your own worth, the worth of others, and your belief in the inherent desire of all human beings to make a contribution. When top-level leaders hold this belief, it empowers employees to produce extraordinary results. Recognize and develop potential in yourself and others by being optimistic, caring, trustworthy, and humble. Always be on the lookout for young talent and coach others so that they may further develop their talents.

Organizations are complex networks

Fostering interdependence. Interdependence is the deep understanding of one's own interconnectedness to others in the larger web of life. The success of top-level leadership depends on recognizing that organizations are by nature interdependent networks. At the top level, you need to know when and how to use collaborative processes to facilitate group learning and decision-making, and be comfortable working across professional, national, gender, and ethnic boundaries.

Try to resist succumbing to stereotypes or false judgments. Learn to listen to the interests and concerns that are often hidden behind position statements, verify whether your judgments are correct, then focus on those concerns that you can address.

For a helpful exercise, please see "The Art of Listening" in the handbook toolkit.

Model integrity and authenticity in your actions

Modeling integrity and authenticity. More than anyone else, leaders at the very top set the tone by acting out the values and displaying the behavior expected of employees up and down the organization. Unless you model integrity and authenticity, your words will hold little meaning. This requires that you be as open and honest in your communications as you can be without betraying confidences and pay attention to what you say and do. If you preach honesty and transparency, be honest and transparent. If you want others to be frugal, be frugal yourself. If you ask for accountability, be accountable.

Assume that everything you say about someone or some organization will eventually reach the people about whom you spoke. It is a much better strategy to talk to people directly so that you can make sure your message is communicated correctly. If it is a difficult conversation to have now, imagine what it would be like after the message reached them indirectly (and presumably, somewhat altered). If you want loyalty and trustworthiness in others, be loyal and trustworthy yourself.

Using authority wisely. Given their power to affect people's lives, it is crucial that top-level leaders use their authority with the common good in mind. Using authority wisely is especially important when there is conflict. It is a common organizational practice in tense or conflicted situations to bypass lower-level supervisors to solve problems or use one's power to deal with messy situations. It is an easy trap to fall into, especially if a problem appears easy to solve from your vantage point. But by solving the problem yourself you undercut the manager whose job it was to manage or resolve the conflict and undermine her success in managing future conflicts. Instead, help her be prepared to solve problems on her own.

Anticipate the consequences of changes

Being a systems thinker. Systems thinking skills refer to the whole system and the interaction of its parts. Systems thinking is the ability to look for connections between seemingly isolated events and to understand the patterns of those events. Understanding these invisible connections helps you anticipate not just the intended consequences of a change but also possible unintended consequences. This is a critical skill for policymakers.

You are also responsible for designing effective systems and processes that enable people to carry out their work effectively. Process skills are one subset of system skills: understanding that how you do something has an effect on the results. "Seeing" the systems can help you understand better how the organizational culture and work climate affect performance and how features of the management systems and external environment shape staff attitudes and motivation.

Assess organizational strengths and weaknesses

Being a strategic thinker. Strategic thinking is not a new skill at this level, but it now has to pervade how you approach any organizational challenge or crisis. Look forward by trying to peek beyond the horizon, read widely, and talk with experts in various fields to help you discern trends and future challenges. Then try to get a good sense of your organization's strengths and weaknesses and convene a group of good thinkers and practical realists to see how you can best position yourselves in ways that respond effectively, and in a sustainable way, to a changing environment.

LEADING AND MANAGING PRACTICES AT THE TOP LEVEL

Represent organizational values

Demands on your time are high at the top level. Many more people from inside and outside the organization will need to meet with you. You will need to be proficient in all the leading and managing practices (see Table 11) and comfortable with working through managers who are leading at other levels in order to achieve results. Your status in the organization increases your influence on the work environment and the impact your values and work style have on others. As a role model, you will be scrutinized, so practicing transparency, honesty, and integrity will reinforce organizational values and inspire others to do the same.

SIGNS OF DERAILMENT

Derailment at this level has a direct impact on people's lives. Chief executives in the private sector who have derailed have dragged their organizations down with them, sometimes destroying their employees' livelihoods and even their savings. In the public sector, executives who derail can undo years of work, prompt a brain drain of good people, compromise program performance at all levels, and create cynicism and ill will among major development partners.

TABLE 11 **Key leading and managing practices
for the top-level manager**

Practice	What to do
Scanning Focusing Planning	■ Spend time with each of your senior team members and learn as much as possible from them about their goals, dreams, how people work, what obstacles they run into, and what relationships they have with other programs. ■ Maintain a broad network of contacts across different sectors, countries, and professional groups. ■ Scan the professional literature, skim reports, or have others produce digests, and find ways to attend professional meetings and international conferences. ■ Talk with participants in training events, visit health centers, meet the people your organization serves, and listen to their concerns. ■ Identify with your top team the three to five issues of strategic importance that your organization needs to address in the next decade. ■ Address critical challenges for your organization now and in the near future. ■ Pay attention to imbalances in your organization and establish taskforces to study the issues.
Aligning Mobilizing Organizing Implementing	■ Make sure your organization is represented in multidisciplinary and multisectoral taskforces so that health concerns are addressed. ■ Look for new donors and supporters outside the usual places. ■ Pretest important decisions and major change initiatives by running them by a group of trusted advisors. ■ Maintain your relationships and participation in multiple networks.
Inspiring Monitoring Evaluating	■ Create a work environment that inspires people to put forth their best efforts. ■ Act with integrity, be humble, and learn to say "I don't know" and "I will get back to you." ■ Check how you are doing from time to time by asking people whom you know will give you honest feedback. ■ Share results and celebrate accomplishments. ■ Articulate what you are learning and apply it to new situations.

Consequences
of derailment
at the top

In all cases, the consequences are disastrous and have ripple effects far beyond the immediate stakeholders. At the same time, bringing attention to derailment at this level requires tremendous courage from the board or carries considerable political cost for senior administration officials. It might have been prevented if derailment had been recognized earlier on. Still, it is always better to recognize derailment before the damage can no longer be undone.

Signs of derailment at the top level

- Uninspired communication with employees or stakeholders outside the organization, especially people from different backgrounds

- Inability to shift perspective from a particular technical focus (e.g., financial, clinical, evaluation) to focusing on the good of the whole organization

- Inability to put together a strong team or hire strong people outside one's area of expertise

- Difficulty with or resistance to grasping the implications of sustainability—the financial, the programmatic, and organizational elements—or focusing on one element over the others

- Time management problems (inability to let go of tactical issues, putting out fires without trusting or supporting the team to handle its own problems)

- Ignoring one's role as custodian of the culture of the organization by engaging in unethical actions or actions that compromise long-term organizational health, such as squandering reserves or endangering the organization's reputation and stakeholders' goodwill

- Little awareness of unspoken norms and of the impact of one's behavior on others

- Self-imposed isolation from receiving useful feedback from staff (or maintaining a culture in which this is not encouraged)

- Low priority of "soft issues" that are not directly linked to business results

Transitions at the very top: Succession management

"Succession planning is perpetuating the enterprise by filling the pipeline with high-performing people to assure that every leadership level has an abundance of these performers to draw from, both now and in the future."

—RAM CHARAN ET AL.
THE LEADERSHIP PIPELINE

Because of the influence top managers and leaders have on the entire organization or ministry, top-level leadership transition is of critical importance. If organizations pay attention to leadership transitions at all levels, managers who lead will emerge with a higher level of competence at each transition—thereby filling the pipeline with several strong candidates for the top position. This leadership pipeline serves the entire organization and reduces the need to go outside to find a suitable replacement for the top executive.

In the absence of a properly filled leadership pipeline—a reality in many organizations—the leadership transition at the top can be a traumatic experience, especially if the outgoing leader is the founder. Elements of ownership, a deep emotional attachment to the organization, and the fusion of the founder's identity with that of the organization tend to compound the task of finding a successor, who has the impossible task of striking out in new ways, while at the same time preserving some of the old ways. In the public sector, political considerations create an equally difficult situation.

For additional resources on how to manage and lead leadership transitions at the very top, please refer to "Planning for Leadership Succession" and "Avoiding Common Mistakes in Recruiting New Leaders" in the handbook toolkit.

Creating a leadership culture

"Participatory management begins with the potential of people."

—MAX DE PREE
LEADERSHIP IS AN ART

The experience of a leadership transition at the top brings into focus the issue of "growing" talent from within or "buying" new talent from the outside. The trauma or disturbance of succession management can trigger new organizational commitment to building and maintaining a pipeline of managers who lead—a pipeline that is kept full and flowing at all times. This commitment means that managers at all levels are taught, coached, and rewarded for lead-

Three dimensions of managing leadership succession in the private sector

Whether a change in leadership at the top is imminent, being contemplated, or sudden, there are always three dimensions at play: a personal, an organizational, and a cultural dimension.

The personal dimension. The founder or long-term leader may be so strongly attached to the organization that it is nearly impossible to let go, since her identity is fused with the identity of the organization. If there is no strong, credible second and third tier of executives, staff or the key stakeholders may not want the former leader to retire, doubting that anyone is ready to take over. When a new leader eventually comes on board, he will need both the blessing of the outgoing leader and to be seen as competent in his own right, as he charts an organizational course that may be quite different.

The cultural dimension. The new leader needs to understand the culture of the organization as well as the wider cultural environment in which the organization operates and be able to play a bridging role between the two. For example, where the organizational culture is energetic and entrepreneurial, and the organization needs to negotiate its affairs with slower government bureaucracies, the organization should find a leader who demonstrates an understanding of those contrasting needs. This dimension is easier to navigate for an internal candidate than for an outsider. The incoming new leader must immerse herself deeply in the culture before trying to change it, especially if she is following in the footsteps of a popular and well-respected leader.

The organizational dimension. As the principal governing mechanism of many organizations, boards of directors play a critical role—as policymakers, evaluators, advocates, and resource mobilizers. To stay on track in a leadership transition, an organization needs a board that is engaged with staff and the outgoing chief executive in the search for the best possible replacement. Board members can also support a culture of leadership development by putting the topic on the agenda, even when an immediate transition is not planned.

ing their teams to produce results and for paying full attention to the needs and concerns of the stakeholders who depend on those results.

Organizations that want to foster such a leadership culture need to pay attention to and encourage transitions at all levels, even the first one, which often goes unnoticed. It is possible to develop and nurture a leadership mindset among managers and staff at all levels. If top executives cultivate the commitment of all their staff to the organization's values and principles, the tent will not collapse when the central pole is taken out. In this way, leadership can pass into the hands of a new generation that is fully prepared and brings fresh views, perspectives, and energy to the evolving challenges.

Questions to consider on . . .

Moving up the leadership ladder

Considering your current level. Think about transitions have you made in your work life. Can you identify which level your current position mostly resembles?

Reflecting on shifts you have made. When you last made a transition, did you notice you had to make a shift in time horizon, priorities, relationships, and tasks? If you did, which ones were easiest for you to handle and which ones were most difficult? If you didn't, looking back some time later, can you see some shifts that you should have made but didn't? Have there been any consequences because these shifts didn't happen?

Preparing others for transitions. How are you supporting people who report to you to prepare them for a role that is appropriate for their level?

Recognizing signs of derailment. Which of the signs of derailment do you recognize in others? In yourself?

Keeping staff on track. Review the signs of derailment for the level of manager that is below you. Can you see any of these signs in your staff? If so, what do you plan to do about it?

Keeping the pipeline full. Is your organization's pipeline filled with people who have good management and leadership potential? If yes, how does the organization keep it moving? If no, what needs to change about the ways you currently groom future leaders and managers?

Planning for leadership succession. How is your organization planning for eventual leadership transitions at the top?

5 Reorienting roles in the health system

". . . the territorial and political subdivisions of the State shall enjoy genuine and meaningful local autonomy to enable them to attain their fullest development as self-reliant communities and make them more effective partners in the attainment of national goals."

—PHILIPPINES LOCAL GOVERNMENT CODE OF 1991

Broad changes in the health system have created new challenges for managers. Three far-reaching changes over the past decade have altered how countries provide and finance health services. First, central governments are moving away from providing services toward overseeing health care and financing health services through health insurance. Second, ministries of health are decentralizing their health systems, so that provinces, districts, and nongovernmental organizations make decisions about health interventions and service mix. Third, demand for health services, especially services related to HIV/AIDS, is rising.

These changing conditions mean that you need to examine the role your level plays in the delivery of health care. This chapter looks at how your level's role has to change within the structure of the health system in order to support and achieve improvements in the health of local populations.

This chapter will help you:

- understand relationships among the district, middle, and central levels;

- become a leader in local health care, if you work at the district level;

- move from director to steward, if you operate at the central level;

- balance national goals with local needs, if you work at the middle level;

- promote phased changes in the health system and negotiate new roles among levels.

Understanding relationships among the health system's levels

"Leadership is about understanding the way people and organizations behave, about creating and strengthening relationships, about building commitment, about establishing a group identity, and about adapting behavior to increase effectiveness."

—MANFRED KETS DE VRIES
"ORGANIZATIONS ON THE COUCH"

If the national health system is undergoing significant reform, it is critical that you understand the new realities that such change often brings. When you do, you will be able adapt your group's role to handle the challenges of this change. Studies of the effects of decentralization (Aitken 1999, Bryant 1999, Kolehmainen-Aitken 1997, Pillay 2000, Stover 1997) in numerous countries as different as Haiti and the Philippines have frequently revealed that:

Unintended side effects of health sector reform

- employees lose their morale;

- health services are disrupted for significant periods of time;

- the financial burden increases for local government or individual users of the system;

- the general population loses confidence in the system;

- national health indicators plummet.

Processes that supported service delivery are often undermined by turmoil and unintended side effects of reform such as mistrust, turf battles, uncoordinated or mismatched resource flows, increased inequities between rich and poor areas, and local political pressures that shift resources away from national health priorities. If these sound familiar, they represent your biggest challenges. How can you and your team change your relationships with other levels and coordinate roles across the system to improve the situation?

REORIENT THE HEALTH SYSTEM TO PROMOTE THE HEALTH OF POPULATIONS

Understanding the attributes of a good health system is an important first step to reshaping your group's role in a reformed health system. The widely accepted attributes of a well-functioning health system (Charoenparij et al., 1999, p. 6) include:

- orientation toward health rather than disease;

- equity, quality, and efficiency;

- decentralization of decision-making;

- accountability and transparency;

- active participation by the population;

- collaboration between the public and the private sectors in producing health services.

Reorienting the health system requires a new mindset

Regardless of their original intent, decentralization and health sector reform can improve service quality, access, and demand for services—and, in turn, improve providers' response to client demand. Envision the kind of health system that has strong local participation and equity, while also serving clients' needs. Figure 10 illustrates the massive shift in mindset that managers must embrace to support a health system, or nongovernmental organization, that is oriented toward supporting health services that exist to help individuals, families, and communities maintain their health. These services can differ from community to community and, if well designed, be quite cost-effective. Because they reflect local populations' needs, these services can promote the health of those populations.

A system driven by local needs can become unstable unless it establishes strong safeguards at other levels. Each level has to provide the supports

FIGURE 10   **Shifting the health system to serve local needs**

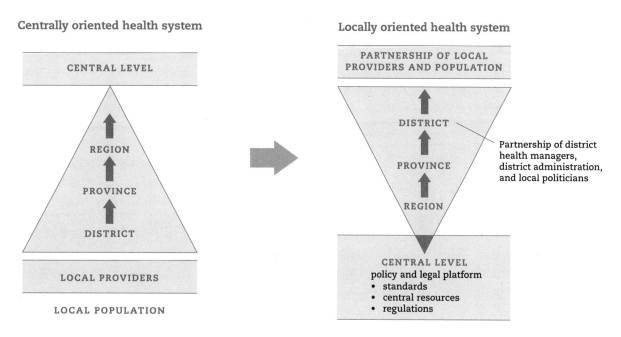

Reorienting a health system toward the local level turns the traditional organizational pyramid upside down and changes the way staff need to think and work.

needed to empower the level above, so that service providers can focus on addressing the health needs of the local population. This means that district health managers, with district administrators and local politicians, need to decide what mix of health services will serve their local communities and mobilize resources for delivering these services. The central level must balance or stabilize the entire health system (or organization) by establishing a strong policy and legal framework that supports equitable and essential preventive and curative services.

Organizational power from supportive relationships

This new orientation gives organizational power a new meaning. Under the former orientation, managers thought of power only as control over resources. The new orientation helps managers expand the meaning to include the power to support. This frees them to focus on relationships between people as a source of power (power "with" instead of power "over").

Like the former health system, the new one represented by the inverted pyramid is composed of the public, private for-profit, and private not-for-profit sectors (Figure 11). To make effective use of available resources and expertise, the central Ministry of Health can expand the policy and legal platform and integrate these sectors as partners in the government-funded, decentralized health system.

FIGURE 11   **Sectors of the health system**

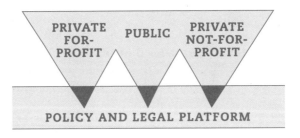

The policy and legal platform integrates these sectors as partners.

SUPPORT LOCAL SERVICES

Roles that support national priorities and local needs

To refocus on local needs, managers at all levels of the health system need to support local services that reflect both national public health priorities and local health needs and interests. Table 12 summarizes the roles of each level. Note that many countries establish a regional or provincial health office as an extension of the Ministry of Health during health sector reform. If this middle level does not exist, these responsibilities belong to the central level.

The following sections explore these new roles at the district, central, and middle levels and examine specific leading and managing practices and priority actions you can initiate at each level. Once you develop a consensus on the challenges that exist at your level, you will be able to identify which actions make sense for your context.

TABLE 12 **Roles that support effective local health services**

Level	Roles
District	Lead local health services by: ■ empowering local communities and program staff to mobilize and apply local and national resources to address specific health care needs in their area; ■ mobilizing new kinds of resources, especially at the community level, to support often underfunded health care services; ■ instilling ownership, responsibility, and accountability for deciding on local health care objectives and for designing, delivering, and monitoring health care services at the district level.
Middle	Balance national health care goals with specific local health needs by: ■ advocating for health care needs and actions at the local level; ■ respecting national priorities and standards.
Central	Become stewards of the health system by: ■ overseeing the delivery of essential services; ■ maintaining national standards and policies for the implementation and quality of services; ■ ensuring equity among regions or provinces.

Leading local health services: The district level

"Diversity, complexity, creativity and adaptability will be the greatest at the local level with an appropriate minimum of regulation to enable the individuals to know what the rules are and what is happening, so that they can collaborate creatively."

—ROBERT CHAMBERS
WHOSE REALITY COUNTS

Increasingly, the level nearest to local communities is accountable for providing the services and information that people need to maintain their health. In some countries, this level is the district and municipality. In others, it may be one level removed (such as the region or province). As you reorient the role your level plays in the system, it is important to accept that you are no longer simply the implementer of ministry directives. Now you need to make strategic choices in order to serve many needs with limited resources. Determine what services your populations need most and how to improve access to, coverage, and quality of these services.

ASSUME RESPONSIBILITY FOR HEALTH IMPACT

Experiences worldwide indicate that the district level will achieve results if it takes responsibility for:

- planning and managing health services to meet local needs while following national policies;

- deploying and using program staff as efficiently as possible to meet local needs and priorities;

- procuring drugs according to national guidelines where the local level has this authority;

- monitoring and evaluating the delivery of local services to ensure quality, impact, and responsiveness to local needs and conditions;

- facilitating community participation in planning, prioritizing, monitoring, and delivering services.

FOCUS ON LOCAL NEEDS

Take
responsibility
for local
services and
providers

To reorient toward addressing the specific needs of your local populations, you will need to lead a shift in focus. As the Director of Human Resources from Nicaragua's Ministry of Health stated, "Health officials at the municipality level now need to make decisions without their provincial- or central-level bosses standing around. They need to take risks where they didn't take risks before." In other words, where you used to take direction from other levels, you now take responsibility for local services and local providers. Table 13 lists the kinds of shifts that managers at this level need to bring about, and what you need to do differently.

APPLY KEY PRACTICES TO TAILOR SERVICES TO LOCAL NEEDS

To make decisions that will result in an appropriate mix of cost-effective services, the district level will need to apply leading and managing practices. At this level, you need to:

- scan to understand local needs by studying data, visiting, and listening;

- plan with the community to address local challenges by setting priorities;

TABLE 13 **Shifts in focus at the district level**

If the district level used to . . .	. . . the district level should now . . .
Respond to central-level requests to develop operational plans to implement the national package of services	Think strategically and facilitate participatory exercises to rally staff around current and anticipated local challenges
Comply with unchanging, uniform national delivery models	Allocate human and financial resources based on local needs and local plans
Utilize staff assigned by the central level	Employ, train, and evaluate staff locally, based on national guidelines
Assume it has the last word on local health-related issues	Understand that health has many types of stakeholders with valid concerns and interests
Ignore local politicians and community leaders, and seek support from other levels in the health system instead	Build local political coalitions for health and promote local ownership to sustain efforts
Adhere to (or quietly ignore) policies, fragmented or inconsistent standards, and norms for service provision that create problems at the local level	Discuss with regional or central authorities and lawmakers the changes in centrally developed policies, norms, and standards that would increase local effectiveness
Provide program and financial information to the middle and central levels	Review program and financial information with local community and staff and adjust services
React to emergencies and call on higher levels to fix problems	Anticipate emergencies and empower staff to deal with them
Have a passive or reactive stance toward development partners, that is, donors and nongovernmental organizations with development projects	Bring the local programs of development partners in line with the local health agenda

- organize services responsive to the health needs of clients and local populations by making the best use of available resources;

- align local stakeholders and mobilize resources by discussing their stake in your success;

- "manage up and across" to align other levels and sectors by requesting support and finding areas in which to collaborate;

- inspire local commitment by producing results and sustaining ownership.

Scan to understand local populations' needs. Ask yourself and others:

- What are the important morbidity and mortality patterns in your district?

- Given the country's essential public health needs, what services would have the most impact on the health of your district's population?

- What services can be most efficiently and effectively provided with the resources available?

- How must these services be provided to be used appropriately?

To answer these questions, you will need to examine existing data and visit district facilities and communities. Take a look at local data from demographic, epidemiological, market research, sociological, and anthropological sources. Focus especially on significant public health problems in your area and consider how your area's health needs match or diverge from national priorities or local interests.

Talk to staff in your health service delivery sites and in the communities about the challenges they see. Also assess the systems that support the district's health service delivery sites, such as facility supervision, supply distribution, in-service training, information systems, financial management, and district-level planning. For this assessment, you will need to work with provincial managers. When you compare all health facilities in your district, you can see which ones are the weakest and may need more attention, support,

---

Resources for scanning local health services and community health

Management of performance improvement (MPI). MPI is an approach adapted from WHO's district team problem-solving methodology to link public health problems with effective interventions. See the issue of *The Manager*, "Managing Performance Improvement of Decentralized Health Services" (MSH 2004).

Service delivery management and assessment (SDMA) protocol. The SDMA, which was developed in Haiti, provides a detailed form and process for collecting data about the management systems and health services of service delivery organizations (MSH 2004). Data from the assessment are used to create an action plan, including plans for training, rehabilitation of facilities, technical assistance, procurement of high-priority supplies and equipment, and monitoring.

Functional service delivery point (FSDP). The FSDP is a framework that helps managers plan, implement, monitor, and upgrade health services so that all the elements needed to deliver high-quality services are present simultaneously. These elements include trained and motivated personnel, adequate infrastructure, a referral system, information about clients and the community, and medicines, equipment, and supplies. See the issue of *The Manager*, "Achieving Functional HIV/AIDS Services through Strong Community and Management Support" (MSH 2002).

or resources. One way you can help weaker facilities is to organize visits to better-performing facilities. Staff can learn from each other and develop connections with the expertise that exists within the district.

As part of your scanning, read policy documents and central office directives to make sure you understand and respect the larger context of health sector reforms. Inform yourself about the current use of local resources and interests of local stakeholders.

Focus and plan to address local challenges with community involvement. You can use all this information to think strategically about local health needs and priorities and to identify your challenges. This process will help you determine which challenges you must address, which you can address immediately with the resources in hand, and which another group can address, with or without your support.

When you plan district health services, invite key stakeholders to participate. Consider engaging political and community leaders, current and potential clients, groups for specific interests, health insurance programs, and program staff. Wide community involvement is the only way to secure broad ownership of a plan and commitment to its implementation.

Once you have agreed on strategic choices, find ways to fit available resources (such as the location and types of services, facilities, personnel, equipment, commodities, and supplies) to these choices. If you manage a clinic, clinic network, or hospital, analyze costs and revenues to see how services can be redesigned and inputs adjusted to reduce costs, increase revenues, and provide the funds to cross-subsidize less profitable public health services. The monitoring and evaluation systems you develop will help you determine the impact of changes in services and indicate whether you need to make adjustments.

To improve the quality of services at service sites, motivate clinic staff who neglect persistent problems to take responsibility for addressing them. For example, low utilization of services and client dissatisfaction can often be addressed by challenging clinic staff to improve at least one area that concerns clients. Don't overlook the importance of coaching health center managers and training them in teamwork, work planning, and the use of information systems. People develop their leadership skills when you challenge them and provide adequate feedback and support.

Align local stakeholders and mobilize resources. A plan that responds to local needs does not necessarily generate the commitment and stimulate the energy of all stakeholders. Align your stakeholders by communicating your plans to groups that were not originally involved in creating the plan. Use existing local channels of communication, such as women's groups, marketplaces, village councils, schools, parent-teacher organizations, and rural radio. Educate the communities you serve about taking responsibility for their health and using health services to prevent illness and restore health. Gather private industries (including private providers and insurance com-

---

Meet with key stakeholders

Fit resources to plans

Challenge and coach clinic staff

Tools for improving the management of health facilities

Analyzing costs and revenues

The Cost and Revenue Analysis Tool (CORE). CORE helps managers of clinics analyze their costs and revenues service by service. They can also examine how their costs and revenues would be affected by changes in prices, staff utilization, service volume, and service mix (MSH 1998).

The Hospital Cost Allocation Tool (HOSPICAL). HOSPICAL offers hospital administrators and financial and department managers a tool for assessing service department costs before, during, and after the allocation of administrative, ancillary, and support costs in order to improve performance (Newbrander and Lewis 2001).

Improving clinic management

Client-Oriented Provider-Efficient (COPE). COPE is a process that service providers can use to build consensus and address challenges in their facilities. Developed by Engenderhealth, Inc., it has been used successfully for decades in many settings (EngenderHealth 2003).

The Clinic Supervisors' Manual. This manual contains guidelines for clinic supervision (MSH 2004). It can be found at http://erc.msh.org. Click on the Health Manager's Toolkit, "Clinical Services and Quality Management."

Communities
take
responsibility
for health

panies), media, religious institutions, and nongovernmental organizations in your area to discuss their stake in a strong local health system.

Many of your resources will come from local sources. You may be surprised to find that you can mobilize diverse resources locally that will further your local health goals. Don't rely on the power of other levels, however, to advocate for local support. This can backfire by creating expectations that are beyond your control and may cause difficulties later.

Manage relationships to align other levels and sectors. Some of your challenges will require regional or even central-level support. Show how you will use the resources or expertise by pointing out the difference they will make. Be as specific as you can, stating, for example, "If we had X, we could do Y, and that would result in Z. Here is why. . . ." Look for ways to integrate with local-level representatives from other ministries, such as education, agriculture, public works, labor, or social services. Identify areas of mutual concern, such as transportation, and then show how each group would benefit from working together and pooling resources, for instance, by doing joint assessments or sharing cars when making field visits.

Inspire local commitment. Reform efforts can be derailed by public cynicism about resource flows and power. When people see no impact, they lose confidence in your ability to bring about change. Your health program can, however, achieve lasting success if all stakeholders become deeply committed

Mobilizing local resources

Approaching groups for money, materials, space, influence, and volunteers can take time, but by being persistent, you can gain crucial support for your program.

Community leaders. Meet individually and in small groups with community leaders and potential benefactors, and paint a picture with them of the kind of local health system that is possible. Encourage them to become allies in your quest for support and specific resources. They will expand your reach by calling on their networks.

Politicians. Contact local politicians who are concerned about health and ask them to help advocate for a fair share of local government resources for the health program. Learn from other sectors that successfully advocate for resources. Through supportive politicians and information about other politicians, you can encourage those who are less interested to support you. Use the language of national priorities if it helps to clarify the political benefits of supporting specific health projects.

Development partners. To support low-resource subdistricts, you can appeal to development partners, if you have the authority. These are the donors and nongovernmental organizations that have projects in your district. Remember that your requests are more likely to succeed when they spring from a compelling vision, are consistent with your strategy, and are supported by data.

Others' experiences. You can learn from the approaches of groups that have successfully obtained resources, both in your country and outside it, through the literature and Internet. For example, in Peru, Comités Locales de Administración Salud (CLAS) operate rural community health centers and have raised local funds to expand services (Taylor and Taylor in Rohde and Wyon 2002). In Bangladesh and India, the Local Initiatives Program, with cadres of local family planning volunteers, has turned overlooked local resources into assets for reaching health goals and empowering women (MSH 2002, "Communities Taking Charge of Their Health"). In Africa, community-based health financing schemes are being tested as ways to increase local revenues while protecting destitute people from losing access to health services (Cripps et al. 2000).

For organizing requests for resources, see "Mobilizing Stakeholders to Commit Resources" in the handbook toolkit. For more information on securing resources for your program, refer to MSH's "Mobilizing Local Resources to Support Health Programs," *The Manager* (MSH 2002), found on the handbook CD-ROM.

to long-term results. This commitment comes about when stakeholders and staff see that they can make a difference despite a chronic lack of resources and other handicaps.

Local commitment comes from creating a compelling, shared vision for better health in your area. Be visible in visiting communities and inquiring

> ### Stimulating political will for local health initiatives—Selected country examples
>
> Local political leaders are gradually realizing that public health is too important to neglect. People of all ages want to be healthy, and improvements in health services and the health status of a population can be quite visible. Around the world, a variety of approaches have stimulated local political leaders to tackle health issues.
>
> **Nicaragua.** In the Waslala Municipality, a program on values-based leadership and social networks inspired community action in remote communities that had suffered from civil war and a devastating hurricane. Mayors and community council members participated in workshops on trust, reconciliation, solidarity, and census taking. Their ability to communicate about community needs and coordinate collective action grew, with visible results: completed clean-up campaigns, new school kitchens, and a facility devoted to the integrated delivery of child health services. As one Nicaraguan mayor reflects, "We realize we cannot achieve our goals alone. We are working together to achieve our dreams. The community sees the fruits of our labor, and they trust us and participate more."
>
> **Senegal.** In Senegal, the District Health Officer of Joal aligned the interests of the mayor and other municipal leaders with those of the Ministry of Health. This alliance quickly mobilized local and overseas funding to improve sanitation in the local health center and repair broken ambulances. The new partnership between health center staff and political leaders improved quality of care: there is more privacy for clients, equipment was updated, and the postpartum wards are less crowded. Community use of formerly underutilized primary care and maternal health services increased.
>
> *(cont. next page)*

Demonstrate the impact of stakeholders' contributions

about the health of residents. Listen respectfully without interrupting, and reiterate what you have heard. Magnify the successes you find when you conduct monitoring and evaluation by publicly celebrating them. Recognize the contributions of individuals or specific groups. Demonstrate the impact of key stakeholders' contributions so they continue their involvement. If you find mistakes, learn from them so that you will not make them again.

In countries around the world, the health sector is finding ways to inspire local politicians and community leaders to support health initiatives.

Stimulating political will for local health initiatives— Selected country examples *(cont.)*

The Philippines. In a number of Philippine municipalities, doctors, agricultural agents, and other professionals have been elected as mayors. They meet periodically and share their wide-ranging experience. By pooling their skills and knowledge, they are finding ways to tackle some of their toughest health and development challenges, in particular childhood mortality, untreated tuberculosis, and risk of HIV/AIDS transmission.

India. Three Indian nongovernmental organizations working in urban slums and isolated rural areas have mobilized health committees to support basic health services delivered by trained volunteers. In the slums of Kolkata, powerful local politicians on these committees have arranged for local clubhouses to serve as health posts. In the mountainous states of Himachal Pradesh and Punjab, health committees of community leaders mobilized support from religious leaders, who provide temples as sites for health clinics and advocate for reproductive and child health services. The committees were also able to use village funds to buy supplies of essential drugs. From 1999 to 2003, the nongovernmental organizations increased contraceptive use rates by 78% on average, child immunizations by 67%, and prenatal care by 78% among the populations served.

These examples illustrate that as staff from the Department of Health and nongovernmental organizations reach beyond the health sector and engage (or become) local leaders, they gain the political commitment, resources, and public involvement they need to achieve impact.

Sources: Adapted from Quick and Urdaneta 2004; Paxman et al. 2005

Moving from director to steward: The central level

"The challenge is trying to redefine the center. We are not just decentralizing everything and letting everyone go off and do their own thing. We are not saying that Headquarters doesn't matter. But we are redefining what the center means in ways that are more inclusive. In ways that allow us to move faster and be more responsive to changes in the market place."

—CHAIRMAN OF MONSANTO
IN FRIEDMAN, THE LEXUS AND THE OLIVE TREE

If you work at the central level or headquarters, your role shifts from directing to being a steward of the health program. Stewardship means making responsible choices about the use of resources (money, time, and talent) that serve the greater good. It involves an attitude of "serving" rather than "being

Serving the greater good

served" and willingness to be held accountable to someone other than your-self and your close supporters. Older generations are active stewards of the common good when they build the capacity of young people to govern them-selves. Organizational stewardship is based on deep concern for principled governance, outcomes, and empowerment throughout the organization.

The central level is the ultimate steward of the nation's health system. As a steward, you have to always be on the lookout for threats to the population's health and to the health system, and take action when they are in jeopardy. You assume vital responsibilities, for equity, standards, and health manage-ment systems. At the same time, you shift your focus away from control toward building coalitions to meet local needs and facilitating the efforts of other levels.

ASSUME RESPONSIBILITY FOR EQUITY, STANDARDS, AND SYSTEMS

Allocate resources to strengthen equity and support local services

Because of your central position, yours is the only level that can ensure an equitable distribution of resources and access to services. When the power of the central level is too weak, health care in poorer regions will suffer. For example, in Papua New Guinea in the late 1980s, poorer provinces expe-rienced reductions in per capita spending and health staff while better-off provinces experienced growth (Thomason et al. 1991). Your level needs to make the hard choices about how to allocate scarce resources across diverse regions or provinces. Your other primary responsibilities include developing standards that support effective local services and maintaining the necessary systems to ensure a continuous, up-to-date flow of information about needs and use of human resources and essential drugs and supplies. Having good information will help you anticipate problems and facilitate resource distri-bution.

Experiences in decentralization from around the world suggest that the central level's responsibilities within the national health system are to:

- lead strategic planning and policymaking;
- draft norms and standards for services that protect the nation's health (norms and standards for ensuring the equity, quality, and sustainability of services and for distributing and using human resources);
- draft national laws and regulations (such as for an essential drug list and for national drug registration);
- set up a system for accrediting and licensing health institutions and professions;
- develop and maintain a national health information system;

- monitor and evaluate policy implementation, regulation enforcement, and progress toward national goals (Kolehmainen-Aitken 1999, Pillay 2000).

A common
set of national
health
indicators

To develop or modify a national health information system, you have to have a common set of national health indicators. Enlist input from all levels, since perspectives will be different. Determine if data items, forms, reporting frequency, or the flow of data need to be changed. To foster effective use of information systems, trace how information currently moves through the system: at what speed it moves, where it hits obstacles, and how it returns (or not) as feedback to those who provided the information.

FACILITATE THE EFFORTS OF OTHER LEVELS AND BUILD BROAD COALITIONS

Facilitate
the work of
other levels

Stewardship does not mean control. Your level will be more helpful if it moves away from providing and enforcing guidelines about how to run health services day-to-day. That power needs to be transferred to government levels or private organizations that are closer to local populations. Instead, try to become a facilitator for the work that other levels need to do. Treat the next level, the provincial or regional level, as your internal customer and make sure it has the necessary resources, training, and support to execute its role as it supports the district level in implementing the national health agenda.

Providing the support that other levels need involves managing relationships with diverse groups. It is important to:

- negotiate with the Ministry of Finance for increased funding for health through financing policies and public investment plans;

- remove obstacles to timely disbursements of funds to the district level;

- take action if irregularities in the flow of resources between the center and districts are discovered;

- provide technical support to other levels, including national procurement and distribution of drugs (or guidelines for procurement at other levels);

- establish links with international organizations and health departments of other countries.

Harmonize
efforts at
all levels

Facing major national health challenges requires a coordinated effort among many organizations. To encourage and harmonize these efforts across the country, you can create opportunities to bring together groups at different levels and in different geographic areas so that they can exchange experiences and coordinate their work. The confidence of local health teams will rise when you offer support for district training and reaffirm their contributions at special events when they assume new responsibilities. At the international level, you can present a compelling case for your vision and support it with evidence that shows how the additional resources you seek will contribute to better health. Getting requested funds will challenge you to fulfill your promise and show results.

ENCOURAGE DIALOGUE

Since you will have less line authority over local services, your level will need to persuade, negotiate with, and solicit input from other levels and sectors in order to implement policies and ensure compliance with national standards. This role means you will need to shift your focus to inviting consultation from many stakeholders in setting policies and defining roles. Table 14 suggests some of these shifts.

TABLE 14 **Shifts in focus at the central level**

If the central level used to . . .	. . . the central level should now . . .
Take a health system's viewpoint toward national legislation	Take a broad, multisectoral view of national legislation
Develop policies based on incomplete data from the district level	Develop policies through dialogue with key stakeholders and affected groups at other levels
Enforce compliance with many unrelated or incomplete standards and norms for services and service providers	Develop coherent, enforceable, and equitable norms and standards and use them to ensure equity and quality
Maintain power at the central level, while giving directives to the district level	Actively work through the middle level to clarify and agree on new management roles and ways to develop local capacity
Accumulate data from other levels with limited feedback to the levels that generate the data	Analyze data from the regions or provinces and provide feedback, support, challenges, and guidance to those who generate the data
Provide direction and resources to health officials in the districts by working through vertical structures	Assist regions and provinces in supporting district health officials by working through horizontal structures, such as coordinating councils, and by getting resources released
Focus on matters at the head office and leave visiting the field to others	Visit and understand local realities; support local ownership for sustained performance

APPLY KEY PRACTICES TO BECOME STEWARDS

To become better stewards, those at the central level need to become skilled in leading and managing various divisions, departments, services, and levels to implement strategic priorities for the entire national health system. This role involves:

- scanning the health, social service, and related sectors to identify how each contributes to the population's health, and considering stakeholders who can help address challenges;

- focusing on a strategic plan to set priorities and bring coherence to the health system's efforts;

- aligning stakeholders to ensure equitable services;

- organizing and mobilizing resources to address priorities that support strategic goals;

- inspiring long-term dedication and monitoring impact to sustain continued performance.

Look at the national picture of health and health care

Scan sectors and stakeholders. The central level is in the best position to scan factors that affect people's health throughout the country and the whole health system. No other level can see the big picture. If your system is overwhelmed by simultaneous reforms, you need to scan what is happening in other sectors to determine their positive or negative impact on health care and to find areas where you can collaborate. For example, a civil service hiring freeze affects the availability of health staff. Find out how health sector reform or general public-sector reforms are affecting the health system at each level.

In doing your scan, ask yourself: What are the new challenges? Where are the breakdowns? Where do ambiguities or overlap exist in the responsibilities of different levels? Your scan will be more meaningful if you analyze the data you collect against the background of information you routinely monitor: trends in the population's mortality, morbidity, demographics, health activities, and finances. (For more discussion on scanning the external environment and sources of data, please see "Scanning the external environment" in chapter 2.)

In addressing your particular challenges, you will need allies among major stakeholders at the central level. When you scan to learn their interests and concerns, consider how to involve them in supporting the changes that are being proposed as part of health sector reform or broader government decentralization efforts. Look for the forces that are supporting or impeding the changes. Among your potential stakeholders, think of people from:

- private industry, including private providers and insurance companies;

- the nongovernmental community, including faith-based health organizations;

- international private voluntary organizations operating in your country;

- labor unions;

- political parties;

- professional organizations;

- regulatory bodies;

- educational institutions;

- other ministries.

Develop a strategic plan. It is vital to keep the combined efforts of the health system focused on the right things and in the right order. To do this, involve your key stakeholders in periodic strategic planning exercises. The results of your scan will give you the information you need to set priorities, develop scenarios about what could happen, and ensure that your team is equipped to face the challenges identified.

Focusing also means making choices about where *not* to spend your energy or resources at this time. In the national political environment, arguments that speak to concerns other than health issues may also be important. It can be critical to place some public health issues in a larger socioeconomic development context where other channels besides health organizations can advance them. The multisectoral approach toward HIV/AIDS is an example. In the mid-1990s in Thailand, government changes in financial support to local governments enabled them to provide nongovernmental organizations with support for a broad range of innovative programs for persons living with HIV/AIDS.

As part of developing the strategic plan, you will need to clarify which challenges can be addressed only at the central level and which should be addressed at levels closer to local populations. As much as is possible and feasible, both legally and politically, push authority to other levels so that the most appropriate level makes decisions. Your job is not to do the work of the provincial or regional level, but to ensure quality and equity of health services through minimum standards and basic packages of services that rationalize health resources. You also need to help your staff perform well in this new central-level role.

Referring to the overall national strategic framework, the district level will need to develop realistic health care objectives to address the needs of its populations. You can help districts do this by providing technical support such as training on how to set strategic priorities and develop plans at their level or how to develop, use, and maintain a management information system that facilitates local decision-making about the accessibility, coverage, and quality of services.

For more information on strategic planning, please see *Strategic Planning: Reflections on Process and Practice* (Vriesendorp 1999). To learn more about developing scenarios and forming coalitions, please see "Coordinating Complex Health Programs" (*The Manager*, MSH 2003).

Align for equitable services. Reorganization efforts in many countries have led to rising inequities among regions, economic instability, and the risk of local governments coming under the heavy influence of special interests (World Bank 1997). To achieve a more equitable flow of resources, you can work with relevant departments and colleagues to align stakeholders around strategies that benefit populations in need of basic health care. For example, you might:

- convene a national forum with key health system stakeholders, such as influential politicians from all political parties, the media, and religious, social, cultural, and educational institutions to address the pressing needs of vulnerable populations;

- link partners in development (donors and nongovernmental organizations) with provinces or districts that lack resources or are lagging in their health statistics;

- initiate national campaigns to encourage communities and families to take responsibility for their own health.

Redesigning processes and anticipating resource needs

Organize and mobilize resources to address priorities. Successfully implementing strategic health priorities depends on effective management processes. Strengthen those processes that are related to your priorities. An institutional modernization process that has been used in several Central American ministries of health and nongovernmental organizations offers a means of redesigning management and operational processes so that they fully support an organization's mission and its core functions. Countries undergoing health sector reform have used this approach to modernize their internal processes so they can exercise their new roles and responsibilities well. Their improved processes have helped them to enhance quality, services (including efficiency of services), and cost-effectiveness.

It is critical to mobilize adequate resources to support the health needs and priorities you identify. Be sure you have an operational planning process that helps managers anticipate resource needs and integrate activities at all levels so they are consistent with the national or organizational strategic plan. When you cannot meet resource requirements with available resources, look for new sources of funding and attract donor interest with compelling proposals or business plans. To be sure you have the people necessary to implement the strategic priorities:

Determining how the system is functioning

There are many approaches to scanning the health system. Focus on those that will give you information on areas you suspect are weak and that will contribute to supporting the system's reorganization.

Management responsibilities. You may need to look at managerial responsibilities for health system functions that may not be working, such as health service delivery, personnel, drugs, supplies, and transport. To do this, you can assess what managers at all levels perceive as their current responsibilities and authority. When you compare these perceptions with the design for national health sector reform (the intention), you will probably uncover areas of confusion, conflicts, or gaps that you can address. *The Decentralization Mapping Tool* at http://erc.msh.org provides a process for assessing managers' perceptions of their actual responsibilities and authority at various levels during health sector reform.

Financial flows. Financial allocations for health services come from diverse financial sources. To find the resources to achieve national priorities, you can begin by tracing the flow of a nation's health expenditures from all public, private (including households), and donor sources. Involve policymakers as you use these data and nonfinancial health data to inform and adjust funding allocations, such as overspending on curative care and underspending on preventive care. National Health Accounts (NHA), a methodology developed by Partners for Health Reform*plus* (implemented by Abt Associates and its partners), can help you in determining the flow of a nation's health expenditures and working to improve funding streams. For more information, see the NHA *Training Manual: Guide for Trainers* (Partners for Health Reform*plus* 2003).

Supply of human resources. With HIV/AIDS and the migration of skilled personnel, many countries are experiencing a severe shortage of the people they need to deliver health services. If your country is experiencing this problem, review the current use and deployment of health personnel, enrollment statistics, trends in graduation, HIV/AIDS-related morbidity and mortality among health workers, and migration statistics. This information will help you determine if appropriately skilled labor will be available to reach your results. Resources about the supply of human resources include "Tackling the Crisis in Human Capacity Development" (MSH 2004) and Kolehmainen-Aitken 2004. You may also want to look at the reasons why some of these statistics are high or low.

(cont. next page)

- work with the Ministry of Finance and civil service to adjust personnel deployment and remuneration policies to support fair distribution among regions and provinces;

- develop staff projections and work with the Ministry of Education to adjust preservice medical and nursing education.

> ## Determining how the system is functioning (cont.)
>
> **Proven practices.** Programs around the world have developed effective ways to address public health challenges and organizational management issues. When you are planning interventions, survey the country's public and nonprofit sectors for innovative and proven approaches to apply. If you do not find any sources for learning about proven practices in your country, you can look on the Internet for practices used in other countries. Two sources of proven practices are the Best Practices Compendium for Family Planning and Reproductive Health (http://erc.msh.org) and the systematic reviews of health care interventions from the Cochrane Collaboration, an international nonprofit organization (http://www.cochrane.org/reviews/index). Summaries of the Cochrane reviews can be read at Informed Health Online (http://www.informedhealthonline.org/).
>
> **Positive and negative forces.** Systemwide changes mandated through the political process rarely state clear outcomes; their goals leave room for interpretation. As a result, various local or national political groups vie with one another to shape the implementation of these changes. Sketching a map of positive and negative forces—political mapping—may help you clarify where you need to focus on advocacy and negotiation (Lindenberg and Crosby 1981).

Inspire long-term dedication and monitor impact. All efforts to bring about fundamental change require willingness to remain engaged for the long term. Without inspired leadership, major setbacks will discourage supporters. Higher pay and better working conditions in other countries can lure away your best workers. To inspire commitment from other levels and stakeholders:

- show how you can transcend group interests by encouraging open communication and negotiating about critical health needs;

- recognize the efforts and successes of others;

- be trustworthy and show willingness to trust others by asking them to become partners in reaching national health goals and giving them the authority and resources to do the job.

Since visible, measurable results are a tremendous motivator, your monitoring and evaluation systems should take a "long view" and examine results from later Demographic and Health Surveys, epidemiological reports, surveillance, and large-scale client satisfaction studies. Make sure health workers see the results of their efforts in the improved statistics. Celebrate victories with all who contributed.

The example on the next page illustrates the experience of one Ministry of Health in reorganizing its management processes to better support district health services.

Use data from research to validate results

Reorganizing a Ministry of Health to support new roles— Example from Nicaragua

When the role of the central level shifts to stewardship of the nation's health system and the middle and local levels become more decentralized, the health ministry's structures, systems, and processes must be changed to support this new role. As part of Nicaragua's health sector reform and decentralization process, the Ministry of Health initiated a host of changes and developed a new national health plan. One group began work on a new health care model, another on the role of the regional and municipal levels, and still others on health care networks. Yet there was a sense that the reforms lacked a coherent vision. There were contradictions among different parts of the health care system in the structure and systems.

The big picture. A multidisciplinary team in the Ministry committed itself to working full-time on reorganizing the Ministry. They first identified how all the different pieces of the health system would fit together: Official health policies would be expressed in the new health care model that defined the basic package of health services. A Ministry structure with fewer levels would support districts and their local networks of facilities in delivering health services. The Ministry would draw on WHO guidelines to define core public health functions and roles at different levels, as well as its vision for the future.

Redesigned support systems. Next the team members defined the operational and management systems needed to support the new roles. For each system, they identified essential processes, procedures, activities, and tasks. Based on extensive input from Ministry of Health staff at every level and interaction with decision-makers, they set performance standards for each administrative and service delivery process. These processes, together with a facilitative supervisory approach, are helping staff do things well the first time, on time, all the time.

Expected results. Teams at the central and service delivery levels are planning the implementation of the redesigned Ministry systems and processes. When all the changes are in place, the country will have a fully decentralized Ministry of Health. Managers and staff will exercise new roles and functions at different levels, supported by efficient systems and processes that will enhance the delivery of health services to Nicaragua's population.

Balancing national goals with local needs: The middle level

"Middles live in a tearing world. It is a world in which people are pulling you in different directions."

—BARRY OSHRY
THE POSSIBILITIES OF ORGANIZATION

Many countries have established an extension of the central Ministry of Health that operates between the national office and the level nearest the local population. The roles of this middle level are often ambiguous and vary from country to country. They are often defined by what they are not: neither policymaker nor operations manager, yet perhaps a little of both. Working away from the capital city, you may enjoy great autonomy and irregular supervision, or you may resent it that your role has been reduced to serving as a conduit of funds (which you cannot spend) for use at the local level and as a cheerleader for local efforts. You may buffer the head office from receiving the brunt of local complaints but also take the blame from the head office for the lagging performance of districts.

A unique view of the central and local levels

Regardless of your assigned functions, being in the middle gives you a unique advantage: you can see both sides. Your level is the only one that can integrate what happens at the central level with what happens at the periphery. By comparing how different districts and communities perform, you can identify where further investigation or immediate action is needed. You can use the successes in one place to help those who are struggling in another by spreading innovative approaches. Disadvantaged districts and communities also need you to be their advocate with headquarters.

To effectively fulfill the role of balancing national goals with local needs, you will need to shift your mindset from being a passive conduit of information and resources to actively supporting local needs. In applying the leading and managing practices, you can initiate, encourage, and influence changes that will result in better health care for local communities.

PROVIDE SUPPORT ABOVE AND BELOW

Your primary task is to support both the central and district levels. You can ensure that on the one hand, national standards meet local needs, and on the other hand, local services meet national standards. For this, you can carry out specific responsibilities:

- arrange technical support to the district level as needed to plan and implement services that meet national and local priorities;

- ensure timely distribution of resources to the district level, if you have the authority;

- advocate for additional support for specific and unique local health care needs;

- help the central level monitor and facilitate local compliance with norms and standards;

- encourage continued attention to national priorities;

- perform epidemiological surveillance and take necessary measures to control epidemics;

- communicate to the central level inspiring stories of local efforts that improved health.

Advocate for
what is needed
to produce
results

It is critical that you and other middle-level managers see yourselves as advocates for what is needed to produce lasting results at other levels. Depending on how the functions and financing of your level have been defined, you may find that the shifts in Table 15 apply.

APPLY KEY PRACTICES TO LINK THE EFFORTS OF ALL LEVELS

To link the efforts of all levels, managers who lead at the provincial or regional level can use the leading and managing practices to:

- scan to fully understand the current health situation and its determinants, anticipate problems, and know who the key stakeholders are, along with their interests and concerns about health system performance at the district level;

- focus on regional challenges, district performance, and national plans;

- align stakeholders and mobilize their resources;

- organize people and expertise around health priorities by building skills;

- support implementation of plans by facilitating local decision-making and stimulating communication with other levels;

- look for encouraging results at the district level to inspire all those involved and encourage those who are watching;

- monitor and evaluate to make sure lessons learned are used and mistakes are made only once.

TABLE 15 **Shifts in focus at the middle level**

If the middle level used to . . .	. . . the middle level should now . . .
Adhere to (or ignore) policies, unrelated, inconsistent standards, and norms for service provision and service providers that impede the middle or district levels	Participate in defining policies, standards, and norms with the central level and advocate for adjusting those that hinder performance at the district level
Collate district reports and send them to the central level	Analyze district reports, synthesize them, and provide meaningful feedback to district health managers to help improve performance
Bundle district plans into regional or provincial plans for submission to the head office	Add value to regional or central plans by ensuring that equity adjustments are made to district or municipal plans and that the plans from different levels form a coherent whole that supports regional or provincial health goals
Ignore or avoid dealing with politicians	Actively work with politicians to influence how they allocate resources for health at the provincial or regional level
Obtain funds from national line (Ministry of Health) departments and account for their use	Bid for most of its budget from provincial nonhealth authorities and account for funds to these authorities
Look to the head office for direction and influence	Look "sideways" to colleagues in other sectors to build coalitions and foster synergies that will promote progress toward common goals
Take a receptive stance towards development partners	Actively work with development partners to make sure their interventions are consistent with provincial health goals and distributed according to need and ability to implement

Untangling
priorities
that conflict

Scan for information to support the district level. You cannot allow unfunded mandates and differing priorities to create confusion among local planners and resource providers on how to allocate resources. Work with your team and others to scan your environment and system. Like managers at the central office, you should research the reasoning behind reorganization as well as its current legal framework. Regularly analyze the health status of the population you serve and discuss the findings with managers and service providers in your districts to increase their understanding of the larger picture.

If you were not involved in creating the country's overall strategic health plan, make sure you understand its priorities for health promotion, protection, and services. Reflect on how well your region's health needs and priorities match centrally determined needs and priorities. Examine the current use and deployment of health personnel in your province or region as well as the curricula and number of students at the educational institutions that train them.

Find out who your stakeholders are and what their interests and concerns are. You should involve some stakeholders during your planning activities, while others may be more important as allies during implementation. Your stakeholders will include:

Recognizing
stakeholders at
the middle level

- political parties and influential politicians who have a stake in improved health services;

- other development sectors;

- faith-based organizations and other nongovernmental organizations operating health services in your region;

- groups of clients with various health care needs and preferences;

- popular organizations (such as women's groups, youth groups, student organizations, sport associations) representing a variety of citizens;

- development partners who have been asked to work in your region by the central government.

Focus on regional challenges as well as national plans. To focus on what you can most effectively do at your level, pay attention to both national plans and district needs. Then make strategic decisions about where to put your greatest effort by identifying a few major challenges that your region is facing. You need to sort out which of these challenges your level can address on its own and which require action from the head office. Your challenges may involve removing obstacles to the delivery of local services, for example, a national policy that interferes with service quality in your region. Work with districts and municipalities to ensure that their plans are consistent with national, regional, or provincial goals, yet flexible enough to meet unique local needs. Provide technical assistance to districts in planning and implementing their plans, if they lack the skills to do this.

Share
information
among
stakeholders

Align stakeholders and mobilize their resources. You will need to share information with all your stakeholders and build coalitions to garner support. For example, to achieve equity among your districts, you may need to advocate for civil service and financial policy reform so that personnel deployment and remuneration policies are geographically equitable. This advocacy will have to be sustained.

Organize staff and expertise around health priorities. To help middle and district levels carry out strategic priorities, find out what technical and managerial skills staff need. Make sure that staff at the district level have the capability to determine costs of services and to use this information in planning and decision-making. It is important that you evaluate district per-

Advocating and coordinating support for health services

Your sources of support will come from the central level and from a number of groups in your own region. You can tailor your approach to each to secure resources.

Central support. Advocating for central-level support is a long process. You can start by building a foundation for advocacy and preparing yourself mentally for the time it will take. Build coalitions with other provincial health staff, and seek advocates for your cause at the central level. Then you will be ready to begin a conversation with the central level to explore changes in roles, responsibilities, and policies that would boost needed reform and gain more support for local services.

Regional support. Nongovernmental organizations and donors operating in your area have resources that potentially can be used to focus on the needs in your region. Through discussions with them, you can work to link their support with geographic areas that lack resources. You can also bring together private industry, media, religious institutions, and nongovernmental organizations in your region to address pressing health needs. You may need to persuade regional authorities from other ministries or state agencies to give you a fair share of provincial resources. You can first try to persuade regional authorities and political parties to focus on high-priority needs. Then you can persuade them to allocate resources to address these needs.

Coordinating support. As groups contribute resources and time to your priorities, it will be important to coordinate their efforts with yours. Gather representatives of these agencies and determine the categories of technical expertise you need to fulfill your program's mandate. Ask each participating agency to identify what they currently do in each technical area. By engaging the group in a discussion about who should take the lead in each area, you can come to an agreement about which agency is the lead agency for an area and what its task involves.

---

formance and take action to address causes of underperformance in specific districts.

Lessening inequalities among districts in your region or province involves skills that the staff at different levels may need to develop. You can evaluate the skills of the district level by keeping informed about local health needs and managing the performance of services. Also determine how well staff at your level can carry out the role of the middle level. Look at their negotiating skills and their ability to be subcontractors of services (especially to private-sector organizations) and coordinators of the health initiatives undertaken in the province or region (Pillay 2000).

Look for results at the district level. Extensive reorganization efforts at the middle level are undermined when staff at this level cannot see direct results from their efforts. They may despair if their roles and responsibilities

Raising
performance
and lessening
inequalities
among districts

are ambiguous. To inspire staff to lead health improvements, work with your team and stakeholders to:

Show staff
the results of
their efforts

- create a compelling vision for better health in your region;

- keep your promises to others and convey your expectations that they do the same;

- delegate some of your tasks to districts and support them while they learn;

- visit the districts as a supporter and facilitative supervisor, not as an inspector;

- look for measurable results, discuss them with district managers, and bring them back to your staff to learn from;

- use findings from monitoring and evaluation to celebrate successes and learn from mistakes;

- recognize the efforts of all who work for better health throughout your region.

The following box illustrates the experience of one middle-level team that reconnected with local facilities and communities.

**Improving morale and resource flows through district outreach—
Example from South Africa**

The Government of South Africa is moving toward a primary health care delivery system based in municipalities. Local governments run by locally elected politicians will eventually assume responsibility for managing primary health care services. Health managers in the Eastern Cape Provincial Department of Health have been working to ensure that, once fully decentralized, primary health care services for very poor populations will continue to improve.

Team visits. The Head of the Provincial Department of Health realized the challenge he faced: how to build consensus around a common vision of improved health for local populations and develop supportive working relationships. To address this challenge, he initiated an outreach program. His top provincial team visited the district with the poorest health indicators and spent most of the day in its various facilities, working side by side with local service providers; meeting with community boards, elected officials, and health councilors; observing services; and talking with staff. During debriefings after the visit, the team focused on commitments made during the visits, priority activities required to meet these commitments, and ways in which team members could support one another in implementing the activities. *(cont. next page)*

Improving morale and resource flows through district outreach— Example from South Africa (*cont.*)

Before the visit, tensions between various stakeholders had led to despair over inequities and other problems. The trip served to open the provincial managers' eyes to the desperate conditions faced by local health workers and their clients. All involved became committed to one thing: improving health services so that local health (as measured by health indicators) would improve.

Obstacles overcome. The head of the Provincial Department of Health used his outreach program to mobilize key stakeholders and inspire them to devote their energy to solving stalemates. This program helped to dispel negative feelings that each group had about others. The health councilors became more aware of the provincial team's goodwill and constraints. The hospital board members, elected by the community, expressed their concerns and helped devise ways to improve hospital services. The provincial team gained a better understanding of pressures in the field. The district health managers felt supported by the top team's visit, and this attention boosted their position in the eyes of local politicians. Each group witnessed other groups' commitment to better health for the people of the Eastern Cape Province.

Roles aligned. Bringing people together, linking conversations to a common, desired future, and showing how each group has a critical role to play were the building blocks for implementing change. These nurtured faith in people's ability to make a difference, no matter what their level in the health system.

Results. As a result of this visit, some longstanding staff vacancies were quickly filled, and badly needed equipment and supplies were ordered. The visit also carried great symbolic value. It indicated to the people working far from the provincial capital that they were important enough for the top provincial team to work with. It greatly motivated clinic and hospital staff. To be involved in problem-solving was unusual and encouraging, especially when the visit resulted in the immediate resolution of some longstanding concerns. Ongoing collaboration and communication between district health managers and local politicians generated progress, enthusiasm among providers, and optimism.

Promoting phased changes and negotiating new roles

"We can refuse to accept and accommodate to familiar realities; we can say no to the predictable responses to the common conditions of organization life; we can create new responses and new, more powerful realities. . . . We can become central to creating what our organizational lives will be."

—BARRY OSHRY
THE POSSIBILITIES OF ORGANIZATION

Knowing the role of your level is an important first step. Now you and others need to lead other people at your level to adopt this role fully. Every national health system (or organization) going through reorientation and structural change has policy directives (or written guidelines, in the case of nongovernmental organizations) that outline new structures and functions. Generally, these documents do not provide the details of how the new design should work, yet experiences worldwide indicate two important lessons for making these designs work:

Making the
redesign
of health
systems work

- widespread structural change should be made in *planned stages* and with selected sectors (or organizational departments), to allow for monitoring results and adapting the next stage to field realities;

- managers at all levels need to *negotiate* (among levels and stakeholders) a realignment of roles, functions, and management systems to address gaps in the design and to make design features work.

To communicate with stakeholders and other levels about realigning roles, you will need to cross lines that separate you from them. Such lines, or boundaries, help you and other groups define yourselves but often create psychological barriers. For example, people may look outside their level and think "You are Central, we are District. We have our own ways of doing things." To cross boundaries and form partnerships, you become aware of your group's ways of working and stay open to the norms, language, and constraints of other groups. Then you can engage other groups in meaningful conversation and create working partnerships.

NEGOTIATE NEW ROLES

Sorting out
new roles for a
better future

Conversations between people can trigger profound changes in their thinking and interactions with others with whom interactions have been difficult in the past. Through conversation and discovery, people learn about things that are not working as they should, and find that many people want these things to change. Translating this awareness into action often takes negotia-

Renegotiating roles among health system levels and stakeholders

Roles that people assume are set in stone are often negotiable. But to negotiate roles, different groups have to talk; many problems arise because people forget to talk with one another. Through structured conversations, people working at different levels and different stakeholder groups can renegotiate their roles so they can cooperate in a reorganized health system to serve local needs and services.

Meet with other levels. Work with representatives of other levels to call a meeting of decision-makers at all levels. You may need the assistance of an outside facilitator to do this. When everyone is gathered, you can set the stage for the participants by turning the pyramid of the health system upside down (see Figures 10 and 11). Then lead a discussion about what each party can do to better support service providers in meeting the needs of local populations. To help shift roles, each level needs to stop blaming and complaining about the other levels and instead make explicit requests for support or information.

For tools to engage other levels and groups, you can refer to "Renegotiating Roles among Health System Levels" and "Making Requests for Better Coordination" in the handbook toolkit.

Create a shared vision. Creating a shared vision creates excitement, generates ownership, aligns different stakeholders and produces a positive atmosphere even in groups that might otherwise be in conflict. While there are different ways to create a vision, you should always involve diverse participants and try to include representatives from key stakeholders, even those with the power to derail implementation. (Be aware of people who may want to undermine the event, and plan countermeasures.) Focus on a measurable result, not on how to get there. The goal is to make people aware that there is agreement about a desired result and that progress will occur if everyone works together.

For an exercise that leads to a shared vision, please see "Creating a Shared Vision" in the handbook toolkit.

Harmonize efforts to achieve a vision. Positive energy created during a visioning exercise may disappear quickly in the face of political or professional differences about how to realize the vision. People at the district level in charge of realizing the vision in their area may need training in how to keep the vision alive during the next phases. It is important that the same groups develop plans together to implement reforms and improve systems, and work together to execute these plans. Managers should monitor performance results through indicators, such as the percentage of certified facilities, and evaluate impact on the population's health.

tion. While everyone may want the same future, they may not want to give up what they have always done. They may also have different ideas about how to get to the future. When topics or issues that were not discussed before are on the table, people have the opportunity to negotiate new roles that will better serve the future.

Negotiating well takes skill. You can learn to solve your differences with people in other levels and other agencies by focusing on their interests rather than their stated positions. You can find ways to establish connection with them, advocate for your point of view, inquire into theirs, and choose a strategy for what you want from them.

The guidelines in "Negotiating to Achieve Intended Results" and other exercises on negotiation in the handbook toolkit can help you negotiate new roles with other levels and stakeholders.

Creating a health system driven by local health needs

"Born of neither the left nor the right, this mosaic of community efforts is not led as much by charismatic leaders or political parties as it is shaped by partners—from neighborhoods, from city hall, and from business."

—CURTIS JOHNSON

A health system that successfully reorients its managers' roles toward promoting health will actively seek to meet the needs of local populations and be directly accountable to them. Its levels will align toward common goals and work collaboratively and productively.

This significant shift in roles and responsibilities requires that managers at each level use leading and managing practices to change how different levels relate to one another and coordinate their work. These shifts will, in turn, produce new and convincing results:

Shifts in roles will produce convincing results

- When the district level directs health services and makes good decisions about their mix and their referral networks, then communities are more likely to use the services and maintain their health.

- When the central level sets fair standards for essential, equitable services, and when it facilitates other levels' efforts to meet these standards, then basic community health care becomes more accessible to the people who need it.

- When the middle level successfully links resource flows from the central level to results at the district level, then health services can function without interruption and respond better to emerging local health needs.

When these linkages are established, the health system can empower people, especially those most vulnerable to diseases and other causes of poor health, to take responsibility for their own health and to actively seek access to services from the health care system when they need them.

Questions to consider on . . .

Reorienting roles in the health system

For all levels

- How do you see your role vis-à-vis the other levels (above and below you)?

- To what degree does complementarity, overlap, or conflict exist in your current roles?

- What are the issues that render your level ineffective? In what programmatic and geographic areas do you want to be more effective?

- Of all the issues you consider to be normally controlled by your superiors, which ones could you address given current legal frameworks for reform?

For the district level

- Which health indicator would you like to improve over the next year?

- What support would you need from the middle level to make this happen?

- What do you need to change in your relationship with the middle level to make this happen?

For the central level

- How could you help address the lack of skilled staff or another challenge that directly affects the delivery of health services at the district level?

- What changes do you need to make in your relationship with the middle level to help this happen?

- What do you need to change in the way personnel are deployed and remunerated, and how can you advocate for these changes?

- What key strategic alliances do you need to cultivate to make these changes happen?

For the middle level

- Which districts' performance could you help improve within in the next year?

- How could you distribute resources more equitably in the areas you are responsible for?

- What are the most important changes you need to bring about in your relationship with the district and central levels in order to help the district level be successful?

6 Leading change for better health

"A principal challenge for managers will be to think about things differently and to get people to do things differently. First, governments need leaders who can imagine a different future. Then, the government needs to be able to communicate this vision in a clear, inspirational, and carefully articulated mission."

—MARGARET NEUSE
US AGENCY FOR INTERNATIONAL DEVELOPMENT

To make significant improvements in health care and in the health of the population you serve—improvements that will last over time—you need to know how to lead and how to influence change within and outside your organization. Whether you are introducing a new clinical practice, making large-scale organizational changes, or scaling up policies and programs nationally, the changes need to be led and managed well using the eight leading and managing practices.

To be successful, you will have to discover new ways to address old problems and face new challenges, and help others embrace and implement new approaches to respond to the changing internal or external environment. Because the health care environment is constantly presenting new challenges, you will need to help your team, and your organization as a whole, to adapt to and thrive in a complex environment. To foster positive change, you will have to examine and adapt your values and practices.

To help you be effective in leading change, this chapter discusses:

- framing your challenge and defining its scope and complexity;

- leading organizational change;

- creating a climate that encourages change;

- supporting change with management systems;

- scaling up changes within and beyond your organization.

149

Defining the challenge of leading change

"No problem can be solved from the same level of consciousness that created it."
—ALBERT EINSTEIN

Addressing
health care
challenges
requires
leading change

To face the enormous challenges of improving the health of the clients you serve, you will have to initiate and carry out many types of changes. You will need to be clear about what you are changing, at what level the changes need to take place, and how to navigate through the change process.

Any country or program that is facing challenges such as the HIV/AIDS crisis, protecting family planning programs in light of competing demands for resources, dealing with infectious diseases, undergoing health sector reform, or responding to reduction or growth in funding for health is experiencing challenges that require leading change. Depending on the scope and complexity of the challenges you are facing, you may need to lead changes in some or all of the following areas:

- clinical or management practices

- organizational structure and systems

- national or organizational policies and strategy.

To lead a change process, you first have to identify the types of challenges that need to be addressed. The Challenge Model discussed in chapter 2 provides a process for addressing your challenges. In most cases, changes will need to be made in multiple areas. By applying the leading and managing practices consistently, managers can make and institutionalize improvements that allow organizations to serve clients better and realize sustainable improvements in the health of their populations.

Revisiting the Leading and Managing for Results Model (Figure 12) is instructive here. The model illustrates how applying the leading and managing practices, fostering a positive work climate, building effective management systems, and strengthening the ability of both the staff and the organization to respond to change all contribute to achieving positive results in health. To start, it is important to understand the complexity of the challenges managers and organizations are facing.

DISTINGUISH BETWEEN ROUTINE PROBLEMS AND COMPLEX CONDITIONS

Leadership means enabling others to face challenges and achieve results under complex conditions. What do we mean by complex? A complex condition is

From *Managers Who Lead: A Handbook for Improving Health Services*. Cambridge, MA: Management Sciences for Health, 2005

FIGURE 12 **Leading and Managing for Results Model**

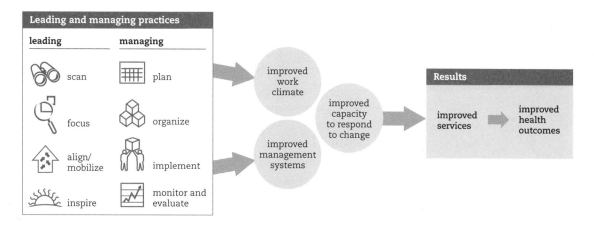

When applied consistently, good leading and managing practices strengthen organizational capacity and result in higher-quality services and sustained improvements in health.

Complex conditions require flexibility and creative thinking

one that is constantly changing or unpredictable. In these situations, we can't apply a prescribed set of steps and count on a predefined outcome. Instead, as conditions in the environment evolve, we must change the way we think and respond. This type of change requires that we learn from day-to-day experience and adapt by applying new values, new ways of thinking, and new practices. There are no easy answers.

To be able to lead change effectively, it is important to understand the difference between routine problems and complex conditions. Table 16 highlights the distinction.

The example on the next page illustrates the difference between routine and complex health problems.

TABLE 16 **Distinguishing between routine and complex**

Routine problems	Complex conditions
The problem is well defined and the solution is known.	The situation must be analyzed and the immediate solution is not known.
The problem can be solved with existing knowledge and practices.	People need to adjust their values, ways of thinking, and practices to address the condition effectively.
A prescribed process can be implemented to solve the problem.	Implementation requires learning new approaches and practices and being flexible as new conditions emerge.
The solution can be applied by a single person or group.	Collaborative work by several stakeholders is required to achieve the solution.

Source: Adapted from R. Heifetz, J. Kania, and M. Kramer, "Leading Boldly," Stanford *Social Innovation Review* v. 2 no. 3 (Winter 2004): 20–31.et al. 2004

For a routine medical problem, such as a simple throat infection, the physician can prescribe a treatment that the patient applies following the medical guidelines. The patient does not need to respond with a change in values or behaviors. In a complex medical condition, such as high blood pressure, there are also treatments the physician can prescribe. But in order to realize a lasting change, the patient needs to adapt his or her values, practices, and behaviors in order get better, and stay healthy. (Heifetz et al. 2004)

In this example, the complex condition of high blood pressure requires that the patient make some fundamental changes in practices and behaviors (such as diet and exercise) to make lasting improvements in his health. In public health programs, a routine problem would be providing specific drugs to rural health posts when they are needed through an existing drug distribution process. A complex challenge would be increasing the vaccination rate in the local population, since people's health care–seeking behaviors and beliefs about the value of immunizations span a wide range.

Encourage staff to try new approaches

As a manager who leads, you need to help people distinguish between routine problems and complex conditions, and help them respond appropriately to each situation. Encourage them to think of new ways to approach their work that are responsive to changing conditions, and support them as they try out new approaches. People who stick rigidly to outdated practices and continue to apply old rules to new situations—whether these situations concern managing people or programs, or how to serve clients and deliver services—will have the most difficulty functioning in this rapidly changing environment.

We will look at the factors that contribute to successful change efforts to help you respond in the best possible ways to the challenges you face in today's health care environment.

Leading organizational change

"How wonderful it is that nobody need wait a single moment before starting to improve the world."

—ANNE FRANK

All successful change efforts require a champion—a person or group of people committed to leading the change process over time and working to overcome the obstacles along the way. The champion (or change team) first needs to clarify her own commitment to the change and believe strongly that the new practice, process, or system is needed to address the challenge the organization is facing.

The champion
must believe
in and fight for
the change

The champion will also need to communicate a compelling case for the proposed change. As part of a strategy for aligning senior management and key stakeholders and gaining their commitment, the champion needs to show that the proposed change is consistent with organizational values and priorities, and explain how the changes can be implemented without seriously disrupting other important organizational activities. Gaining this critical commitment from other stakeholders will help ensure that necessary resources will be made available to support the change effort. At the same time, the champion must regularly monitor and report on the progress of the effort, and those involved in implementing the changes must be responsible and accountable for using resources appropriately.

> The handbook toolkit provides a group exercise, "Understanding the Process of Leading Change," to help you and your staff learn more about what is involved in leading change.

LEAD THE CHANGE PROCESS

Apply the
eight factors
of successful
change

Once you are certain that a change is needed and have identified the types of challenges you are facing, your job is to initiate and lead the change process. Doing so requires knowing and incorporating the critical success factors in your change effort.

The challenge of leading organizational change is enormous. Many change efforts fail because they are not led and managed well. Such efforts waste precious organizational resources and create pessimism about the organization's ability to change.

The eight factors shown in Table 17 largely determine whether a change effort will be successful. The lessons are drawn from John Kotter's work in researching thousands of organizations undergoing organizational change. They also draw on MSH's approach to developing managers who lead at all levels of an organization. These lessons can serve as guidelines for managers leading a change process.

> For an exercise that helps reinforce these success factors and helps a change team apply them in a change effort, please see "Applying the Factors of Success in Leading Change" in the handbook toolkit.

To be successful in implementing these success factors, managers need to create an environment that supports and encourages change. This means creating a work climate that rewards staff for trying new ways of doing things and acknowledges them for their efforts and commitment while also holding staff accountable for their work.

TABLE 17 **Key factors in leading organizational change**

Success factor	Consequences of not taking this step
Communicate urgency by framing the challenge clearly	**Complacency.** People will not be mobilized to change if they think everything is fine the way it is. They need to understand the challenge they are facing and how it affects their work and their organization.
Build the core team	**Going it alone.** If there is not a group of "early adopters" who are committed to the change, it will falter in the face of opposition. Include key stakeholders and authority figures on the change team in order to get organizational buy-in.
Create a shared vision	**Lack of commitment.** If the vision is not created together with all of the stakeholders, there is no clear picture of and path toward a desired future, and energy and commitment will be dispersed. Be inclusive in creating the vision.
Include others in planning and implementation	**Lack of involvement.** If the vision is not communicated clearly and regularly and used as a guide for shared planning, it will not have an impact on organizational activities. Engage others in creating the implementation plan.
Overcome obstacles together	**Demoralization.** When obstacles remain in place, and little or no effort is made to remove them, people will not be able to sustain the energy to continue. Work together to identify the root causes of obstacles and overcome them.
Focus on results and create short-term wins	**Lack of sustained effort.** When people do not see any positive results in the short term, it is hard to keep them engaged. Focus on results and how to achieve them.
Maintain support for facing ongoing challenges	**Shifts in attention.** While the first positive results may be encouraging, they are not a substitute for lasting change. The risk of declaring victory too soon is that people's attention shifts to something else, and the effort to keep the change moving is lost. Continue to frame the new challenges.
Make change stick in organizational systems and culture	**Changes that don't last.** If the changes do not become part of the organization's systems and culture, it is unlikely that the changes will last. Incorporate new values, behaviors, and processes into routine organizational systems.

Source: Adapted from "Leading Change: Why Transformation Efforts Fail" by John P. Kotter, *Harvard Business Review*, March–April 1995, p. 61.

Creating a climate that encourages change

"The most powerful agent of growth and transformation is something much more basic than any technique: a change of heart."

—JOHN WELWOOD

Any successful change process—whether it is a single practice or an organization-wide system—relies foremost on a manager's desire to make changes. The manager needs to be willing to reflect on his own values and behaviors. This proactive attitude is a prerequisite to leading any change effort. Indeed no significant changes are made that don't begin with a change in oneself. Change requires that you think about and be willing to question long-held beliefs, since often our beliefs are the biggest obstacles to change.

Change begins with oneself

Managers also need to help staff examine their own attitudes and behaviors so that they can respond appropriately to changing conditions. Change is a learning process and requires that you have the ability to question assumptions and test new ways of acting. You will be much more credible as a leader of change if you show in your daily life that you are also making the changes you request of others.

Model changes to influence others

As a manager who leads, you model your attitudes and values (sometimes even without knowing it) and influence how others act and respond. If you show that you want to learn and adapt, that you are willing to admit when you are uncertain, do not know the answer, or when you are wrong, then, in time, others will do the same. Setting an example will support a climate in which people are engaged in thinking and working together to address challenges and achieve results.

HELP OTHERS RESPOND TO CHANGE

Support others' shifts in attitudes and behaviors

When a work unit or organization is undergoing a change, people will have a range of responses. Some adapt quickly to new changes and seek them out. Others are more reluctant and need time to understand and accept the changes before they can commit to them. People have to absorb what the changes mean to them and make their own shifts in attitudes and behaviors before the change will take hold in their daily work.

The diagram in the box on working with people's responses to change shows the range of responses that people have to change. The important job of those leading a change effort is to understand these responses, recognize where people are in the change process, and know how to work with them so that they can help support and institutionalize the changes in the long term.

Working with people's responses to change

It is important to understand the responses people have to change and provide support and encouragement that is appropriate to where people are in their own process.

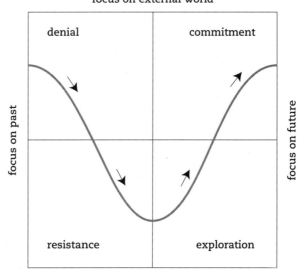

focus on external world

focus on past

focus on future

focus on internal world

denial

commitment

resistance

exploration

When people are in a place of...

Denial. Provide them with more information so that it becomes difficult to stay in denial.

Resistance. Create opportunities for people to express their feelings. Resist the impulse to explain or defend, which will make things worse. Show empathy for and understanding of the losses people experience.

Exploration. Make available opportunities and resources for discovering what is possible in the new situation. Encourage people to get together and support one another.

Commitment. There is no need to "manage" the change process at this point, since people will manage themselves. Get out of the way.

ADDRESS RESISTANCE TO CHANGE

Resistance is a common response to change. People usually resist change because they view it as losing something that is important to them. They may oppose changes and seek to sabotage them because they weren't included in the decision-making that led to the changes. People also resist change if the proposed changes strongly contradict their ideas or appear to threaten their survival.

When you run into resistance, allow people to express their fears and feelings of loss. Don't rush them into seeing things your way, but consider how the change appears to them.

Scan to understand who is resisting and why. Different people or groups may resist a change for different reasons. Find out what people think they stand to lose. Look for examples elsewhere of successful change efforts that you can learn from. Sharing experiences and providing support to one another is important. Tap into networks of people who may have dealt with similar challenges.

Focus on the early adopters. Look at the causes of the resistance, not just the symptoms, and form a strategy for dealing with the resistance. One strat-

Use leading and managing practices to manage change

How to . . .

Deal with resistance

Use reason. Make the case (as in a legal argument) for the change you propose, by pointing out the pros and cons of the change, showing the consequences of not addressing it.

Debunk myths. Directly (but tactfully) challenge myths stemming from long-held beliefs, wrong or outdated ideas, or misinformation passed on by others.

Reinforce the desired new behaviors or practices. Provide resources and rewards (which may be publicity, public recognition, awards, extra resources, or opportunities for growth) to those who apply the new behaviors or practices.

Describe the vision in a variety of ways. Provide opportunities for people to "try on" the new vision for themselves.

- Tell a compelling story about the vision and show how the changes are inevitable.

- Recognize that people take in information in different ways. Some need to see numbers presented in graphs or tables. Others prefer to see pictures or hear or see quotations.

- Use movies, poetry, or visual arts to help people understand the benefits of the change.

(cont. next page)

How to . . .

Deal with resistance (cont.)

Look at yourself. Reflect on your habitual ways of communicating, of telling the story. Maybe something you do needs to change. Your own style may be strengthening the resistance!

- Maybe you are moving too fast and are too impatient.

- Maybe you need to use a different way of communicating with people. Presenting slides from a podium may not be the right way. Consider sitting around a table and exploring the implications of the change with those whose support you need most.

- Spend less time communicating your point of view and more time listening.

  See the exercise "Balancing Advocacy and Inquiry: Changing the Pattern of Conversation" in the handbook toolkit.

- Practice what you preach. If the change involves setting and maintaining high standards, then you too should live up to those higher standards. If you tell people that treating clients with respect is your message, then show respect in every interaction; if you made a mistake, admit it, apologize, and move on.

Expose the resisters to other people or places. Arrange meetings with other people who have been through significant changes. Take staff to visit clinics to see or talk with clients to make the impact of the change visible. These contacts will help demonstrate the (possible) positive effects of the changes you are proposing.

Address slow changers indirectly. Studies on the diffusion of innovations show that a small percentage of almost any group will lag behind in making a change. Do not focus your efforts on this group, sometimes called "slow changers," but let improved results speak for themselves. When a change in practice becomes official, changes in standards will eventually motivate these slow changers to adopt the new practice (Rogers 2003).

egy is to focus on early adopters, those people who buy in and become change agents themselves early on, especially those who are already opinion leaders. Start by including them in your deliberations. It will be a small group at first, but each additional member increases your momentum.

Align and mobilize other people with your change efforts. With your core group, seek allies and the support of influential people to get political support and credibility. Mobilize the opinion of others who are in favor of the change both inside and outside your work group by connecting the benefits of the change to the expressed needs of the clients you serve.

Inspire others to work toward the vision. Appeal to a shared vision and to people's deeply held values, such as equity, justice, and fairness. This advocacy will build a common foundation with others and cause them to reflect on how they can connect what is most meaningful in their lives with the changes that are underway or being proposed.

LEARN AND SHARE KNOWLEDGE

Share experience to encourage new thinking

An important factor in supporting a climate in which people think about new ways to approach new challenges and learn from others' experience is to support systems and norms for regularly sharing and exploring what has worked (or not worked) well and why. Having a process for exchanging information, synthesizing it, and making it available to people when they need it supports an environment in which people learn from each other and find new ways to improve performance.

Knowledge management involves establishing processes and work norms that support generating knowledge (information sharing and synthesis); collecting, storing, and packaging the information for easy access; and helping people to apply the information. Create opportunities for sharing knowledge and reward people who engage in this process.

Provide opportunities for sharing knowledge and experience

Share experience in public forums. Encourage people who have completed a project, gone on a mission or field visit, or presented at or attended a conference to present what they learned to the rest of the organization.

A common practice in the United States is to conduct a "brown bag," named after the brown paper bag that people often use to carry their lunches. These presentations occur around lunch time and people are invited to eat their lunches while listening. (Because the atmosphere is informal, eating is not considered disrespectful.) In this way, the organization does not have to disrupt work schedules and the presentation is limited to one hour.

Brown bag presentations give people a chance to learn about colleagues' work (challenges and successes) and also provide an opportunity for people to practice their presentation skills. These presentations also allow those who have little direct contact with the ultimate beneficiaries of their work to see the connection between their work and the well-being of those served by the organization.

Write up and publicize your results. When a program or intervention has been underway for some time, particularly when it has yielded significant results, work with a small team to produce a flier, brochure, book, newsletter or journal article, curriculum, guide, video or photo montage, or even a conference (virtual or traditional). Creating a product compels you to distill the essential lessons from experience in a form that is accessible to others.

(cont. next page)

Provide opportunities for sharing knowledge and experience (*cont.*)

Evaluate progress and share lessons learned. Routine monitoring and periodic focused evaluations allow you to continuously learn from your activities. Be sure to look carefully at data and information from routine monitoring, discuss the results of evaluations, and apply what you have learned so that you can improve your organization's ability to serve your clients and communities.

Another way to discuss lessons learned is to hold an "after-action review" meeting. The after-action review brings together members of a team who have worked over a period of time to achieve an objective. The members discuss what worked well (and should be continued in another initiative) and what didn't work as well as intended (and should be done differently next time). To be effective, this process requires that the participants be honest and provide constructive feedback, be open to hearing others' perspectives, and be willing to make changes.

For an exercise on conducting after-action reviews, please refer to "Learning from Experience: The After-Action Review" in the handbook toolkit.

Supporting change with management systems

"Pit a good employee against a bad system and the system will win most of the time."

—GEARY RUMMLER

Align management systems with changes

Systems are the interdependent processes that support and enable an organization to do its work and reach its intended results. Good management systems support an organization's capacity to manage resources well and provide better health care. As the Results Model indicates, well-functioning and efficient management systems are essential in order for an organization to effectively produce its intended results as well as to manage change.

As a manager who leads, you have to make sure that your systems can support you, your team, and the entire organization in addressing your current challenges. Do they provide you with the critical information you need in a timely manner? Do they enable you to respond quickly to opportunities and requests? Do they help you see trends and problems, and provide warning signals in time? Can they compensate for the inevitable knowledge and experience gaps when you lose seasoned staff?

Those leading the change process must make sure that the organization's management systems are appropriate and functioning well—or that they are modified, if necessary—so that they align with and support the changes being

The role of management systems in supporting change

Whether you are leading a senior team or a team at a lower level within a program or organization, how well your organization's management systems function affects your ability to achieve results and the sustainability of your entire organization. All the systems need to be aligned with the larger change effort so that you can achieve your intended results.

Operational planning. Operational plans specify the projects and activities that will be conducted over the short term and establish the measurable objectives, timetable, resources needed, and persons or groups responsible for completing the activities.

By developing operational plans that reflect and address the changes you are making, you help your organization align people, ideas, and resources to take effective action. By conducting annual or semi-annual operational planning, you can significantly increase your ability to reach your goals year after year.

Human resource management. Good organizational performance is more likely if you have appropriate staffing levels and (at a minimum) people who perform their jobs according to established job standards. If you do not have enough staff who are performing to these standards, all your other management systems will be compromised. To sustain strong performance, your human resource management system should support:

- planning of human resource needs
- deployment of staff in response to changing work requirements
- creation of a resilient and motivated workforce
- a culture of shared learning and teamwork.

Quality assurance. Assuring the quality of services that your organization provides is central to improving the health of your client population. A good quality assurance system provides managers with critical data from their most important stakeholders—clients. By establishing a system for assessing and improving the quality of services and training staff to use the system regularly, you will be supporting ongoing improvements in your organization's performance. You will also build client satisfaction, which will likely increase demand for your services (a key ingredient of sustainability).

Information management. Good information systems (including data collection, analysis, and use of information), coupled with effective monitoring and evaluation, are essential to support the scanning and focusing functions of managers who lead. Data can be used to inspire your teams when they show progress toward meeting organizational objectives. Analysis of data and the causes of not reaching objectives can help you make midcourse corrections so you can reach your goals by the end of a performance period.

(cont. next page)

The role of management systems in supporting change (*cont.*)

Monitoring and evaluation. Monitoring and evaluating are critical not only for checking that planned activities are completed, but also for analyzing whether the work is resulting in the achievement of objectives. Evaluation helps you determine whether you are "doing the right things" to align staff and make a lasting and positive impact on health, and not just "doing things right." Institutionalizing evaluation practices across the organization is critical to supporting change and learning. A well-functioning monitoring and evaluation system also enables you to share knowledge on best practices, and sustain program and organizational improvements.

Financial management. The financial management system allows the organization to implement appropriate financial controls, collect and analyze financial data, and make sound financial decisions based on the analyses. Sound financial management is essential for good organizational performance, including fulfilling commitments to donors, whether they are your government or an external funding source.

Managers who are leading change efforts need to be skilled in using financial information for planning, implementing, and analyzing activities and for making decisions. In the current environment of health reform and the decentralization of responsibility for health programs to lower levels in the health system, it is more critical than ever that managers be able to apply sound financial management practices and have a strong financial management system to support them.

Revenue generation. One element of organizational finance is identifying and generating new sources of revenue to support services and other organizational programs. Leadership in this area centers on creating and implementing a long-term revenue generation strategy that will mobilize

(*cont. next page*)

implemented by the organization. The management systems to pay attention to are:

- operational planning
- human resource management
- quality assurance
- information management (data collection and use of information)
- monitoring and evaluation
- financial management
- revenue generation
- supply management.

The role of management systems in supporting change (*cont.*)

diverse revenue sources and allocating those resources to meet current and future program and organizational needs. Leading a change effort may require that you to find new ways of generating revenue to support your new or expanded activities.

Supply management. An effective supply management system ensures that the right drugs or other commodities (equipment, expendable supplies), in the right quantities, get to the right place at the right time and are used correctly. The availability of drugs is as critical to organizational performance in health as is the availability of competent staff. You can use the pharmaceutical and commodity management cycle as a systematic approach to make certain that all drugs for services are available and appropriately used according to an effective treatment strategy and timeline. This cycle covers:

- selecting essential pharmaceuticals
- procuring selected pharmaceuticals
- distributing procured pharmaceuticals
- using distributed pharmaceuticals.

For further information about the management systems discussed here, please refer to the many issues of *The Manager* that are available in full text on the handbook CD-ROM.

For extensive information on operational planning and program management, please refer to *The Family Planning Manager's Handbook* (Wolff et al. 1991). For a comprehensive manual on supply management, please refer to *Managing Drug Supply* (MSH and WHO 1997).

All these systems influence how effective the organization will be in achieving results as it evolves and grows over time.

Analyzing the management capacity in your organization, including how well your management systems function, and making plans for improvement are important components of leading organizational change. There are many tools and processes available for assessing management capacity. One tool developed and applied extensively by Management Sciences for Health is the Management and Organizational Sustainability Tool (MOST). MOST guides you through a process, over the course of a few days, to assess your organization's mission, values, strategies, structure, and systems, and provides a framework for developing an action plan to make organization-wide improvements.

You can use MOST as part of a change process to help align your strategies, structure, and systems with your vision for change. The complete MOST tool and guidelines for applying it are available on the handbook CD-ROM.

Assess and strengthen management capacity

Scaling up changes within and beyond your organization

"Whatever you can do, or dream you can do, begin it. Boldness has genius, power, and magic in it."

—JOHANN WOLFGANG VON GOETHE

Scaling up is a type of change that involves building on a successful experience in addressing a challenge and expanding the approach to a wider arena or significantly larger population. To scale up an initiative, new practice, service, or national policy, you will need to work closely with others within and outside your organization. You must have compelling evidence first that the positive results from the approach applied on the smaller scale are significant enough to make the approach worth scaling up. Scaling up can occur only when results are evident to others.

Build on successful experience to expand to a wider area

There are many innovative initiatives underway to improve public health. Many are experiments being conducted in small areas, targeting specific groups that receive special attention and extra resources for a specific period. Critics sometimes claim that these small-scale interventions are not appropriate models for expanding beyond the experimental phase, because the enormous amount of attention and resources lavished on the pilot project or site cannot be maintained when the project scales up beyond its narrow boundaries.

The encouraging news is that there are many examples of small organizations or working groups that have introduced innovations and spurred huge changes in the larger health and reproductive health environment, within and across national borders. Such examples usually begin with a small number of committed leaders, who end up making dramatic and often permanent improvements in the health of their fellow citizens. In some parts of the world, such projects have been remarkably effective in lowering maternal and child mortality rates, increasing the use of family planning, and preventing and treating devastating infectious diseases like tuberculosis and HIV/AIDS.

For example, Fazle Hasan Abed, the founder of BRAC—a large Bangladeshi NGO—took on the challenge of testing a formula for oral rehydration solution to save the lives of children with diarrhea. By the end of 1990, BRAC had trained 12 million families to prepare this solution at home. Community women who worked as trainers created their own innovative practices to simplify the process of preparing the solution and help mothers make accurate measurements.

APPLY THE LEADING AND MANAGING PRACTICES

To scale up a policy, program, or practice beyond your local group or organization, use the leading and managing practices, and be sure to incorporate the eight key factors of successful change in your plan (see Table 17, Key Factors in Leading Organizational Change). These will support you as you reach wider audiences and adjust management systems to support the scale-up.

Scan for factors
that inhibit or
support change

You will need to scan the larger environment and the factors that inhibit and support change. This scan includes seeking to understand new stakeholders and their needs, and creating strategic priorities that respond to their needs. You will have to work hard to align and mobilize resources for the change. It takes "political" skill to build larger coalitions to support scale-up: You will need to know with whom it is critical to align and how you can best mobilize them to support the change.

Your management practices are also very important in scaling up, because to be successful you must create a solid plan, achieve buy-in for it from other stakeholders, and make sure that the necessary resources have been committed to implement that plan. You may also need to enlist others who are especially good at managing large projects to lead the scaling-up process.

Take stock of
successes and
share lessons
with others

What are the lessons we can learn about effectively scaling up our successes? How can we share what works with others in ways that will allow them to adapt and use the lessons to produce results in their own situation? The following examples illustrate a few of the many successful initiatives to change the way managers work. They began small and gained momentum through strong leadership, management, and collaboration, which led to broader commitment and participation as more people saw the positive results.

Scaling up clinical practices

When you have found, through experience or research, a practice that has effectively addressed a challenge you are facing, first test the practice in your own organizational setting. Once you have established that the new practice is effective in a pilot test and have decided to scale it up within your organization or in the entire region or country, you will need to build a broad base of support.

To scale up the new practice, use all the leading and managing practices, attend to the key factors of successful change, and work closely with a wide range of stakeholders. It is important to be persistent and patient, since it often takes a long-term effort to change and scale up even simple practices throughout an organization, region, or country.

For a detailed discussion on leading changes in health processes and practices, please refer to *The Manager*, "Leading Changes in Practices to Improve Health" (MSH 2005), found on the handbook CD-ROM.

WORK WITH MULTIPLE STAKEHOLDERS TO SCALE UP CHANGES

The challenge of scaling up is particularly relevant in the fight against HIV/AIDS. The urgency of addressing the pandemic and dealing with its conse-

> ## Scaling up changes in the way health managers work—Selected country examples
>
> A variety of approaches that change the way local health managers work are being scaled up. Some focus on leadership skills while others develop district-level decision-making. These approaches all engage managers and their teams in intensive work on just a few real organizational challenges (one to three) over several months as part of their regular work day. These approaches also encourage managers to rely mainly on local resources to achieve results, but scaling up often depends on some central-level support for materials, guidelines, or facilitation.
>
> **Nicaragua.** The Nicaragua Leadership Development Program has effectively improved staff morale and work climate as it has helped municipal health managers develop their key leadership competencies. The program has grown rapidly since its inception in 2001 in 12 rural municipalities in northern Nicaragua with 36 participating district managers. It has reached thousands of managers, who oversee 70% of the primary health care facilities, and has covered the majority of the municipalities in the country. In an initial Leadership Dialogue across the Ministry of Health, the Ministry identified its challenges and needed leadership competencies. A pilot test gave the program a solid start.
>
> Close partnership among the Ministry of Health's central, regional, and district levels was the key to scaling up the program. An extensive network of Ministry facilitators at all levels received training, participant materials, and a facilitator's manual. Now a champion for the program in the Ministry of Health's human resource office promotes its spread through continuous education programs regularly offered by the Ministry and municipalities.
>
> **Egypt.** When Aswan Governorate's pilot Leadership Development Program ended in June 2003, the 10 participating teams were so enthusiastic about the results that they continued the program with their own resources and worked with local facilitators. By the beginning of 2005, the program had spread to cover over 78 rural health units in five districts of Aswan Governorate. At the same time, groundwork is being laid to scale up the program nationally. Program materials are standardized, new facilitators are recruited and trained, and a management process for achieving sustainability is being created to provide continued support for this program. Other governorates across Egypt are benefiting from this process of working in teams and using the Challenge Model to achieve results.
>
> *(cont. next page)*

Coordination
is key in
scaling up

quences calls for concerted action on a large scale. Large global and multi-donor funding arrangements (such as those used to support initiatives focused on eradicating a specific disease), sectorwide funding strategies, and basket funding mechanisms often carry an imperative to create partnerships among sectors and stakeholder groups in order to use the funds to scale up national programs effectively.

**Scaling up changes in the way health managers work—
Selected country examples** *(cont.)*

Guinea. After participating in a Leadership Development Program, seven regional health directors, who formerly worked in relative isolation, joined forces with a number of central-level directors and advisors to become a strong team, even though they work at a distance from one another. They consult regularly and come to each other's aid on challenges ranging from difficult employees to dealing with fraud or leakage of resources. The group has created a culture of "questioning oneself first" and become more systematic in dealing with crises and new challenges using leadership practices. In their regions, as they use more teamwork and delegate more, their staff have gained confidence and developed their skills. The regional and central directors are also conducting the Leadership Development Program in districts and district hospitals in these and other regions.

Indonesia. As the Indonesia Ministry of Health rapidly decentralized authority to the district level, it also worked to improve the performance of health services. The central level developed a framework to define essential public health functions and minimum service standards. At the district level, managers assessed district performance of essential public health functions against the standards and used a performance improvement planning and budgeting process called PROSPEK to identify the essential services most in need of strengthening. They designed and implemented cost-effective interventions related to these services to rapidly enhance service delivery performance.

Over two years, the national mandate for essential services and minimum service standards, a committed team of national and provincial facilitators, and clear, tested procedural guidelines, made it possible for 18 districts in five provinces to carry out the assessment and planning process. The Ministry of Health has published and distributed the syllabus for the assessment and planning process to all provincial and district/municipal health offices. Schools of public health are using the methodology to train health managers, and donors are funding the use of this process in the provinces and districts they assist.

Coordination across sectors is absolutely necessary to address most public health crises. When many organizations operate in the same general area, they must coordinate activities to serve the needs of their client populations. Whether it is HIV/AIDS, education of women and girls, family planning, or the elimination of harmful practices, coordination requires planning with key stakeholders. Coordination efforts usually illuminate common hopes and dreams, along with potential conflicting agendas.

DEFINE ROLES AND RULES OF COLLABORATION

When coordinating with other stakeholders, a group composed of representatives of each organization needs to develop a shared vision, find common ground, and establish a common language. In doing so, they make visible the intricate interdependencies among the various partners. Leading such a process requires the kinds of skills we have discussed throughout this book. If it is done well, each stakeholder group will understand how it can contribute its unique strengths, expertise, experience, and position to support a successful scale-up. If it is done poorly, it will create cynicism, waste resources, and compromise the most precious resource we have: people's energy and their commitment to a common cause.

Because the professional and organizational cultures of the various stakeholder groups will vary, it is important to be clear about how you will work with other stakeholders so that together you can realize the greatest benefit from your collective interests, experience, and capabilities. To effectively engage with other stakeholders, you will need to know:

- how decisions will be made (Will the leader make the final decisions? Will you vote? Will you seek consensus?);

- what the criteria will be for accepting or rejecting plans, or modifying them when circumstances change (Are you looking at time, cost, scope, impact?);

- who will need to agree on which kinds of decisions (Will consultative groups need to agree only on broad strategy but not on the details of implementation?).

Deciding together on the process and structure of your collaboration will establish a strong foundation for the future. Irritations frequently arise out of mismatched expectations about how people will work together, what processes and outcomes are acceptable (and which are not), and how credit and accountability will be handled. Establishing ground rules is important because they state what people's responsibilities are for approving, implementing, and evaluating activities. By agreeing on the rules, people will know what they will be held accountable for and what the consequences will be if they don't follow through on their responsibilities.

In the end, change is always a process of aligning and mobilizing stakeholders. In most situations, other people have commitments, beliefs, and expectations that differ from our own. If we are really going to lead change successfully, we have to consistently seek to understand others' views and create shared visions to bring new realities into being.

(margin notes)

Establish interdependencies among partners

Be clear about expectation and accountability

Taking the lead in scaling up

Coordination is an important mechanism for managing large-scale change or scaling up small successes beyond one group's pilot project. Coordination involves more than meeting periodically. To turn a coordinated effort into a true partnership you need to actively shape it. The following actions will help you lead a diverse group of partners as they prepare to scale up a practice or service on a regional or national scale in partnership with one another.

Develop a common view

- Alignment is key. Develop a common view of the central challenge that the partnership needs to address.

- Coherence provides focus. Agree on the central goal of the initiative or program. Make sure everyone agrees with "what success looks like."

Recognize opportunities and constraints and plan to address them

- Recognize that each group contributes in specific ways to addressing the common challenge and achieving the partnership's goal. Define clear roles in line with each partner's strengths.

- Acknowledge that individual groups cannot do everything even in limited geographical zones. Map out who will do what and where in order to build on each partner's strengths and geographic presence, and look for complementarities within and across regions.

- Be aware that coordinated action creates new work or tasks that may require additional resources that are not already programmed in annual plans and that pose human capacity challenges in particular. Include plans for how the additional resources will be mobilized and deployed.

- Know that when diverse groups work together, conflict is inevitable. Discuss at the outset how you will address obstacles to good coordination (such as competition, technical and style differences, resource needs and uses) and make agreements or ground rules to fulfill the potential that your diversity offers.

Help partners grow and develop

- The scope of the collective task may require individual partners to move beyond their traditional roles and geographic area. Therefore, help them to take on their new responsibilities.

- Working in partnership makes new demands on managers and leaders. Help them look at their leadership and management roles in the scale-up effort and determine where they need to strengthen their capabilities to carry out their roles successfully.

For additional guidance on working with stakeholders and gaining their commitment, please refer to "Analyzing Stakeholder Interests and Concerns" and "Mobilizing Stakeholders to Commit Resources" in the handbook toolkit. For further discussion on coordinating with stakeholders, please see the issue of *The Manager* "Coordinating Complex Health Programs" (MSH 2003) on the handbook CD-ROM.

For a comprehensive manual on scaling up HIV/AIDS programs, please refer to *Scaling Up HIV/AIDS Programs: A Manual for Multisectoral Planning* (Helfenbein and Severo 2004).

Turning visions into reality

"If one advances confidently in the direction of his dreams, and endeavors to live the life which he has imagined, he will meet with a success unexpected in common hours."

—HENRY DAVID THOREAU

This chapter has made clear the critical role that managers have in leading change. As a manager who leads, your commitment will inspire the commitment of others. Be clear about what you want to create, and align and mobilize others around a shared vision. You can make these changes, although they may seem overwhelming at times.

Change takes time. You will be making incremental changes along the way, and then one day a major stakeholder who was not fully committed aligns with you, or a new group adopts the change. If you are working with integrity and are consistent in your approach and clear in your values, you will make steady progress toward your vision.

You will know you have been successful when you see:

- people who are free to question and innovate;
- relationships between supervisors and staff that inspire and motivate;
- initiatives that promote continuous learning and seeking out of best practices;
- a climate in which people are acknowledged and held accountable;
- programs that are supported by the community and clients.

Inspire and model change

Mahatma Gandhi once said, "We must be the change we wish to see in the world." When you take on this challenge, you allow yourself to think and act in new ways. In turn, you give permission to others to do the same. Face your fears and your challenges. Make sure to ask for and get support from others, and know that your vision can be achieved only by working with others—never by working only by yourself.

To improve the health of the world's most under-served people is a great challenge. By taking the responsibility to lead your teams and organizations to face this challenge and turn your dreams for a better future into reality, you *are* changing the world.

You follow in the footsteps of others who are committed to health for all. As you move forward and make progress, you form new pathways—creating opportunities for others to lead as well. We need to continually expand this body of leaders to create a world in which all people have access to high-quality health care. We share this challenge with you and hope that this handbook will support you and your teams in facing your challenges and realizing lasting improvements in health.

Questions to consider on . . .

Leading change for better health

Influencing and leading change

- What are your organization's most important challenges in its efforts to improve the health of those you serve?

- What do you need to change first?

- What will be your biggest obstacles in leading this change in your organization?

- Who can you work with to make this change happen?

Encouraging a climate for change

- With respect to the change you are considering, ask yourself and your staff:

  - How might this change benefit my team or my organization?

  - What might I/we learn from this change?

  - What new opportunities will this change present?

- What qualities do you need to develop in yourself and your staff to encourage an environment of flexibility and change?

- What can you do to encourage people to have meaningful conversations about the needs in your organization?

- What do you do to promote learning among the members of your team?

Supporting change with management systems

- How will the change that you are advocating for be institutionalized in the organization's systems?

- What are you doing to ensure that the management systems and practices you have developed and supported will endure if you leave the organization unexpectedly?

Scaling up changes

- What processes, systems, or practices have to be adjusted to scale up this change within your organization?

- Are the potential benefits or improvements in health worth the cost of the resources required to make the change (people, time, energy, money, supplies)?

- Who are the key stakeholders with whom you need to align yourself to implement and scale up your proposed change?

- What are the stakeholders' interests and how will you gain their commitment?

Resources to support managers who lead

This toolkit provides managers and facilitators with exercises and tools to improve managers' skills in leading and managing teams and strengthening individual and team performance to produce results. Each resource provides step-by-step guidelines for facilitating small or large group work and practicing leadership and management skills.

The resources in the toolkit are organized in the order in which they are first referenced in the handbook chapters. Many of these resources are also referenced in other chapters since they are core resources to help managers lead and manage their teams—at any level and in any context. To look up resources by subject, please refer to the index in the back of the book.

Contents

EXERCISE   Understanding leading and managing practices

PURPOSE

This exercise helps participants identify key leading and managing practices, and connects participants' own experience with the practices in the Leading and Managing Framework. It can be used as an introductory exercise with a large group or a small team, and serve as a springboard for more focused leadership and management activities.

RESOURCES NEEDED

- ❑ flipchart and markers
- ❑ four-by-six-inch cards or removable self-stick notes
- ❑ enlarged copy of the Leading and Managing Framework for posting on a wall, or a copy of the framework on two flipchart pages taped together
- ❑ copies of Handout: The Leading and Managing Framework

PROCESS

Preparation

- ■ Make enough copies of the Leading and Managing Framework (Handout) for all participants.

- ■ Prepare nine flipchart pages with one practice written at the top of each page (scanning, focusing, etc.), and one page with the heading "Other."

- ■ Post the flipchart pages around the room and cover the headings.

- ■ Set up the room so that there are four to six participants at each table.

Step 1. Introduce the definition of leading

- ■ Ask the group what they think of when they hear the word "leader."

- ■ Record some responses on the flipchart and reflect on the answers.

- ■ If all answers relate to famous and charismatic people, explain that this is not the type of leading they will be discussing here, but that leading is an activity or practice that anyone—at any level—can engage in.

- ■ Write the definition of leading on a flipchart: "Leading is enabling others to face challenges and achieve results in complex conditions."

Step 2. Reflect on practices of managers who lead

- ■ Ask the participants to think of a person they know personally who leads and manages well.

- ■ Use the definition of leading—"enabling others to face challenges and achieve results in complex conditions"—to guide their thinking.

- ■ Ask them to think about what this person actually does (identify the practices).

- ■ Have them work individually and write down on a piece of paper as many practices they can think of, trying to be as specific as possible.

Step 3. Gain agreement on key practices

- ■ In small groups, ask the participants at each table to review the practices noted by each person.

- Have them develop a list of key practices that everyone in the group agrees are characteristic of managers who lead well.

- Ask them to write each practice on a four-by-six-inch card or on removable self-stick notes.

Step 4. Match practices identified by participants with the Framework

- Uncover the headings on the nine flipcharts that are hung around the room.

- Explain what each means; provide and ask for examples.

- Ask the participants to tape or stick their cards on the flipchart that best describes each practice they identified. (Use the flipchart marked "Other" for practices that do not appear to fit under any of the eight headings.)

- After all the cards are posted, in plenary, ask for volunteers to read the cards posted on each flipchart.

Step 5. Present the Leading and Managing Framework and reflect on practices

- In plenary, pass out copies of the Leading and Managing Framework to each participant.

- Discuss similarities to or differences with the practices they identified.

- Explain that the framework and this common set of practices were the result of research conducted with high-performing managers, research similar to the inquiry and discussion the participants have just conducted.

Step 6. (Optional) Tally strong and weak practices among participants

- Ask participants to reflect individually on the *one* practice in the framework that is their strongest and the *one* that is their weakest.

- For each practice on the framework, tally the number of participants who named it as their strongest. Do the same for the weakest practice.

- Mark the one practice that was identified most often as a strength and the one that was identified most often as a weakness. (This analysis may indicate trends in the organization.)

Wrap up and plan next steps

- Discuss with the group how these eight practices are all needed to effectively produce results in an organization. This framework will help them assess what they need to improve upon to lead and manage better, and will provide guidance for future activities.

- If the session is intended to be an introduction to managing and leading, Step 6 may provide a focus for subsequent sessions.

From *Managers Who Lead: A Handbook for Improving Health Services*
Cambridge, MA: Management Sciences for Health, 2005

HANDOUT   **Leading and Managing Framework**

Practices that enable work groups and organizations to face challenges and achieve results

Leading	Managing

 scanning

- identify client and stakeholder needs and priorities
- recognize trends, opportunities, and risks that affect the organization
- look for best practices
- identify staff capacities and constraints
- know yourself, your staff, and your organization—values, strengths, and weaknesses

ORGANIZATIONAL OUTCOME
Managers have up-to-date, valid knowledge of their clients, the organization, and its context; they know how their behavior affects others

 focusing

- articulate the organization's mission and stategy
- identify critical challenges
- link goals with the overall organizational strategy
- determine key priorities for action
- create a common picture of desired results

ORGANIZATIONAL OUTCOME
Organization's work is directed by well-defined mission, strategy, and priorities

 aligning/ mobilizing

- ensure congruence of values, mission, strategy, structure, systems, and daily actions
- facilitate teamwork
- unite key stakeholders around an inspiring vision
- link goals with rewards and recognition
- enlist stakeholders to commit resources

ORGANIZATIONAL OUTCOME
Internal and external stakeholders understand and support the organization' goals and have mobilized resources to reach these goals

 inspiring

- match deeds to words
- demonstrate honesty in interactions
- show trust and confidence in staff; acknowledge the contributions of others
- provide staff with challenges, feedback, and support
- be a model of creativity, innovation, and learning

ORGANIZATIONAL OUTCOME
Organization displays a climate of continuous learning and staff show commitment, even when setbacks occur

 planning

- set short-term organizational goals and performance objectives
- develop multi-year and annual plans
- allocate adequate resources (money, people, and materials)
- anticipate and reduce risks

ORGANIZATIONAL OUTCOME
Organization has defined results, assigned resources, and an operational plan

 organizing

- ensure a structure that provides accountability and delineates authority
- ensure that systems for human resource management, finance, logistics, quality assurance, operations, information, and marketing effectively support the plan
- strengthen work processes to implement the plan
- align staff capacities with planned activities

ORGANIZATIONAL OUTCOME
Organization has functional structures, systems, and processes for efficient operations; staff are organized and aware of job responsibilities and expectations

 implementing

- integrate systems and coordinate work flow
- balance competing demands
- routinely use data for decision-making
- coordinate activities with other programs and sectors
- adjust plans and resources as circumstances change

ORGANIZATIONAL OUTCOME
Activities are carried out efficiently, effectively, and responsively

 monitoring and evaluating

- monitor and reflect on progress against plans
- provide feedback
- identify needed changes
- improve work processes, procedures, and tools

ORGANIZATIONAL OUTCOME
Organization continuously updates information about the status of achievements and results, and applies ongoing learning and knowledge

EXERCISE   "Understanding leading and managing practices"

From *Managers Who Lead: A Handbook for Improving Health Services*
Cambridge, MA: Management Sciences for Health, 2005

EXERCISE Using the Challenge Model

PURPOSE

This exercise is designed to familiarize a group with the process of applying the Challenge Model. To implement the Challenge Model in its entirety, follow the guidelines in Chapter 2 of this handbook.

The Challenge Model provides a systematic approach to achieving results in which groups identify and face one challenge at a time. The model leads you through a process of forming commitment to a shared vision that contributes to realizing your organization's mission, defining and owning a challenge, prioritizing actions for implementation, and working together to achieve results.

RESOURCES NEEDED

❑ flipchart and markers
❑ copies of Handout: The Challenge Model

PROCESS

Preparation

- Make enough copies of The Challenge Model (Handout).
- Review the steps and decide which other handouts you will need from other parts of the toolkit to introduce and review the Challenge Model process with your team.

Step 1. Review your organizational mission and strategic priorities

- With your team, form a common understanding of your organization's mission and strategic priorities. This understanding will help you shape your vision and make sure that it contributes to larger organizational priorities.

Step 2. Create a shared vision

- Work with your team to create a shared vision of the future that contributes to accomplishing the organization's mission and priorities. This shared vision will inspire the team to face each new challenge.

Step 3. Agree on one measurable result

- Pick an aspect of your shared vision and create one measurable result that you all want to achieve. This measurable result is what will drive your work. Because it is measurable, it allows you to monitor and evaluate your progress toward achieving it.

  Note that *finalizing* the result is an iterative process. As you learn more about the current situation and obstacles you need to overcome, you may need to adjust your stated result so that it is appropriate and realistic.

Step 4. Assess the current situation

- Scan your internal and external environments to form an accurate baseline of the realities or conditions that describe the current situation in relation to your stated result.

Step 5. Identify the obstacles and their root causes

- Make a list of obstacles that you and your team will have to overcome to reach your stated result. Use root cause analysis tools to analyze the underlying causes of these obstacles to make sure you are addressing the causes and not just the symptoms.

Step 6. Define your key challenge and select priority actions

- State what you plan to achieve in light of the root causes of the obstacles you have identified. (It helps to begin your challenge statement with "How will we . . . ?") Then select priority actions that you will implement to address the root causes.

Step 7. Develop an action plan

- Develop an action plan that estimates the human, material, and financial resources needed and the timeline for implementing your actions.

Step 8. Implement your plan and monitor and evaluate your progress

- Support your team in implementing the plan, and monitor and evaluate your progress toward achieving your result.

From *Managers Who Lead: A Handbook for Improving Health Services*
Cambridge, MA: Management Sciences for Health, 2005

Mission

Vision

Measurable result:

_____

_____

_____

_____

_____

**Priority
actions**

_____

_____

_____

_____

**Obstacles and
root causes**

Current situation:

_____

Challenge:

_____

[How will we achieve our desired result in light of the obstacles we need to overcome?]

EXERCISE   "Using the Challenge Model"

From *Managers Who Lead: A Handbook for Improving Health Services*
Cambridge, MA: Management Sciences for Health, 2005

EXERCISE   Creating a personal vision

PURPOSE

This exercise helps to familiarize a group with the process of crafting a vision. It can be used as a warm-up exercise for creating a shared vision for a team or a whole organization. It is based on the questions about your personal vision on p. 204 of Senge et al. 1994.

RESOURCES NEEDED

- ❑ flipchart and markers
- ❑ copies of Handout: The Challenge Model

PROCESS

Preparation

■ Make enough copies of the Challenge Model for all participants.

Step 1. Introduce and discuss vision

■ In plenary, ask: "What is a vision?" Record some responses.

■ Explain what a vision is: "A vision is an image of hope, something you truly wish to create."

■ After discussing the use of visions in general, conduct an introductory exercise, "What's in a name?"

■ Say: "Many names come from our parents or our family's vision for our future."

■ Ask the following questions and have participants share their responses with one other person:

■ What is the meaning of your name?

■ Where does it come from?

■ What did your parents envision for your life?

■ Discuss some examples of visions that were in our names.

Step 2. Create a personal vision

■ Ask the participants to think about what they want for their own lives. Ask them to put down all papers, and close their eyes if they wish.

■ In a quiet voice, ask the following four questions, allowing a lot of time between questions to imagine what they are creating.

■ Think about your personal life. What do you want your state of health or level of fitness to be? Imagine yourself and your body exactly the way you want it to be. What activities and hobbies do you want to be doing? Imagine yourself doing these activities.

(Pause to allow people time to think.)

- Think about your family and your relationships. Imagine yourself and others doing things and being exactly the way you most want yourself and them to be. See a picture of yourself and them together in this happy state.

(Pause to allow people time to think.)

- Think about your work. Imagine where you most want to be working. Who are you working with? Who are you serving? What are you doing?

(Pause to allow people time to think.)

- Think about your contribution to the world. What would you most like to contribute, to give back? What does it look like when you are giving something to society or your organization that you are proud of?

- After the participants have reflected on these questions, ask them to open their eyes and take a few notes on what they saw in their mind's eye.

- Put the headings for each question on a flipchart for them to refer to (personal life, family/relationships, work, and contribution to society).

- Ask the participants to find one other person and share their vision in the present tense with this person. (For instance, say "I am" or "I have. . . .")

- Give the participants about five minutes to share their thoughts. Then ask each person to find one more partner and repeat the sharing for five more minutes.

- If some participants are willing to share their personal visions with the larger group, ask for some examples.

Step 3. Discuss the elements of the Challenge Model

- In plenary, discuss how creating a vision is the first step in using the Challenge Model. (The next step is to identify a measurable result that will move them closer to their visions.)

- Discuss the elements of a vision and how the Challenge Model provides a framework for identifying ways to realize the vision.

- Discuss what the participants thought of this exercise. (Usually participants will report that the exercise was an energizing, inspiring, and unusual experience.)

Wrap up and plan next steps

- Close the conversation by pointing out the shift in energy as a result of the vision work.

- Ask the participants why they think the shift took place.

- Ask why they think a personal vision is relevant to people working together in a team or organization. This conversation can then be used as a bridge to creating a shared vision.

From *Managers Who Lead: A Handbook for Improving Health Services*
Cambridge, MA: Management Sciences for Health, 2005

Mission

Vision

Measurable result:

Priority
actions

Obstacles and
root causes

Current situation:

Challenge:

[How will we achieve our desired result in light of the obstacles we need to overcome?]

EXERCISE   "Creating a personal vision"

From Managers Who Lead: A Handbook for Improving Health Services
Cambridge, MA: Management Sciences for Health, 2005

EXERCISE   Creating a shared vision

PURPOSE

This exercise, an adaptation of the exercise in chapter 2 of the handbook, can be used to guide a very large group through the process of creating a shared vision.

PROCESS

Step 1. Imagine the future

■ Say: "We are going to create a shared vision. This is the picture of what we want to create in the future together. We are not going to discuss the obstacles now, but what we most want to see happen."

■ Ask the participants to think about a time in the future.

■ Say: "Imagine it is two (or more) years from now and we are looking back. We have accomplished all that is important to us. What picture do you see in your mind that represents that accomplishment?"

■ Ask each participant to write a newspaper headline reporting on the group's accomplishments in the year 20_ _ (two or more years from now). Each individual writes a statement to describe what he is most proud of.

Step 2. Integrate your vision with others

■ Group the participants in pairs and ask them share to their visions of their future accomplishments with each other.

■ Ask each pair of participants to create one shared vision combining the best aspects of both visions.

■ Have groups of four (two pairs), discuss the combined visions.

■ Have each group of four further combine the visions to arrive at one shared vision.

Step 3. Record key elements of vision statements

■ Ask each group of four to record the key elements or phrases of their vision statement on four-by-six-inch cards or removable self-stick notes. (Give each group six to eight cards; groups should write only one element or key phrase on each card.)

Step 4. Organize elements and key phrases into categories

■ Ask each group, one group at a time, to tape its cards showing key elements on the wall (or on a set of flipcharts taped to the wall).

■ Ask each successive group to place its cards with other cards that have similar elements. If a card doesn't fit with any other card, it stands alone.

■ Once all the cards are posted, ask the participants to come up to the wall and move the cards around, grouping similar messages and phrases together until they are all arranged into categories. (For example, put all the cards related to serving clients in one category, and all the cards related to clean clinics in another category.) It is okay to have a lot of people moving the cards around, since this process tends to generate good discussion.

- Alternatively, this categorization can be done in a plenary session, in which you ask the participants to suggest which cards should be grouped together (or remain apart).

- Decide on a name for each category, write the name on a new card (of a different color), and place the card above the appropriate groupings of cards.

- Read all the categories aloud.

Step 5. Draft a shared vision statement

- Have a small team synthesize the messages that pertain to each category and write a statement that reflects the shared vision. Remind the team to retain the pride and feeling that the vision expresses. This synthesis is best done overnight or during lunch break.

Step 6. Present the draft shared vision statement

- Write the shared vision on a clean flipchart.

- Put the shared vision statement in the front of the room for all to see. This initial shared vision statement will probably need to be fine-tuned. It should help guide further discussions and refinement.

Wrap up and plan next steps

- Decide on a deadline for finalizing this draft vision statement and who needs to be involved in finalizing it, and finalize the vision statement.

- Discuss with the group how to use the vision as an alignment tool:

  - Discuss the final vision statement with people (other stakeholders) outside your immediate group who need to know your vision or could help you move closer to realizing the vision.

  - Make the vision statement accessible (and easily visible) to everyone who will be involved in working to achieve it.

- Remember that the process of creating a vision together is what makes it powerful. Giving the statement to others who were not involved in the process will not have the same power.

From *Managers Who Lead: A Handbook for Improving Health Services*
Cambridge, MA: Management Sciences for Health, 2005

EXERCISE Creating a shared vision in a picture

PURPOSE

This exercise guides a group through the process of creating a shared vision using images and pictures rather than words. Use it as a precursor to using the Challenge Model. The drawing keeps people from writing down clichés or abstractions that have little personal meaning or fail to inspire them.

RESOURCES NEEDED

❑ flipchart and markers for each group
❑ crayons or pencils (preferably in several colors)

PROCESS

Preparation

- Have handy blank flipchart paper for each table and a set of markers and pencils or crayons (colors are nice to have but not essential).

Step 1. Create a picture of a desired future state

- Divide the participants into small groups of four to six people.
- Ask everyone to dream about the future of their group or organization.
- Have each participant make a quick sketch of an image that come to mind.

Step 2. Share drawings with other group members

- Ask the participants to show and explain their images to the others in their group.

Step 3. Prepare one drawing per group

- Ask each group to prepare one large drawing (flipchart size) that captures the collective dream of the members in their group. (This process encourages the participants to defend elements that are important to them and omit elements they do not care strongly about.)

Step 4. Present small-group drawings

- Ask each group to present its large drawing to the plenary group. (If necessary, have the group clarify parts of the drawing that are not clear. If other participants criticize what a group has drawn, the group should defend the dream in such a compelling way that the rest of the groups accept it.) The drawings can be altered at any time.
- While the small groups present their drawings, summarize the elements and concepts that the drawings portray on a separate board or wall chart.

Step 5. Review the elements and concepts represented in the drawings

- When all the groups have completed their presentations, review (in plenary) the elements and concepts that you recorded.

Wrap up and plan next steps

- Invite a small group of people who write well to transform the elements of the vision into an inspiring piece of prose. Some groups have found it inspiring to hold on to the picture.

- You might also ask a local artist to take the sketches and do an artistic rendering of the result of the exercise.

- Explore in a closing reflection with the group how this image of their shared vision might change as they work together.

From *Managers Who Lead: A Handbook for Improving Health Services*
Cambridge, MA: Management Sciences for Health, 2005

EXERCISE   Recognizing your sphere of influence

PURPOSE

This exercise helps people think about what is under their control to change and what is not given their role or position in their program or organization. It helps them learn about where they can be most successful in influencing changes and provides guidelines for aligning and mobilizing others.

RESOURCES NEEDED

❏ flipchart and markers

PROCESS

Preparation

- Prepare a flipchart with three concentric circles of increasing diameter.

- Write the serenity prayer on another flipchart page: "Give us grace to accept with serenity the things that cannot be changed, courage to change the things which should be changed, and the wisdom to distinguish the one from the other." Keep this page covered until the end of the exercise.

Step 1. Define circles of control and influence

- In plenary, discuss the three circles with the participants to distinguish between:

  - inner circle: what we have direct control over

  - middle circle: what we can influence

  - outer circle: what we have no influence over

- Ask for examples for each circle, such as:

  - inner circle: our behaviors, our actions, our attitudes

  - middle circle: our neighborhood, our church, our work environment, friends, colleagues, family (We can influence them but we cannot control them.)

  - outer circle: natural phenomena such as earthquakes or weather, politics and policies that fall far outside our personal reach, the behavior of people we have no contact with

- Ask the participants in which circle they spend most of their mental energies and which circle is the source of many of their worries and conversations.

- Discuss how they can divert their attention to the inner and middle circles and how doing so can indirectly affect the outer circle.

Step 2. Discuss practices that help people have a positive influence

- In small groups, ask the participants to reflect on and discuss what practices they need to use to be effective in influencing others.

- Ask them to make a list to present to the larger group.

Step 3. Present practices that support influencing others

- In plenary, have the teams present their reflections on influencing practices.

- When the participants are making presentations, coach them about their influencing skills related to how they communicate (for example, are they well prepared? making eye contact with their listeners, speaking effectively overall?)

Wrap up and plan next steps

- Present the flipchart with the serenity prayer.

From *Managers Who Lead: A Handbook for Improving Health Services*
Cambridge, MA: Management Sciences for Health, 2005

EXERCISE Developing measurable results

PURPOSE

This exercise helps participants create a measurable result for their vision. It shows how to define measurable results when using the Challenge Model. This exercise should be used after the group has created a shared vision.

RESOURCES NEEDED

- ❏ flipchart and markers
- ❏ copies of two handouts:
   Handout 1: SMART Criteria
   Handout 2: The Challenge Model

PROCESS

Preparation

- Make enough copies of two handouts for all participants: the SMART criteria (Handout 1) and the Challenge Model (Handout 2).
- Draw the Challenge Model on a flipchart.

Step 1. Choose a desired result as one element of the vision

- In plenary, ask the participants to pick one aspect of their vision to put into action. For example, if the vision is "Patients receive the best and safest care in our unit," ask participants what would be a compelling result that would indicate that they are moving in that direction.
- Distribute the handout of the Challenge Model and reveal the flipchart with the Challenge Model.
- Write the vision in the top in the image of the cloud.
- Ask them what would be a compelling, measurable result that would indicate that they are moving in that direction?
- Give the participants some time to come up with a number of results that they believe will get them to their vision. Write these on a separate flipchart.

Step 2. Write desired results that meet SMART criteria

- Distribute Handout 1, the SMART criteria. Using a few examples, show what each letter of the acronym means.
- Divide the participants into small groups and ask them to make the measurable results written on the flipchart "SMARTer" and/or brainstorm other results.
- Check the groups' work in plenary to see whether they meet the SMART criteria. Coach groups individually if they need more help.

Step 3. Define measurable results in the Challenge Model

- Ask the groups to develop one measurable result that everyone can agree on.
- Have each group write its measurable result in the Challenge Model, Handout 2.
- Ask each group to discuss the current situation in relation to the intended result.
- Have each group articulate its challenge: "How do/can/will we . . . ?"

Wrap up and plan next steps

■ Explain how this gap between what the group wants as a result in the future and what is currently in place creates a tension. This tension, like any tension, seeks resolution. The natural tendency to resolve tension will give the group the energy to move toward its vision.

■ Once the challenge is framed, remind the group that they can now apply the managing and leading framework (scanning, focusing, etc.) to their challenge to better understand it and find out what to do to address it.

From *Managers Who Lead: A Handbook for Improving Health Services*
Cambridge, MA: Management Sciences for Health, 2005

HANDOUT 1 **SMART Criteria**

One of the single most productive things a group can do is make its intended results clear.

When you decide on a desired result, make sure that you have a clear set of indicators. To meet the SMART criteria, results must be:

Specific . . .
  clearly written to avoid differing interpretations

Measurable . . .
  to allow for monitoring and evaluating progress toward achieving the result

Appropriate . . .
  to the scope of your program or work activities, so that you can influence or make changes

Realistic . . .
  achievable within the time allowed

Time bound . . .
  with a specific time period for completion.

Example of a measurable result

For a program whose mandate is to prevent the spread of HIV/AIDS:
  The number of voluntary counseling and testing sites in the district will increase by 50% in the next 12 months.

From *Managers Who Lead: A Handbook for Improving Health Services*
Cambridge, MA: Management Sciences for Health, 2005

HANDOUT 2   **The Challenge Model**

Mission

Vision

Measurable result:

_____

Priority actions

_____

_____

_____

_____

_____

_____

Obstacles and root causes

_____

_____

_____

_____

_____

Current situation:

_____

Challenge:

_____

[How will we achieve our desired result in light of the obstacles we need to overcome?]

EXERCISE   "Developing measurable results"

From *Managers Who Lead: A Handbook for Improving Health Services*
Cambridge, MA: Management Sciences for Health, 2005

EXERCISE	Analyzing stakeholder interests and concerns

PURPOSE

This exercise helps a group of people or organizations that have come together to pursue a common goal to identify key stakeholders (individuals and groups), understand their interests and concerns, and strategize on how to get their support.

RESOURCES NEEDED

- ❑ flipchart and markers (or an over-head projector to use in Step 4)
- ❑ copies of Handout: Stakeholder Analysis Worksheet

PROCESS

Preparation

- ■ Make enough copies of the Stakeholder Analysis Worksheet (Handout) for all participants.

Step 1. Reflect on the role of stakeholders when pursuing a new initiative

- ■ Explain that "having a stake" means being affected by the outcome of an activity and/or being able to influence the outcome positively or negatively.

- ■ Suggest that sometimes we approach stakeholders as if we know what their concerns and interests are. If our assumptions turn out to be wrong we may distance them, rather than align or mobilize them. Find out if people in the room have had this experience (for example, when dealing with groups with which they ordinarily have little contact).

- ■ Explore people's experiences with ignoring stakeholders' concerns by asking, "What happened when we don't pay attention to a particular group that has a stake in the outcome of an initiative we pursue?"

- ■ Ask for ways in which they can find out about stakeholders' concerns and interests.

Step 2. Identify stakeholders

- ■ Referring to the common goal, ask participants: "Who are the people (groups or individuals) who have a stake in the success of our initiative?"

- ■ Brainstorm and record answers. If the list gets very long, create categories to group the answers (for example, private for-profit, NGOs, international donors, government agencies, community groups, professional and educational institutions, religious or political entities).

- ■ Identify the most critical people or groups with an asterisk, or circle them.

Step 3. Identify stakeholder interests and concerns

- ■ Divide the participants into small groups of four to six people per group.

- ■ Divide up the stakeholders that were marked as most critical among the small groups.

- Ask each small group to fill in the Stakeholder Analysis Worksheet (Handout) for the stakeholder group(s) assigned to them.

- Remind the group that there may be representatives from some of the stakeholder groups in the room, making it easy to verify assumptions.

- Have them make a note if there is a stakeholder group they know very little about. This is a reminder to do more scanning later.

Step 4. Verify conclusions and assumptions

- In plenary, ask each small group to present its filled-in worksheet (on a flipchart or using an overhead projector).

- Ask the large group to add missing information, complement the analysis, and correct any errors. If there are representatives from stakeholder groups in the room, ask them to comment. This is a great opportunity to check assumptions.

- If specific actions need to be taken to get stakeholders on board or engaged, decide who will do what. Record the decisions made so that they can be revisited at a future meeting.

Wrap up and next steps

- Compile all the information from the worksheets produced by each small group into one master worksheet including all stakeholders.

- If specific resources are needed from particular groups, use the exercise "Mobilizing Stakeholders to Commit Resources" to create a detailed plan for making requests to stakeholders to commit resources.

From *Managers Who Lead: A Handbook for Improving Health Services*
Cambridge, MA: Management Sciences for Health, 2005

HANDOUT   **Stakeholder Analysis Worksheet**

Stakeholder group or individual	What are they most interested in?	What is their biggest concern?	What do we need to do to get their support?

EXERCISE   "Analyzing stakeholder interests and concerns"   From *Managers Who Lead: A Handbook for Improving Health Services* Cambridge, MA: Management Sciences for Health, 2005

EXERCISE	Diagnosing root causes: The Fishbone and Five Whys Techniques

PURPOSE

This exercise helps participants to understand how to diagnose root causes in the Challenge Model. Use it in conjunction with the Challenge Model to make sure that you are planning actions that target the root causes of obstacles, not just the symptoms.

RESOURCES NEEDED

- ❏ flipchart and markers
- ❏ copies of two handouts: Handout 1: The Fishbone Technique Handout 2: The Five Whys Technique

PROCESS

Preparation

- Make enough copies of the Fishbone Technique (Handout 1) and the Five Whys Technique (Handout 2) for all participants.

Step 1. Introduce the Fishbone and Five Whys techniques

- In plenary, draw on a flipchart a picture of a tree, showing its roots.

- Explain that root cause analysis helps us see beneath the surface to understand the causes of a problem or obstacle.

- Say to participants: "We are learning to diagnose organizational problems, in the same way that we learn to diagnose medical problems."

- Explain that we need to ask "why" to understand the underlying causes of symptoms.

- Draw a picture of the Fishbone Diagram on the flipchart, and label each bone: People, Policies, Processes and Procedures, and Environment.

- Explain that these four areas help us diagnose the causes of organizational problems or obstacles that are preventing you from achieving your desired result.

- Use a concrete example that participants can relate to (for example, people are not coming to the clinic for prenatal care).

- Ask participants to come up with reasons for this state of affairs according to the categories.

- Write on a separate flipchart next to the tree: Why? Why? Why? Why? Why? For each of the fishbone categories, ask "why" five times to come up with the root causes for the example chosen.

Step 2. Practice the Fishbone and Five Whys techniques

- Divide the participants into small groups of four to six people and ask each group to select a desired, measurable result to work with.

- Ask them to identify one obstacle that is preventing them from achieving that result.

- Distribute the Fishbone and Five Whys handouts.

- Ask each group to brainstorm the root causes of that obstacle, using the categories of the Fishbone and the Five Whys in the same way as was demonstrated in plenary.

- Circulate among groups or listen closely to the group's deliberations and remind them to go beyond statements such as "lack of resources." Push them to a high-quality analysis.

- Have participants mark those causes that they can do something about.

Step 3. Report on progress

- In plenary, ask each team to report on its progress.

- Discuss any concerns or questions.

- Have the teams continue to work on their analyses of root causes until they are completed for one obstacle.

Wrap up and plan next steps

- Explore with the participants how they felt after the analysis. It is important for people to gain a sense of control, especially if they usually feel powerless.

- This analysis can help participants become aware of areas in which they can actually change things. The exercise should create significant energy for change.

From *Managers Who Lead: A Handbook for Improving Health Services*
Cambridge, MA: Management Sciences for Health, 2005

HANDOUT 1   **The Fishbone Technique**

PURPOSE

To identify the root causes of the obstacle(s) you have identified
that is keeping you from achieving your intended result.

PROCESS

Step 1. Write your obstacle in the Fishbone Diagram

- In the box on the far right side of the diagram, write one obstacle you have defined in
  your Challenge Model.

Step 2. Brainstorm possible causes

- Discuss each category (main factors) and brainstorm possible reasons why this
  obstacle is creating a gap between your intended result and the current situation.

  People. Knowledge, skills, feedback, motivation, support

  Policies. Rules and regulations that you can affect

  Processes and procedures. Standards, equipment

  Environment. Ministry of Health, community, other stakeholders

  The categories are designed to help organize your ideas. As a group, look for the
  possible causes of the performance gap, and classify them in accordance with the
  categories. You can select other categories if these don't apply to the group's situation.

Step 3. Connect the categories to the central spine of the diagram

- Draw arrows from each category to the central spine, as shown in the diagram.

Step 4. Identify the causes that are most responsible for the problem

- For each category, probe deeper to understand the factors that sustain the current
  situation and keep you from moving to your desired result. Use the Five Whys
  technique to help you probe.

- Brainstorm and write the group's ideas directly on the diagram.

- Think about and select those causes that, if successfully addressed, will allow you to
  make significant progress toward the desired result. Circle these causes.

EXERCISE   "Diagnosing root causes: The Fishbone
            and Five Whys Techniques"

obstacle

processes and procedures

policies

environment

people

From *Managers Who Lead: A Handbook for Improving Health Services*
Cambridge, MA: Management Sciences for Health, 2005

EXERCISE   "Diagnosing root causes: The Fishbone
and Five Whys Techniques"

HANDOUT 2   **The Five Whys Techniques**

PURPOSE

The Five Whys exercise is a questioning technique, developed by Imai Masaaki, for getting beyond obvious symptoms and identifying the primary or root causes of a problem. Asking "why" five times prevents mistaking symptoms for causes, so that you can work on addressing the underlying factors that are causing the problem rather than working on the wrong causal factor.

PROCESS

When you are working with a cause-and-effect diagram and have identified a probable cause, ask, "Why is that true?" or "Why is that happening?" To each answer ask "why" again. Continue asking "why" at least five times, until the answer is "That is just the way it is, or that is just what happened."

EXAMPLE

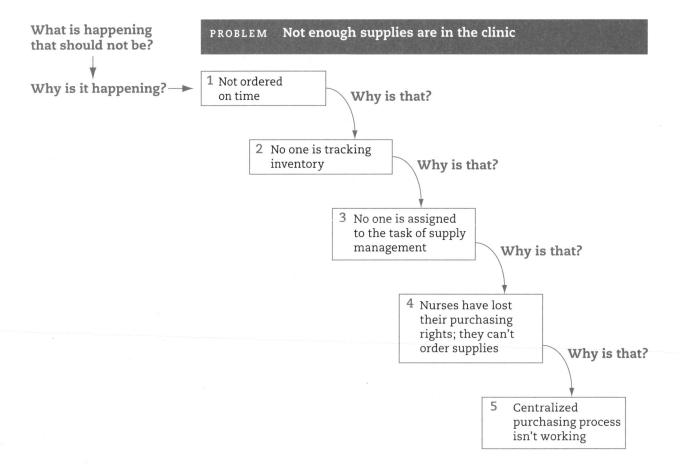

EXERCISE   "Diagnosing root causes: The Fishbone and Five Whys Techniques"

From *Managers Who Lead: A Handbook for Improving Health Services*
Cambridge, MA: Management Sciences for Health, 2005

EXERCISE   Distinguishing challenges from problems

PURPOSE

This short exercise introduces participants to the idea of "facing challenges" as a leadership activity. It is an inquiry into people's positive experiences in facing challenges. Use it as an introduction to visioning, a conversation about leadership, or as a warm-up for a planning process.

RESOURCES NEEDED

❑ flipchart and markers

PROCESS

Step 1. Introduce the concept of a challenge

- In plenary, ask: "Think of something that you have accomplished in your life that you are proud of, something that was a challenge for you and that involved overcoming big obstacles."

- Have the participants turn to their neighbors and talk about this. Make sure each person gets a turn.

- In plenary, ask for some examples. Note how in each case there was a shift from seeing something as a problem (for someone else to solve) to turning the problem into a personal challenge.

Step 2. Share what you have learned about facing challenges

- In small groups, discuss what you learned about what it takes to face a challenge and overcome obstacles.

Step 3. Reflect on what it takes to face a challenge

- In plenary, ask the groups to share what it takes to face a challenge (for example, persistence, hard work).

- Record responses on a flipchart.

Step 4. Discuss the difference between a problem and a challenge

- A problem is "out there" and something that often is blamed on external forces.

- A challenge is something you own.

- A challenge entails overcoming obstacles to achieve a result you are committed to achieving.

Wrap up and plan next steps

- Make an agreement with the group that before calling something a problem they will think about whether it may be a challenge that they are willing to own and practice their leadership skills on.

From *Managers Who Lead: A Handbook for Improving Health Services*
Cambridge, MA: Management Sciences for Health, 2005

TOOL   Setting priorities using the Priority Matrix

PURPOSE

The Priority Matrix helps participants rank actions based on their time to complete, cost, importance to quality, and availability of resources. This tool can be used to prioritize strategies and actions as part of developing an action plan. It assumes that participants have completed a root cause analysis first, so that the selected actions address the root causes of the problem and not just the symptoms.

RESOURCES NEEDED

❑ copies of two handouts:
Handout 1: Sample Completed Priority Matrix
Handout 2: Priority Matrix Worksheet (blank)

PROCESS

Preparation

■ Make enough copies of the Sample Completed Priority Matrix (Handout 1) and the Priority Matrix Worksheet (Handout 2) for all participants.

■ Draw the sample matrix (not filled in) on a large piece of paper so that everyone can clearly see it.

Step 1. Demonstrate the tool and list priority actions

■ Distribute copies of the Sample Completed Priority Matrix (Handout 1) and explain how to use the matrix.

■ Using a real challenge that one of the groups is facing, choose three actions that address the root causes of the obstacles that are preventing them from reaching their desired result.

■ Using Handout 2, have the participants list the actions in the three boxes in the row under "Priority actions." (These actions need to be based on the outcome of a root cause analysis.)

Step 2. Rank each priority action on a scale of 1 to 3

■ On a scale of 1 to 3 (with 1 providing the least benefit and 3 the most benefit), rank each priority action according to the time needed, cost to implement, potential for improving quality, and the availability of resources.

Step 3. Calculate the total points for each priority action

■ Add the numbers in each column to see the total score for each action.

■ The higher the score, the higher the priority of the action based on the criteria listed. (You may choose to add or change criteria to suit your specific needs.)

Wrap up and plan next steps

Check whether the priorities make sense to the participants and make sure that they feel they can actually implement these actions without having to wait for someone else's approval or resources.

From *Managers Who Lead: A Handbook for Improving Health Services*
Cambridge, MA: Management Sciences for Health, 2005

HANDOUT   **Sample Completed Priority Matrix**

Criteria *rank from 1 to 3*	Priority actions		
	Train counselors	**Conduct community education seminars**	**Renovate clinics**
Time to implement *1= the most time* *3= the least time*	2	2	1
Cost to implement *1= the highest cost* *3= the lowest cost*	2	3	1
Potential for improving quality in the long term *1= the least potential* *3= the most potential*	3	2	2
Availability of resources *1= the least available* *3= the most available*	1	3	1
Total	8	10	5

This example illustrates that conducting community education seminars should be a priority. It doesn't mean that you don't carry out the other actions, but you should focus on those that will have the most impact on achieving your result, taking into account time and money.

EXERCISE   "Setting priorities using the Priority Matrix"   From *Managers Who Lead: A Handbook for Improving Health Services*
Cambridge, MA: Management Sciences for Health, 2005

HANDOUT 2   **Priority Matrix Worksheet**

Criteria *rank from 1 to 3*	Priority actions		
Time to implement 1= *the most time* 3= *the least time*			
Cost to implement 1= *the highest cost* 3= *the lowest cost*			
Potential for improving quality in the long term 1= *the least potential* 3= *the most potential*			
Availability of resources 1= *the least available* 3= *the most available*			
Total			

From *Managers Who Lead: A Handbook for Improving Health Services*
Cambridge, MA: Management Sciences for Health, 2005

EXERCISE   Mobilizing stakeholders to commit resources

PURPOSE

This exercise provides a planning process for aligning and mobilizing resources and other forms of support from stakeholders. It should be used after you have identified your measurable results and obstacles in the Challenge Model. It will help you focus your plans for approaching stakeholders and inform your action plan for achieving results.

RESOURCES NEEDED

❑ flipchart and markers
❑ copies of Handout: Resource Mobilization Request Form

PROCESS

Preparation

- Make enough copies of the Resource Mobilization Request Form (Handout 1).

Step 1. Brainstorm stakeholders

- Brainstorm with your team to develop a list of stakeholders from whom you need resources in order to overcome your obstacles and achieve results. (Stakeholders could include local community groups, other health units, other levels of the health system, local hospitals, or other organizations in your area.)

- Make a list of all stakeholders that could support you in achieving your results.

Step 2. Brainstorm resources desired and how to get them

- Discuss what resources each stakeholder has that you need. (Resources could include: skills, equipment, vehicles, funds, or nonmaterial resources such as support, endorsements, and ideas.)

- Brainstorm the request(s) you want to make of them.

Step 3. Fill in the Resource Mobilization Request Form

- Distribute the Mobilization Request Form (Handout 1) and together decide how you can get these stakeholders to support your effort to achieve your intended result(s).

- Decide what specific requests you will make of each stakeholder, who will be responsible for making the requests, and what the timing of the requests will be.

Wrap up and next steps

- Include the activities and timeline you have identified in your overall action plan.

From *Managers Who Lead: A Handbook for Improving Health Services*
Cambridge, MA: Management Sciences for Health, 2005

HANDOUT　**Resource Mobilization Request Form**

Name of stakeholder and resources needed	What specific request will we make of this stakeholder?	Who will make this request?	When will the request be made?

EXERCISE   Developing an action plan that leads to results

PURPOSE

This exercise helps groups develop an action plan incorporating the priority actions to be implemented to achieve the desired results and showing the human resources needed and the timeline for completing the actions. The exercise assumes that teams have defined their challenges, measurable results, obstacles and root causes, and priority actions using the Challenge Model.

RESOURCES NEEDED

❏ copies of two handouts:
   Handout 1: Action Plan
   Worksheet (blank)
   Handout 2: Action Plan (blank)

PROCESS

Preparation

- Make enough copies of the Action Plan Worksheet (Handout 1) and Action Plan Format (Handout 2) for the participants.

- Draw sample formats on large paper for all to see (not filled in).

Step 1. Demonstrate how to use the worksheets

- In plenary, give all the participants a copy of the two handouts.

- Explain how to complete the Action Plan Worksheet.

Step 2. Complete the Action Plan Worksheet

- Have participants work in their teams, each team working on its own challenge.

- Ask the teams to fill in the blank Action Plan Worksheet and discuss their reasons for choosing the priority actions to justify their choices.

Step 3. Complete the action plan

- Instruct teams to transfer the activities from the Action Plan Worksheet and enter them into the blank Action Plan.

- When they are filling in the Action Plan, ask the groups to:

  - list each priority action and the related sub-actions in the far left column;

  - assign a person who will be responsible for each activity;

  - note needed resources to complete the activity;

  - indicate the weeks or months during which this activity will be implemented.

- When the groups have drafted their action plans, have them present them in plenary or to you.

Step 4. Discuss action planning process

- In plenary, answer any questions that participants have about the action planning process.

- Remind them that they will be reviewing the action plans with their local managers and completing their plans with the entire team that has to implement the plan.

- Make sure that these action plans will be integrated with existing work plans and that individuals discuss activities outside their planned scope of work with their supervisors if the supervisors are not present in the group.

Wrap up and plan next steps

- List all your priority actions on a timeline showing when each activity and sub-activity will be carried out, who is responsible, and what resources are required.

From *Managers Who Lead: A Handbook for Improving Health Services*
Cambridge, MA: Management Sciences for Health, 2005

Transfer the information from your work with the Challenge Model and insert it in the appropriate places in this chart.

Health District/Unit: _____

Challenge	Current situation (baseline data)	Measurable result
Root causes	**Priority actions**	

From *Managers Who Lead: A Handbook for Improving Health Services*
Cambridge, MA: Management Sciences for Health, 2005

HANDOUT 2   **Action Plan**

Health District/Unit: _____   Measurable result: _____

Actions	Person(s) responsible	Resources needed (human, financial, material)	Timeline			
			1st month	2nd month	3rd month	4th month

From *Managers Who Lead: A Handbook for Improving Health Services*
Cambridge, MA: Management Sciences for Health, 2005

EXERCISE   "Developing an action plan that leads to results"

TOOL   Putting first things first: The Important and Urgent Matrix

PURPOSE

This tool, developed by Stephen Covey (Covey 2004), helps individuals and groups set priorities and learn how good management means putting first things first and organizing and carrying out work based on priorities. This tool will help individuals and groups learn that the most important thing is not managing time; it is managing ourselves!

RESOURCES NEEDED

❑ flipchart and markers
❑ copies of Handout: Important and Urgent Matrix and discussion notes

PROCESS

Preparation

- Draw a large version of the Important and Urgent Matrix on a flipchart.

Step 1. Identify work activities using the Important and Urgent Matrix

- With large groups, divide the participants into small groups of four to six people.
- Present the empty matrix and explain the four quadrants. We spend our time on activities in one of four ways, by working on:
  - urgent and important things
  - urgent but not important things
  - important but not urgent things
  - not important and not urgent things.
- Clarify the words: *urgent* means it requires immediate attention. It is the NOW stuff! *Important* has to do with results: important activities contribute to your mission, values, and high priority goals.
- Ask each person to look at the matrix and think about the kinds of work-related activities she typically engages in.
- Since no one likes to admit that he is engaged in nonurgent and nonimportant activities, ask the group members to come up with a description of a typical work week for a manager like them and then slot the activities into the four quadrants.
- Calculate the total number of hours spent by this fictitious manager in each quadrant.

Step 2. Calculate the time you spent last week working on activities in each quadrant

- Have individuals do a similar exercise for themselves. For example, if you work a total of 40 hours in a week and you spent 20 hours in Quadrant I, that would mean that you spent 50 percent of your total work week doing urgent and important things (Quadrant I).
- Tell the participants: Once you have finished working on your matrix, turn to the person next to you and share your results.

- Ask small group members to discuss how they can shift the percentages so that there is more time for the important stuff (putting first things first).

Step 3. Discuss results in plenary

- If some participants are willing to share their results, note the percentage of time each person spent in each quadrant, then make a group chart.
- You can also discuss how they think they could do things differently to focus more on important priorities.

Step 4. Make a plan to put first things first

- Ask participants to:
    - make a list of what is most important in their work;
    - share this list with another person;
    - discuss what each person could do differently to put first things first.

Wrap up and plan next steps

- Relate this exercise to the organizational challenge that the group or each team is working on.

HANDOUT **The Important and Urgent Matrix**

	URGENT	NOT URGENT
IMPORTANT	**I** **Activities** ■ Crises ■ Pressing problems ■ Deadline-driven projects that are critical to your strategic priorities	**II** **Activities** ■ Preventing problems and anticipating future activities ■ Creating strategy, planning ■ Relationship building ■ Recognizing new opportunities ■ Recreation
NOT IMPORTANT	**III** **Activities** ■ Interruptions, some calls ■ Some mail, some reports ■ Some meetings ■ Pressing matters	**IV** **Activities** ■ Trivia, busy work ■ Interruptions ■ Some mail ■ Some phone calls ■ Time wasters

Quadrant I represents things that are "urgent and important." Quadrant I activities are usually "crises" or "problems." They are very important, but look out! Quadrant I can consume you. As long as you focus on it, it keeps getting bigger and bigger until it dominates your work. There will always be crises that require immediate attention, but how many things are really urgent?

Quadrant II includes activities that are "important but not urgent." It is the *quality* quadrant, where we plan and anticipate, and prevent things that otherwise might become urgent. *Quadrant II is the heart of effective personal management.*

Quadrant III includes things that are "urgent, but not important." Plenty of us spend too much time in this quadrant. The urgency sometimes is based on someone else's priorities. It is easy to believe that something that is urgent is also important. Look at what you classified as "urgent and important" in Quadrant I. Ask yourself if the urgent activity contributed to an important strategic objective. If not, it probably belongs in Quadrant III.

Quadrant IV includes activities that are "not urgent and not important." It is the "waste of time" quadrant. Chatting, reading jokes, and gossiping are examples of these activities.

Impact of each quadrant on your energy and effectiveness

Results of living in Quadrant I: Stress, burnout, crisis management, always putting out fires

Results of living in Quadrant II: Vision, perspective, balance, control, few crises

Results of living in Quadrant III: Short-term focus, crisis management, feeling victimized and out of control

Results of living in Quadrant IV: Irresponsibility, work not completed on time (or at all), loss of your job

> **SEVEN KEY PRACTICES OF QUADRANT II**
> ■ Improving communication with others
> ■ Better preparation
> ■ Better planning and organization
> ■ Caring for yourself
> ■ Taking advantage of new opportunities
> ■ Personal development
> ■ Knowing what is important
>
> The key practice is **knowing what is important!**

Most of your time should be spent in Quadrant II, Important and Not Urgent.

EXERCISE "Putting first things first: The Important and Urgent Matrix"

Source: Stephen R. Covey, *The 7 Habits of Highly Effective People: Restoring the Character Ethic,* pp. 151, 152–54, text adapted (Fireside edition, 2004).

| EXERCISE | Coaching your team through breakdowns |

PURPOSE

This exercise is helpful when a group has experienced a breakdown and needs a process to resolve the issues. Designed for use with a small team that has been working together on an initiative or project, it helps make the process of addressing and resolving breakdowns a nonthreatening learning experience.

RESOURCES NEEDED

- ❏ flipchart and markers
- ❏ copies of Handout: Breakdown Conversation Worksheet

PROCESS

Step 1. Discuss what a breakdown is

A breakdown is any situation that:

- threatens progress toward a commitment
- presents uncertainty or difficulty
- stops effective action
- presents obstacles to our commitments.

Breakdowns normally lead to:

- minimizing or ignoring the problem
- blaming each other
- erosion of teamwork, trust, and effectiveness.

Step 2. Discuss new ways to approach breakdowns

Explain that:

- all large commitments have breakdowns;
- the greater our commitment, the more and greater the breakdowns: *"No commitment, no breakdown"*;
- breakdowns (when well handled) are a major source of breakthroughs: "finding a new way" to meet your commitments together.

Step 3. Practice a conversation about a breakdown

- Divide the group into pairs and distribute the Breakdown Conversation Worksheet (Handout).
- If the group consists of people who normally work together, ask the pairs to apply the questions from the worksheet to a real breakdown.
- If there is no common experience of a breakdown, participants can ask each other the questions from the worksheet about a personal experience.

Wrap up and plan next steps

- In plenary, have the pairs present their work.
- Summarize what participants have learned by asking: What else did you learn from this exercise?

HANDOUT 1   **Breakdown Conversation Worksheet**

Think of the breakdown your team has recently experienced, and answer the following questions related to that breakdown.

1. What was the breakdown? Briefly describe what happened.

_____

_____

_____

_____

2. What were you committed to? Describe the commitment of you or your team.

_____

_____

_____

_____

3. What was missing that caused the breakdown to occur?

_____

_____

_____

_____

4. What did you learn?

_____

_____

_____

_____

5. What actions could you take now?

_____

_____

_____

_____

EXERCISE   "Coaching your team through breakdowns"   From *Managers Who Lead: A Handbook for Improving Health Services*
Cambridge, MA: Management Sciences for Health, 2005

EXERCISE   **Creating a climate of hope and possibility**

PURPOSE

This exercise helps create a spirit of hope in a group by focusing on what is good, what is working, and what is most fulfilling. It is particularly useful for groups that have seen many problems, have little confidence in their ability to change things for the better, and lack a shared positive vision of the future. It is well suited to serve as preparation for an exercise on developing a shared vision or when there is much conflict or diversity in the group. It is suitable for a first meeting of a coordinating committee because it emphasizes our common humanity and common aspirations.

The theory of Appreciative Inquiry into organizational life, on which this exercise is based, was articulated by two professors (David Cooperrider and Suresh Srinastva) at the Weatherhead School of Management at Case Western Reserve University.

RESOURCES NEEDED
❑ flipchart and markers

PROCESS

Preparation

Review the following questions and make adjustments to the text that is in brackets to fit the group's situation. Prepare a handout for each participant.

1. Tell me about a time that stands out for you as a high point in your work as [your function], when you most successfully joined with others in bringing about positive organizational change in health services delivery. (If you have very recently joined the organization, think about your previous workplace.)

2. Tell me what it was about you that made this a high point. What values, characteristics, or qualities did you bring to the effort that made it so successful?

3. Imagine yourself as a helicopter hovering above your team. What do you see as the essential "life-giving" elements that sustain you as a work group?

4. Looking at the world around you in [your district, region, province, or country], what trends do you see that give you a sense of hope and confidence and that indicate to you opportunities for your organization to fulfill its mission?

5. [Omit this question if you plan to continue with a shared visioning exercise.] Imagine that we have all gone to sleep and woken up in the year 20__ [10 or 15 years from now]. What would you like to see around you as you wake up? Think about your family, your organization, and health [in your region, the world].

Step 1. Appreciate what is good and fulfilling

- Group the participants in pairs and ask each person to interview her partner using these questions. (Plan about 20 minutes for this first step.)

Step 2. Share stories in plenary

- In plenary, introduce the sharing by talking briefly about the importance of stories in our life, especially stories that nurture the human spirit, give hope, and encourage people to go on when circumstances are difficult.

- Instruct participants to present the essence of the story that emerged from the answers to questions 1, 2, and 3. In large groups (more than 20 people), ask participants to share some of the stories at their tables. For smaller groups, share in plenary.

- Make sure that people tell the stories about their partners, not themselves. Bragging is not acceptable in many cultures. In this way each interviewer can show appreciation for his partner.

Step 3. Debrief and record responses to Question 4

- Ask all interviewers if they heard a story that was particularly surprising or wonderful to them.

- After each person has told a story, ask the "owner" of the story if the recounting of it was more or less correct (but don't let her retell the story).

- Ask the interviewer why he thought the story was so amazing. Then move on to the next person. Try to do this swiftly. If you have a small group you can cover all the stories; otherwise take a sampling of stories.

- Record the answers to question 4 on a flipchart (or have small groups summarize them and then record the summaries in plenary).

- Do the same for question 5 if it was asked.

Step 4. Review the results of the exercise and changes in perspectives

- Review what you have done.

- How did you feel when you came in this morning? How do you feel now? What caused the change?

Wrap up and plan next steps

- Have the participants reflect on everything that was discussed in the session and ask:
  - What can you use right away?
  - How?
  - Who would you like to have hear about the ideas we explored?
  - How can you create a similar sense of possibility in your own team?
- Suggest that people write about their intentions in a journal, if they wish.

From *Managers Who Lead: A Handbook for Improving Health Services*
Cambridge, MA: Management Sciences for Health, 2005

EXERCISE   The art of listening

PURPOSE

This exercise helps participants become more aware of their listening habits. It is useful for groups that need to improve their listening to clients, stakeholders, staff, or colleagues.

RESOURCES NEEDED

❏ flipchart and markers

PROCESS

Step 1. Introduce "bad" listening

- In plenary, tell the participants that they are first going to practice "bad listening."
- Conduct a role play in the front of the room.
  - Choose a person to do the role play with you.
  - Ask this person to try to tell you something that is important to her.
  - Role-play bad listening (for example, responding to interruptions, taking phone calls, reading other materials, giving short unresponsive answers, or bringing up other topics).

Step 2. Experience "bad" listening

- Group the participants in pairs and have one person talk for two minutes about something that he really cares about.
- Ask the other participant to show signs of not listening.
- Reverse roles and repeat this exercise for two minutes.

Step 3. Share how you felt not being listened to

- In plenary, ask participants how it felt to be listened to like that.
- Optional: Record responses on a flipchart.
- Summarize the consequences of not being heard (for example, reduced motivation, decreased personal and organizational performance).

Step 4. Introduce "good" listening

- Conduct a role play in the front of the room.
  - Choose a person to do the role play with you.
  - Ask this person to tell you something that is important to her.
  - Demonstrate good listening by paying attention and responding to her concerns.

Step 5. Practice "good" listening

- Group the participants in pairs and have one person talk for two minutes about something that he really cares about.

- Ask the other person to show that he is listening carefully by looking at the person speaking and occasionally asking questions for clarification.

- Reverse roles and repeat this exercise for two minutes.

Step 6. Share how you felt being listened to

- What does it feel like to be listened to well?

- Does it take more time to listen well than to listen badly?

- What is the impact of listening well on motivation and performance?

Wrap up and plan next steps

- What lessons do you take from this exercise?

- Who can we use these skills with?

- Discuss ways to practice better listening.

- Have people report to one another (colleagues, spouse, friends) what changed as they started to listen better to others.

From *Managers Who Lead: A Handbook for Improving Health Services*
Cambridge, MA: Management Sciences for Health, 2005

EXERCISE   Balancing advocacy and inquiry: Changing the pattern of conversation

PURPOSE

This exercise can be used to analyze the types of conversations and questions that block group learning and those that encourage it. Use it with groups or individuals that overuse either inquiry or advocacy. It can help you change the pattern of conversation in a group; encourage outspoken members to spend more time listening; and encourage reticent members to participate more fully.

RESOURCES NEEDED

❏ two flipcharts and markers

PROCESS

Preparation

- Prepare five flipcharts to be completed in plenary:

  Flipchart 1: Balancing Advocacy and Inquiry (see model below, Step 1)

  Flipchart 2: Inquiry that blocks learning (see model below, Step 2)

  Flipchart 3: Inquiry that encourages learning (see model below, Step 2)

  Flipchart 4: Advocacy that blocks learning (see model below, Step 3)

  Flipchart 5: Advocacy that encourages learning (see model below, Step 3).

Step 1. Discuss characteristics of advocacy and inquiry

- In plenary explain the difference between advocacy and inquiry

  - *Advocacy* is when you promote your own view, hoping others will accept it and change their minds.

  - *Inquiry* is when you are curious and try to understand the other's thinking and reasoning.

- In the first flipchart, fill in the four quadrants with behaviors (as shown in the chart below) as you answer the questions:

  - What types of conversations are high in advocacy? Low in advocacy?

  - What types of conversations are high in inquiry? Low in inquiry?

- Point out that anything in excess can create an undesirable situation. Mark these examples on the flipchart with an unhappy face:

SAMPLE COMPLETED ADVOCACY AND INQUIRY CHART (FOR FACILITATORS)

		ADVOCACY	
		HIGH	**LOW**
INQUIRY	**HIGH**	Dialogue: conversation to achieve deep understanding Discussion with learning as objective (interactive lecture)	Interview Focus group Survey Asking questions Interrogation
	LOW	Lecture Speech Explanation Sales pitch Imposing a point of view	Observation Disengagement

Source: Based on the Inquiry/Advocacy Matrix developed by Diana McLain Smith, in Senge et al. 1994, p. 254

Step 2. Discuss different types of inquiry

- In plenary, remind participants of the definition of inquiry: *Inquiry* is when you are curious and try to understand the other's thinking and reasoning.

- Ask for examples of questions we commonly use to elicit information, and reflect on the effects these questions have on others.

- For each question, ask "Does it encourage participation and learning, or block participation and learning? " Write the responses on the appropriate flipchart.

- List the questions from the brainstorming in the appropriate column to distinguish inquiry that encourages learning from inquiry that blocks learning by making others feel defensive.

SAMPLE COMPLETED TABLE OF TYPES OF INQUIRY

INQUIRY THAT BLOCKS LEARNING (DEPENDING ON TONE)	INQUIRY THAT ENCOURAGES LEARNING
- Don't you agree? (especially when said in an intimidating way) - Did you do that because of X, Y, or Z? - Do you really think you did a good job? (when you think he did not.) - Why don't you just try what I'm suggesting? - Why didn't you just tell me? - Why are you so defensive? - Why don't you . . . ? - What's the matter with you?	- How do you see this differently? - What's your reaction to . . . ? - What led you to that conclusion/action? - Say more about that. - Why is that so? - What makes you . . . ? - What kept you from telling me? - How have I contributed to that? - How can I/we . . . ?

Step 3. Discuss different types of advocacy

- Identify types of advocacy (promotion) we use to persuade, and reflect on how these affect people (for example, a sales promotion for a new service or behavior change communication in a workplace AIDS prevention program).

- How does the type of advocacy affect people's stance toward you or what you are promoting?

- List types of advocacy in the appropriate column to distinguish types that encourage learning from types that block learning.

SAMPLE COMPLETED TABLE OF TYPES OF ADVOCACY

ADVOCACY THAT BLOCKS LEARNING	ADVOCACY THAT ENCOURAGES LEARNING
That is how it is! (withholding reasoning) Because I say so! (no discussion possible) Statements with "always" and "never"	When you do this, I . . . It seems to me that... Because of . . . , I believe that . . . My experience is that . . . What I see is that . . .

Wrap up and plan next steps

- In plenary, reflect on the consequences of having too much inquiry or too much advocacy, and point out the importance of balance between the two to encourage learning.

- Discuss and identify future opportunities to practice this balance (such as tallying the number of instances of inquiry versus advocacy in a meeting).

From *Managers Who Lead: A Handbook for Improving Health Services*
Cambridge, MA: Management Sciences for Health, 2005

TOOL   Exploring each other's thinking: The Ladder of Inference

PURPOSE

This tool provides a systematic way to look at how your assumptions influence your conclusions and helps you see another's points of view. It can help you develop an awareness of your thought processes; select different data to reach new conclusions; and have more effective discussions with people who disagree with you or each other. The Ladder of Inference is most useful when you are faced with a view with which you disagree and you seem to be at a standoff.

RESOURCES NEEDED

❏ copies of Handout: Ladder of Inference

PROCESS

A. When someone disagrees with you . . .

Step 1. Ask yourself if you are open to learning from the other person

- Am I willing to be persuaded by a reasonable argument?
- Am I open to new information?

Step 2. Reflect on and disclose your data and interpretations

- Explain, "This is what I am thinking, and this is how I reached this conclusion," slowly move up the Ladder of Inference.

Step 3. Explore your understanding and that of others

- Ask the other person, "Does this make sense to you?" or "Do you see any gaps in what I just said?"
- Encourage the other person to explore your data and interpretations.

Step 4. Ask, "What do you see?"

- Solicit the views of others.

B. When faced with a view with which you disagree . . .

Step 1. Ask, "What happened?"

- What were the actual events that took place or the words you heard?

Step 2. What is your interpretation of those events?

Step 3. Listen, explore, and offer your own interpretation

Step 4. Listen for a larger meaning

- Do you see a different meaning emerging from sharing different interpretations?

C. When at a standoff . . .

Step 1. Explore what data and information are known and not known

Step 2. Listen to ideas with a fresh perspective

Step 3. Look for information that will help move people toward consensus

- Ask from time to time, "What do we need to do to move forward?"

From *Managers Who Lead: A Handbook for Improving Health Services*
Cambridge, MA: Management Sciences for Health, 2005

HANDOUT   **The Ladder of Inference**

Conclusion
the final opinion
or decision you reached

Interpretation
the meanings and
assumptions you added

Selected data
what you observed
or chose to focus on

Observable data
what people actually
said and did

EXERCISE   "Exploring each other's thinking:
The Ladder of Inference"

Source: Adapted from Argyris 1982 in THE FIFTH DISCIPLINE
FIELDBOOK by Peter M. Senge, Charlotte Roberts, et al.,
copyright © 1994 by Peter M. Senge, Charlotte Roberts, Richard
B. Ross, Bryan J. Smith, and Art Kleiner. Used by permission of
Doubleday, a division of Random House, Inc.

TOOL   Reflecting on communication: The ORID method

PURPOSE

This tool provides a simple way to reflect on and reduce miscommunication in conversations with people at all levels of an organization. The process represents one of many applications of the ORID method, which stands for: be Objective, Reflective, Interpretative, and Decisional. It represents the natural process of the brain as it moves from observation to decision through a number of distinct phases. It encourages more detailed reflection than the Ladder of Inference and helps people to distinguish facts from emotions and make decisions about next steps to take.

RESOURCES NEEDED

❑ copies of Worksheet:
   The ORID Method

PROCESS

Preparation

- Think of a specific conversation or meeting that resulted in conflict or negative feelings—perhaps a time when you had to tell a work group that they needed to improve their performance.

- Identify the person or people you spoke to and the purpose of your conversation.

- For each step, write your answers in the framework provided in Handout: The ORID Method.

Step 1. Consider the facts (objective level)

- Consider the objective aspects of the conversation—the facts.

  - What did you observe?

  - Who was there?

  - What did you see?

  - What did you hear?

Step 2. Reflect on your feelings and the other person's feelings (reflective level)

- Reflect on the emotional aspects of the conversation.

  - What did you have positive feelings about?

  - What did you have negative feelings about?

  - Were you ever excited, frustrated, pleased, or angry?

  - What did you assume about the other person's feelings?

Step 3. Interpret the significance of the conversation (interpretative level)

- What seemed most important to you?

Source: ORID was developed by the Institute of Cultural Affairs, a nonprofit organization with offices in Washington, DC, and other cities throughout the world. Adapted from *Winning through Participation: Meeting the Challenge of Corporate Change with the Technology of Participation* by Laura Spencer (Dubuque: Kenndall/Hunt Publishing, 1989)

- What was confirmed?
- What was not confirmed?
- What new insights did you get from this reflection?

Step 4. Decide on steps to take (decisional level)

- What conclusions did you come to?
- What change is needed?
- What are you going to do in the short term?
- What will you do in the long term?
- What do you need to explore further?

Wrap up and plan next steps

- Reflect on the insights you gained about yourself as a result of this exercise and think about what you will do differently next time.

SAMPLE COMPLETED ORID WORKSHEET

OBJECTIVE LEVEL—WHAT DID YOU OBSERVE?
Two people were present—myself and a doctor I supervise. We sat in my office, where it was hot and stuffy. The sun coming in the window was very bright. I had shut the door to reduce the noise from the hallway and keep our conversation private. I had several comments from the suggestion box that were complaints from clients who had to wait because the doctor had arrived late. When the doctor sat down, she looked expectantly at me. When I had shared my concerns with her, she turned red and waved her hands and talked in an agitated way. After that, she gave short answers to my questions.

REFLECTIVE LEVEL—WHAT DID YOU FEEL? WHAT DID YOU ASSUME ABOUT THE OTHER'S FEELINGS?
I had felt quite anxious at the start of this conversation and my stomach had been in a knot. I had determined that her behavior was unacceptable, no matter what the excuse might be! I had taken a few deep breaths to steady myself. I think the doctor was also nervous and perhaps resentful. After I read the comments from the suggestion box out loud, she appeared angry. I felt my own anger rise and tried unsuccessfully to repress it. I was angry about her lack of sympathy for our clients. After her outburst, the doctor seemed to withdraw and become emotionally distant.

INTERPRETATIVE LEVEL—WHAT NEW INSIGHTS CAN YOU GET FROM THIS REVIEW?
Perhaps because the conversation was very emotional, I failed to find out why the doctor was arriving late almost every day. I focused exclusively on the clients and their needs but did not explore the doctor's needs or the reasons for her arriving late. As her supervisor, I could have focused on enlisting her help in figuring out what had to be changed in order for her to arrive on time. Maybe it would have helped to discuss the negative impact that her behavior was having on the work climate of our group. For example, it is hard on her colleagues when they must deal with resentful clients.

DECISIONAL LEVEL—WHAT IMMEDIATE ACTION CAN YOU TAKE? WHAT DO YOU NEED TO EXPLORE FURTHER?
I will approach her with a friendlier demeanor and set up another supervisory appointment. For this next meeting, I will set an agenda, share it with her ahead of time, and stick to it in the meeting. I will put on my air conditioner and pull the blinds, so we will be more comfortable and feel more private. We will explore the root causes of her persistently late arrival and try to solve the problem together. We will set benchmarks for new behavior and arrange a follow-up meeting to discuss her progress.

OBJECTIVE LEVEL—WHAT DID YOU OBSERVE?

REFLECTIVE LEVEL—WHAT DID YOU FEEL? WHAT DID YOU ASSUME ABOUT THE OTHER'S FEELINGS?

INTERPRETATIVE LEVEL—WHAT NEW INSIGHTS CAN YOU GET FROM THIS REVIEW?

DECISIONAL LEVEL—WHAT IMMEDIATE ACTION CAN YOU TAKE? WHAT DO YOU NEED TO EXPLORE FURTHER?

TOOL   "Reflecting on communication: The ORID Method"

EXERCISE   **Giving useful feedback**

PURPOSE

This exercise helps people learn how to give constructive or positive feedback to others about their behavior. Use it when people feel awkward about giving each other feedback or when there is much indirect complaining or negative talk behind people's backs.

PROCESS

Preparation

- Make enough copies of the Feedback Form (Handout) for all participants.

- Write the following four lines on a flipchart:

  - When you _____

  - I feel _____

  - The impact (on me or on the work) is _____

  - I would like it if you [request] _____

Step 1. Introduce giving feedback

- Check to see whether everyone in the group has received feedback at some point in their work life.

- Ask the participants to think of a time when they received feedback that was helpful. When it was not helpful?

- Have each participant talk about these two experiences with another person in the group.

- In plenary, ask for examples.

- Summarize the lessons from the individual stories as follows:

  - *Be specific* about the action that bothered you. Don't generalize by using words such as "always" or "never."

  - *Be specific* about an action that you liked, that had or would have a positive impact, and that you want to reinforce.

  - *Describe the impact* (positive or negative) of the action on you and your work.

  - *Make a specific request* for another action when an action or behavior has a negative effect.

Step 2. Practice giving feedback through a role play

- Divide the participants into pairs, provide each person with a copy of the Feedback Form (Handout) and explain the role play.

- Write the role play instructions on the flipchart as follows:
  - "Think of someone to whom you want to give feedback. This person may or may not be in the room. You will be practicing giving this feedback to your partner."
- Ask everyone to fill out the Feedback Form individually.
- Have each person practice saying what she has noted on the Feedback Form and provide any background if necessary for the partner to understand the context.
- Reverse roles so that the other person can practice giving feedback about a specific action or behavior of another person.

Step 3. Share experiences in giving effective feedback

- In plenary, ask the participants what it was like to give and receive feedback in this way.

Wrap up and plan next steps

- Discuss ways to practice giving useful feedback at work or at home.
- Ask the participants to report the results of their practice to someone else.

From *Managers Who Lead: A Handbook for Improving Health Services*
Cambridge, MA: Management Sciences for Health, 2005

When you are giving feedback, remember to:

- talk about a specific action
- talk about its effect on you and the work
- make a specific request for a different action.

Remember to speak respectfully: "Say what you mean, but don't say it meanly."

When you _____

[do something, a specific action]

I feel _____

[disrespected, etc.]

The impact is _____

[how it affects you or your work]

I would like you to _____

[do something, a specific action]

EXERCISE   "Giving useful feedback"

From *Managers Who Lead: A Handbook for Improving Health Services*
Cambridge, MA: Management Sciences for Health, 2005

EXERCISE   Making effective requests and reducing complaints

PURPOSE

This exercise enables participants to be more effective in communicating requests and reducing the tendency to complain. Use it when there is much complaining and little direct contact about the issues that are being complained about. It is designed to be used with a large group composed of subgroups in an organization.

RESOURCES NEEDED

- ❏ flipchart and markers
- ❏ copies of Handout: Complaints versus Requests

PROCESS

Preparation

- Make enough copies of Complaints versus Requests (Handout) for all participants.

Step 1. Transform complaints into requests

- In plenary, explain to the participants that in organizations people usually have a lot of complaints.
- Ask them to give you some examples of complaints they have in their organizations.
- Record the examples on a flipchart.
- Take a few of the complaints and transform them into requests. Write the following on a flipchart and fill in the requests in the blanks in plenary.

  - Will you _____ (specific person)
  - please do this _____ (specific action)
  - by this time _____ ? (specific time)

- Write on flipchart:

  Three ways to respond to a request:

  - Yes
  - No
  - Counteroffer: "No, I can't do that, but I can do this, or I can do it by some other time."

Step 2. Practice writing out complaints as requests

- Distribute Handout: Complaints versus Requests to the participants.
- Ask each participant to write down three complaints.
- Ask them to rewrite these complaints as requests.

Step 3: Share your request

- Group the participants in pairs and ask each person to share his requests with his partner to see if it has all the characteristics of a good request.

Step 4. Report out on experiences

- In plenary, have the participants share examples of good requests.

Wrap up and plan next steps

- In plenary, review the box in the Handout: Complaints versus Requests.

- Encourage the participants to use these practices. They can make a request of someone soon after the workshop and note how that person handles the request differently from a complaint.

From *Managers Who Lead: A Handbook for Improving Health Services*
Cambridge, MA: Management Sciences for Health, 2005

Complaints and requests: Principles in effective organizations

- People complain only to someone who can do something about the situation.

- People state their complaint in the form of a request.

- If you receive a complaint you cannot do anything about, you decline to listen to it, and refer it to someone who can do something about it (avoid gossip).

- If you receive a request, you are free to respond in the three ways (yes, no, or counteroffer).

Take one complaint and transform it into a request using the following format.

Request form

1. Will you _____ *(specific person)*

2. please do this _____ *(specific action)*

3. by this time _____? *(specific time)*

Three ways to respond to a request

- Yes

- No

- Make a counteroffer: "No, I can't do that, but I can do something else, or I can do it by some other time."

From *Managers Who Lead: A Handbook for Improving Health Services*
Cambridge, MA: Management Sciences for Health, 2005

EXERCISE   **Inspire through building trust at work**

PURPOSE

This exercise engages participants in a reflection about trust in the workplace. Use it to help people discover how to inspire others through building trust.

PROCESS

Preparation

- Write the following definitions of trust on a flipchart; then cover the flipchart:
  - Trust: A firm reliance on the integrity, ability, or character of a person.
  - To trust: To increase one's vulnerability to another whose behavior is not under one's control in a situation where there may be risk.

Step 1. Conduct an inquiry about trust

- Introduce the topic of trust with a question: "Why is trust important for managers?"
- After getting some answers, ask people to think of someone they trust. What has this person done to earn your trust?
- Then ask them to think of someone they don't trust. What has this person done to lose your trust?
- Divide into pairs and have them discuss their thoughts about trust.

Step 2. Discuss earning and losing trust

- In plenary, ask pairs to share what they learned form this conversation about earning and losing trust.
- Record responses on flipchart with two columns labeled: How was trust gained? How was trust lost?
- Show them the definition of trust on flipchart. Ask whether this definition rings true.

Step 3. Review leadership practices that improve trust

- Divide the participants into small groups and ask them to discuss what leadership practices they can use to improve trust in their work.
- Have each group present its findings.
- Check whether the following practices are included (otherwise add them):
  - Treating others with respect
  - Cooperating rather than competing
  - Supporting and helping others
  - Looking for causes of problems in work processes rather than blaming people

- Using knowledge and competence rather than official status to influence others
- Admitting one's own mistakes and uncertainties.

Wrap up and plan next steps

- What can we take away from this exercise that can help us make our workplace more "trustful"?
- Record the participants' responses on a flipchart.
- Ask someone to type up the responses and distribute them to all participants.

From *Managers Who Lead: A Handbook for Improving Health Services*
Cambridge, MA: Management Sciences for Health, 2005

EXERCISE **Gaining commitment, not just compliance**

PURPOSE

This exercise increases people's understanding of the difference between compliance and real commitment. This exercise can help a work group or a group of managers generate commitment to a set of complex tasks or a work plan. Use it when there seem to be problems with commitment in a group, or when people appear to comply out of fear.

PROCESS

Preparation

Make copies of Commitment versus Compliance (Handout) to hand out during Step 2 of the exercise.

Step 1. Reflect on motivating factors of commitment

■ In plenary, ask the participants to reflect individually on a time when they were really committed to doing something.

■ Ask them to write down the factors that motivated them.

■ Then ask them to think about another situation, where they were forced or obliged to do something.

■ Have them create a new list with the reasons why they complied. Then instruct them to label their first list "Internal motivators" and their second list "External motivators."

Step 2. Discuss the meaning of commitment and compliance

■ Distribute Handout: Commitment versus Compliance to the participants.

■ Lead a group brainstorming session to discuss the following questions (alternatively, break up into smaller groups for this discussion, and share key group learning in plenary):

  ▪ What is commitment?

  ▪ What is compliance?

  ▪ What is the difference in the types of performance they produce?

  ▪ Explore when compliance is important.

Wrap up and plan next steps

■ Ask the participants to reflect on their workplace situations and what they need to do to move from external to internal motivation.

■ Ask the group to seek to make a commitment in instances when compliance can be turned into commitment.

From *Managers Who Lead: A Handbook for Improving Health Services*
Cambridge, MA: Management Sciences for Health, 2005

HANDOUT   **Commitment versus Compliance**

Source of motivation	Feeling	Outcome
Commitment (internally driven) You want to do something extraordinary You believe in it	Caring about the work Persevering in the face of obstacles Bringing new possibilities and options to the work and feeling empowered to overcome obstacles	Good results that you are proud of and care about
Compliance (externally driven) You have to do something	Acting to satisfy an external standard or requirement	Obedience to orders and working according to a plan
Formal compliance You do just what is required and no more	Usually sufficient to achieve organizational objectives Doing what one has to but is a routine way	Results that are expected
Noncompliance You don't do what is required	Refusing to cooperate and participate in work activities	No results
Malicious noncompliance You purposely do the wrong thing, although you may not object openly	Following the "letter of the law" but undermining desired results	Negative or sabotaged results

EXERCISE   "Gaining commitment, not just compliance"   From *Managers Who Lead: A Handbook for Improving Health Services*
Cambridge, MA: Management Sciences for Health, 2005

EXERCISE   Coaching to support others

PURPOSE

This exercise gives participants an opportunity to practice a short coaching conversation and explore its use in helping individuals become more effective. Use it when working with teams that are working on a challenge and need to build their coaching skills in order to sustain effective action.

RESOURCES NEEDED

❑ copies of:
   Handout 1: Coaching Principles
   Handout 2: Three-Person
   Coaching Exercise

PROCESS

Preparation

- Make enough copies of Coaching Principles (Handout 1) and Three-Person Coaching (Handout 2) for all participants.

Step 1. Introduce the concept of coaching

- In plenary, explain to participants the concept of coaching. A coach might be:
  - a midwife who supports a woman in delivering her baby;
  - a sports coach who helps a team win without actually being a player.
- Coaching is a leadership tool to support others to successfully address challenges and produce results.
- Coaching is: *enabling another person to reflect on his commitments and find new ways to achieve his intended results.*

Step 2. Conduct a role play demonstrating critical feedback

- In plenary, you and another facilitator (or you and a prepared participant) conduct a role play, presenting the following:

  First scene: A supervisor comes to visit a staff member to criticize her performance.

  - Rather than listening to her, the supervisor immediately starts to look at clients' records and logs and criticizes the staff member for some mistakes.
  - Rather than discuss the causes of the problems, the supervisor immediately begins to give solutions.
- Discuss the role play. Ask . . .
  - Does this situation seem familiar?
  - How does the person being coached feel?
  - Is her performance likely to improve from this interaction?

Step 3. Conduct a role play demonstrating effective coaching

- In plenary, you and another facilitator (or you and a prepared participant) conduct a second role play, presenting the following:

  Second scene: The supervisor coaches the staff member.

  - The coach first greets the staff member and asks how he thinks things are going.
  - The coach then asks questions to try to understand what:
    - ◆ the staff member is trying to achieve
    - ◆ actions she has taken
    - ◆ she thinks needs to be done next.
  - The coach stays in the "inquiry" mode and asks questions without offering solutions.
  - The coach gives the staff person an opportunity to think through her problems and offers her support by trying to understand how she sees the problem.

- Discuss the role play. Ask . . .

  - How does the staff member feel now?
  - Was she able to generate some solutions?
  - Is she likely to be more motivated now to perform?

- Distribute Handout 1: Coaching Principles and go over the principles in light of the role plays.

Step 4. Practice effective coaching

- Distribute Handout 2: Three-Person Coaching Exercise, and divide the participants into groups of three.
- Read the instructions and role for each person to practice coaching.

Step 5. Report on experiences

- In plenary, ask the participants to report to the large group on their experiences:

  - Hear from the observers what they saw.
  - Review the experiences of being coached: what was good and what could have been better.
  - Then review the experiences of coaching: what was easy and what was difficult.

- Discuss the challenges of being a coach and help the participants identify what they need to work on to become better coaches.

Wrap up and plan next steps

- Have the participants select an opportunity to coach or be coached at work and encourage them to practice.
- If all the participants work in the same organization or team, they may consider forming a coaching support group to periodically discuss progress and common challenges.

From *Managers Who Lead: A Handbook for Improving Health Services*
Cambridge, MA: Management Sciences for Health, 2005

HANDOUT 1   **Coaching principles**

Coaching is a conversation in which the coach is committed to the development and success of the person being coached.

A coach helps the other person:

- clarify her commitments and intended results;

- see new possibilities and actions, and expand her range of behavior choices;

- understand her own contribution to recurrent problems and see the consequences of choices made;

- think more clearly and see new ways of achieving her intended results.

A coach does not:

- evaluate and judge

- blame, criticize, and scold

- give solutions.

An effective coach:

- builds a relationship of trust and support

- cares about the person being coached/has the other's growth in mind

- listens well

- asks questions to clarify and illuminate a goal or challenge.

To be coached, you have to:

- want to learn and change

- be open to feedback from others

- take responsibility for your own actions.

EXERCISE   "Coaching to support others"   From *Managers Who Lead: A Handbook for Improving Health Services*
Cambridge, MA: Management Sciences for Health, 2005

Three-Person Coaching Exercise

Step 1. Divide the participant into groups of three and assign each a letter:

- Person A is the coach.

- Person B is the person being coached.

- Person C is the observer.

Step 2. The person being coached describes a challenging situation

- This situation could be an obstacle that stands in the way of achieving a result that the person cares about. This is a real problem that he is facing in either his work or personal life. The person being coached takes about five minutes to describe the situation.

- The coach listens to the entire story with great care and without interrupting.

Step 3. The coach *only* asks questions and does not provide solutions

Following are some of the questions the coach can ask:

- What are you committed to achieving?

- What have you achieved so far?

- What obstacles are you facing?

- Why do you think you are stuck?

- If it could turn out exactly as you dreamed, how would it turn out?

- What actions could you take to overcome your obstacles?

- What support do you need from others?

- How can I support you?

Step 4. The observer watches and reviews how the coach performs

- Allow 10 minutes for each round. Then B becomes the coach, C becomes the person coached, and A is the observer. Repeat again in third round, with C being the coach, A the one coached, and B the observer.

- Make sure each person takes a turn in each role. The complete exercise, not counting instructions or debriefing, will take at least 30 minutes. The observer gives feedback on the coaching.

  - Was the coach supportive?

  - Did she listen well?

  - Did she ask questions to help the staff person think through the issues?

  - Did she avoid giving solutions?

  - Did she leave the person more motivated to perform?

EXERCISE "Coaching to support others"

From *Managers Who Lead: A Handbook for Improving Health Services*
Cambridge, MA: Management Sciences for Health, 2005

TOOL   Improving coaching skills: The OALFA checklist

PURPOSE

OALFA—which stands for Observe, Ask, Listen, give Feedback, Agree—is a technique for coaching staff. Use this checklist before or after a coaching session. It can also be used in preparation for coaching as a reminder about what you need to pay attention to. It can also help you see what you need to improve in your coaching skills.

PROCESS

To use the OALFA checklist, review the items and questions in each step and place a checkmark in the columns marked Yes or No as appropriate.

OALFA Checklist		
STEP 1: OBSERVE	YES	NO
1. Observe the person you will be coaching while you: ■ say hello to him ■ invite him to sit down ■ call him by his name ■ ask a personal question. 2. What do you observe about his emotional state?		
STEP 2: ASK	YES	NO
1. Explain the reason for the conversation using data to set the context for your questions. 2. Ask questions that aim to understand the point of view of the person being coached. 3. Follow answers with questions that probe deeper.		
STEP 3: LISTEN	YES	NO
1. Show signs of active listening when the person being coached talks, for example, lean forward, nod, or maintain eye contact. 2. Paraphrase the words of the person being coached to verify understanding. 3. To confirm your understanding, reflect in your words your understanding of his feelings.		
STEP 4: GIVE FEEDBACK	YES	NO
1. Summarize the information provided by the person being coached. 2. Present observations. 3. Use words that are specific rather than generalizations. 4. Use words that are descriptive rather than judgmental. 5. Focus on observable behavior.		
STEP 5: AGREE	YES	NO
1. Ask questions that require the person being coached to generate alternatives. 2. Help him make a decision to face the problem. 3. Confirm the agreement. 4. Agree on next steps. 5. Discuss consequences in case of failure or nonperformance.		

From *Managers Who Lead: A Handbook for Improving Health Services*
Cambridge, MA: Management Sciences for Health, 2005

EXERCISE   Diagnosing performance problems

PURPOSE

This exercise helps participants identify what may be at the root of performance problems. Use it in situations where problems recur and people focus their energy on treating symptoms rather than root causes.

RESOURCES NEEDED

- ❏ flipchart and markers
- ❏ copies of Handout: Diagnosing Individual Perfrmance Problems Tool

PROCESS

Preparation

- Make enough copies of the Diagnosing Individual Performance Problems Tool (Handout) for all participants.

Step 1. Discuss what it means to perform at your best

- In plenary, ask participants:
  - When do you perform at your best?
  - Why are you able to perform at your best?
  - What systems are in place that help you to do your best work?
- Capture their responses on a flipchart.
- Explain to the group that unless there are clear performance expectations, job descriptions, evaluations with adequate feedback, supplies, equipment, job aids, functional systems, motivation, support, information, and skills in place, it can be difficult to do their jobs to the best of their abilities.

Step 2. Introduce the Diagnosing Individual Performance Problems Tool

- Distribute Handout: Diagnosing Individual Performance Problems Tool.
- Ask the participants to fill out the tool individually.
- Divide the participants into small groups and ask them share their results.
- Ask them to reflect on their experience and consider the gaps they discovered in their performance in relation to what was present or missing that should be in place for optimum performance.

Step 3. Report and reflect on small group work

- In plenary, have the small groups report on their results.
- Identify patterns that require organization-wide solutions.

Wrap up and plan next steps

- If there are people in the room with the authority to act on organizational solutions, agree on priorities, responsibilities, and a time to report back to the group.

From *Managers Who Lead: A Handbook for Improving Health Services*
Cambridge, MA: Management Sciences for Health, 2005

HANDOUT   **Diagnosing Individual Performance Problems Tool**

	YES	NO	SOMEWHAT
1. PERFORMANCE EXPECTATIONS			
a) Do you know what is expected of you?			
b) Do you have an up-to-date job description?			
2. PERFORMANCE FEEDBACK			
a) Do you know whether your performance matches expectations or not?			
b) Do you have periodic conversations with your supervisor about your performance?			
3. WORK CONDITIONS			
a) Do you have the necessary job aids, supplies, and equipment to perform your job?			
b) Is the work climate (environment) conducive to good performance?			
4. MOTIVATION			
a) Do you have any external motivation (such as recognition or financial reward) to perform well?			
b) Is the actual performance of staff influenced by external motivators?			
5. SUPPORT FROM HIGHER LEVELS			
a) Does the district health management team or your organization's management team support you in performing well?			
b) Do policies and procedures support good performance?			
6. THE SKILLS AND INFORMATION YOU NEED TO DO THE WORK			
a) Do you feel that you have the right skills and information to do your job well?			
b) Are there other skills and information you need?			

LIST THREE AREAS YOU NEED TO DISCUSS WITH YOUR SUPERVISOR TO IMPROVE YOUR PERFORMANCE

1.

2.

3.

EXERCISE   Understanding roles in teamwork

PURPOSE

This exercise helps a team reflect on the various roles of its members. Use this exercise to discover ways to improve team members' interactions. This exercise is based on Kantor's Four Player System (Kantor 1999).

RESOURCES NEEDED

❏ flipchart and markers

PROCESS

Preparation

- Prepare a flipchart with the four roles of team members written on one page: Initiate, Follow, Oppose, Observe

Step 1. Present four roles of team members

- In plenary, present the four roles to participants, saying:
  - these are the four roles you can play in a team: *Initiate, Follow, Oppose, Observe;*
  - all these roles are important;
  - a healthy team has people playing all four roles in order to get results.
- Explain that:
  - someone needs to "initiate" an idea or action;
  - someone else needs to "follow" or accept the idea;
  - someone needs to "oppose" or question the idea to make sure that decisions or actions aren't made impulsively and to improve the quality of the team's thinking;
  - someone needs to "observe" to give feedback on how the team is doing.
- Point out that these roles can also be played in a nonproductive way. (For example, one person can do all the initiating and dominate, or someone can only follow and never question the value of the actions. One person can get stuck in opposing and never go along with the proposals of the group. Finally, someone can be too passive and only observe and never actively participate.)
- Explain that for a team to function well, it needs all four roles played in a productive way. For a team member to be effective, she must be able to play any of the four roles.

Step 2. Practice team roles

- Divide the participants into small groups.
- Select two people from each group to act as "observers." It is good to choose natural "initiators" for this role, because it gives them a challenge to stay quiet and observe.
- Ask the observers to write the four team roles (Initiate, Follow, Oppose, Observe) on a piece of paper.

- Have the observers mark on the paper when they see members of their team playing one of these roles.
- Give the teams a topic or challenge to discuss that is sufficiently real to generate a spirited conversation. This topic should relate to their work, so that they won't be self-conscious.

Step 3. Share what it felt like to be an observer

- In plenary, ask the observers what it was like to be only an observer. Was it difficult?
- Ask them what they observed. Did they see each of the four roles played?

Step 4. Give teams feedback

- Have the observers give feedback to their teams.
- Go around to each team and ask the team members whether the four roles were present in a balanced way, or whether there was too much of one role or the other.
- Have the teams discuss the feedback and propose ways to correct imbalances.

Wrap up and plan next steps

- Emphasize that there are no wrong roles, only sometimes that the roles are not balanced.
- Point out that we all need to learn how to be more effective in the roles that don't come most easily to us.

From *Managers Who Lead: A Handbook for Improving Health Services*
Cambridge, MA: Management Sciences for Health, 2005

GUIDELINES   Planning for leadership succession

PURPOSE

These guidelines can be used in the process of top-level
leadership succession, when the departure of a senior leader is
imminent.

GUIDELINES

Preventive action is always preferable to curative medicine. If you are the chief executive
who is contemplating your departure—even if you feel ambivalent about the move—start the
conversation now to prepare your organization for your departure. Obtain perspective and support
by engaging your staff and the board early and actively in succession planning. The more open
the organizational culture, the more involved your colleagues will be. If they know that the board
functions independently in the best interests of the organization, staff members' feedback is
the more likely to be candid and truly representative. Gilmore (1993) has distilled the succession
management process into a sequence of nine steps.

Step 1. Engage the stakeholders

- Engage your organization's *internal* stakeholders in succession planning directly, in
  a series of organization-wide conversations, or indirectly, through a committee that
  circulates questionnaires and issues regular updates on its progress.

- Convince *external* stakeholders, such as donors, investors, partners, collaborators,
  customers, and other influential individuals, of the necessity of a leadership change
  and of the importance of their full support before, during, and after the transition.

Step 2. Analyze strategic challenges

- If your organization has recently conducted a strategic planning exercise, you should
  have a clear picture of the challenges facing the new leadership.

- Changes in the organization's strategic challenges should be reflected in management
  strategies for human resources. These strategies include the choice of a new top
  executive.

Step 3. Formulate the selection criteria and job description

- Select criteria for evaluating the most promising candidates.

- Use the selection criteria to help develop the job description. It should translate
  strategic directions into leadership needs—what sort of leadership the organization—
  will need in the future and job qualifications for the top executive position.

- Since the perfect candidate doesn't exist, explore the most critical qualifications
  needed in the new leader and where you might find people in your organization who
  have those essential qualifications.

Step 4. Design a search and selection process

- The board should have (or develop) a generic search and selection process that needs only minimal adaptation to be used for this recruitment process.
- The board chairperson normally activates the process when succession has become an issue (which may be sudden or occur after the chief executive has spent many months or years contemplating a change).
- If there are no obvious candidates for the chief executive post, the chairperson should put together a search committee (see the box entitled "Using a Search Committee") with the mandate of recommending a suitable candidate to the board.

Step 5. Prepare senior management

- As the search proceeds, start preparing reports to document your understanding of institutional history, vision, mission, culture, and managerial mechanisms for your senior management team.
- The outgoing leader should gradually transfer authority and decision-making to managers, so that they are prepared to help the new leader get a good start.

Step 6. Screen candidates

- The search committee must find equilibrium between looking too close to home (that is, considering only candidates whom people in the organization already know) or casting the net too wide (bringing in many inappropriate résumés and creating unproductive work).

Step 7. Select and interview the finalists

- The committee uses the selection criteria to develop a short list of the most promising candidates.
- The committee interviews each finalist.

Step 8. Arrange for reference checks and interviews

- The committee checks the references of promising candidates to find out how they performed in previous jobs.
- Consider candidates' track record in fulfilling the leadership functions that are required at the top level (see the description of the transition to Level Four in chapter 4).
- Try to visit work sites of the short-listed candidates and talk with subordinates, peers, board members, and clients.
- Collect impressions of the work environments that the prospective new leaders have created.

Step 9. Offer the job to the candidate selected

- The committee reviews it impressions of each candidate's experience, qualifications, character, and fit with the organization, and comes to consensus on one candidate.
- The committee makes a final recommendation to the board and outgoing CEO, and the board chairperson offers the position to the candidate who was selected.

Step 10. Manage the transition within the organization

- The change in leaders involves three stages: an ending, a neutral period, and a beginning. Pay attention to the departure of the old leader and to how the new leader is brought on board.

- In the *ending period,* organize tributes and gatherings where people can reflect on the past and say goodbye.

- In the *neutral period,* prepare for the future by giving staff opportunities to review and reflect, surrender some old ways of doing things, and regenerate and renew their sense of the organization and their roles within it.

- Take care that the push for results and increasing productivity does not interfere with personal reorientations that will give a solid base to a new beginning.

- In the *beginning* of the new leader's tenure, the new leader, the rest of the staff, and the board must share their expectations of how they will work together.

- Do not ignore the legacy of the organization (its good and bad parts) that is the launching pad for the new beginning.

From *Managers Who Lead: A Handbook for Improving Health Services*
Cambridge, MA: Management Sciences for Health, 2005

USING A SEARCH COMMITTEE

The board chairperson usually names a board member to head a search committee. The committee chairperson forms the search team, which should reflect the stakeholder groups and include other members, possibly some senior management staff, and—when required—outside executive recruiters. The key to a successful search is an active approach, which depends on close linkages in the process of identifying candidates and managing information generated by the search. The whole process can easily take six months or longer.

Working with a search committee

- Develop ground rules for the committee (on confidentiality, decision-making procedures, recourse after decision-making, and transparency in taking actions).
- Review the organizational context, strategic plan, and cultural environment and how they shape the profile of a new leader.
- Conduct a survey among staff and volunteers to develop selection criteria.
- Use the criteria to develop a job description for the new leader.
- Specify minimum requirements to screen out inappropriate candidates.
- Develop a system for managing and sharing information.
- Identify where candidates may be found and sources of leads for candidates.
- Identify the most promising candidates for interviews.
- Strengthen interviewing skills among committee members (if necessary).
- Develop interview questions and an interview process (number of interviewers, duration, place, recording, and reporting).
- Conduct interviews and reduce the pool of candidates.
- Inform rejected candidates.
- Complete background and reference checks for remaining candidates.
- Conduct site visits to the workplaces of remaining candidates, if possible.
- Conduct final interviews.
- Make the final choice and recommendation to the board.

From *Managers Who Lead: A Handbook for Improving Health Services*
Cambridge, MA: Management Sciences for Health, 2005

GUIDELINES   **Avoiding common mistakes in**
recruiting new leaders

PURPOSE

Use these guidelines to familiarize yourself with the process
of top-level leadership succession and avoid making common
mistakes in the recruitment of a new leader.

GUIDELINES

These guidelines look at how the organization deals with the process of leadership succession,
both before and after the handover of power. As the principal governing mechanism of many
organizations, boards of directors play a critical role: as policymakers, evaluators, advocates, and
resource mobilizers.

To stay on track in a leadership transition, an organization needs a board that is engaged with
staff and the outgoing chief executive in the search for the best possible replacement. A key factor
is the quality of the relationship between the board (or a senior team) and the chief executive. A
chief executive may deliberately appoint a weak board that agrees with everything the chief says
or does. Such a board is not going to be very helpful in managing the succession. Alternatively,
a board may undermine the trust and confidence of the staff by promoting the interests of the
outgoing chief or a particular candidate for political reasons. Sometimes board members pursue
personal interests or the interests of their constituency, which may not coincide with those of
other stakeholders.

If the chief executive has not developed strong, credible second and third tiers of executives, she
might find that staff or key stakeholders will not want her to retire or withdraw from routine tasks.
They may feel that no one has had enough experience with executive management functions to
run the organization in her absence. Avoid this situation by constantly building the leadership
capacity of managers within the organization and grooming senior managers for executive roles in
the organization.

The following summary applies not only to boards but also to individuals in key leadership
positions.

From *Managers Who Lead: A Handbook for Improving Health Services*
Cambridge, MA: Management Sciences for Health, 2005

COMMON MISTAKES IN RECRUITING NEW LEADERS AND WAYS TO AVOID THEM

COMMON MISTAKES	WAYS TO AVOID THE MISTAKES
Considering candidates and the search process too quickly, before reviewing the strategic direction of the organization	Look at your strategic plan and ask: ■ What is our "business"? ■ What products and services do we produce? What are our values? ■ Why are we good at producing them? What is our relative advantage or competence compared with that of others? ■ Why do people value what we produce? ■ How does the role of the potential leader contribute to our strategy? ■ Where should we look to find candidates who do similar or compatible work?
Not thinking about the leadership of the organization and the board together	Be sure there is stable board leadership to provide continuity and support to the new leader. Avoid choosing new boards and a new organizational leader at the same time.
Distancing yourself from the search process too quickly	Remain engaged even if you have appointed a search committee or hired a search firm. The board cannot delegate the search process entirely. Each board member should help in shaping specifications, suggesting candidates or sources of names, and "networking" about the vacancy.
Not clarifying the role of staff in the search process	Decide whether staff members will serve on the selection committee or participate in the final selection. If they cannot be involved, they should be kept informed about the process and time frame. They can contribute by helping to translate strategy into job specifications, meeting with candidates, and offering their opinions.
Placing too much value on the interviews with candidates	Structure and focus the interviews with challenging questions. After the interview, identify areas of possible concern and check references specifically about such areas. If possible, visit the workplaces of the most promising candidates and interview colleagues and subordinates about their work style.
Relying only on written responses for references	Engage referees in direct conversation, face to face or by phone, with a skilled interviewer, to create an environment in which all shades of opinion can emerge.
Not using the final selection to establish expectations on both sides (new leader and board) and a process for evaluating the new leader's performance	Talk about expectations and agendas. Negotiate roles and responsibilities that are not codified in the organization's bylaws. Answer questions about the role of the outgoing leader and agree about how or when to revisit issues later.
Pulling out of the transition process too fast	During the "honeymoon" period after the new leader is recruited, the board should: ■ help the new leader to balance needs for continuity and change, in the context of the organization's history; ■ help connect the leader with external resources; ■ set ground rules for how the board and leader will interact; ■ encourage staff and outsiders with concerns to speak directly to the leader rather than complain to the board.

Source: Adapted and reprinted with permission from *Finding and Retaining Your Next Chief Executive: Making the Transition Work* by Thomas N. Gilmore, a publication of BoardSource, formerly the National Center for Nonprofit Boards. For more information about BoardSource, call 800-883-6262 or visit www.boardsource.org. Copyright © 1993 BoardSource. Text may not be reproduced without written permission from BoardSource.

TOOL   Preparing for a successful negotiation

PURPOSE

This is a tool to help you prepare for a successful negotiation. Use it when you know that you need to negotiate an issue with someone else or with another group and when you are not sure that you are up to the task.

PROCESS

As you prepare for the negotiation, remember that the outcome of your negotiation depends partly on *how* you negotiate. There is the aspect of the substance of the negotiation (what you are negotiating about) and then there is the relationship between you and the other party.

Use *advocacy* (presenting your own point of view) to establish your voice in the negotiation and use *connection* to establish and nurture your relationship with the other person. Decide which is more important as you plan your strategy to reach a negotiated agreement.

Step 1. Get a good understanding of the substance of the negotiation (scan)

- Take stock of what you bring to the table (for example, skills, information, experience).
- Look for hidden resources you are not using.
- Recognize what makes you vulnerable and plan how you are going to deal with that.
- Get facts about the substance of the negotiation, the other person, and his situation.
- Develop alternatives.
- Seek fresh perspectives to avoid becoming trapped in your own thinking.
- Anticipate reactions from the other party to you, your viewpoint, and your proposals.

Step 2. Attract the other party to the table

- Make sure the other party sees that you have something of value and that you will not give this value away for free.
- Make negotiation unavoidable. For instance:
  - issue a credible threat that forces the other party to choose;
  - make the consequences of the choice tangible to the other person;
  - raise the cost of not dealing with you;
  - show your alternative to a negotiated settlement, or show that no action is not an option, because change will definitely happen.
- Level the playing field by establishing your authority and credibility. If you are lower in status than the other party, secure explicit authorization from your superior(s).
- Build support for your agenda by using allies as intermediaries, strategic partners, and promoters of your cause.

Step 3. Make the connection

- Invest time and energy in relationship building, participation, and staying engaged (keeping the dialogue going).

- Get everyone to own the problem by pointing at the negative consequences for all of not reaching agreement.

- Examine your own story. Separate fact from fiction.

- Listen to the other person's story, appreciating his situation, feelings, ideas, and need to save face.

- Look for links between your two stories.

- Recognize, however, that sometimes the other party is playing by different rules and is unwilling to engage in negotiation with you. Sometimes the power imbalance between you and that person is so great that you must give in. If so, show appreciation for being invited to the table, so you at least receive a hearing and may receive a hearing in future situations.

ENVISION TROUBLE SPOTS AND MENTALLY PREPARE YOUR RESPONSE

TROUBLE SPOT	PREPARE YOUR RESPONSE
When the other party challenges you	■ Respond positively, calmly, and respectfully to moves aimed at placing you at a disadvantage.
When the other party upsets you	■ Take a break, end the session and schedule another one in a few days, or change the pace or venue.
When the other party raises inappropriate issues	■ Point out the ineffectiveness or inappropriateness of this tactic, or highlight the tactic's unintended consequences. ■ Characterize the tactic as counterproductive. ■ Ask for repetition ("Could you repeat what you just said?") since innuendo does not stand up to repetition in public, which usually embarrasses the speaker. ■ Name hostile or exclusionary moves. ("Could you please explain your rationale for leaving the beneficiaries out of this conversation?")
When the other party tries to distract you from the issue under negotiation	■ Shift the conversation back to the main issue and away from personal accusations. ■ Look ahead rather than back at past mistakes. ■ Substitute a better idea for earlier ideas that did not receive sufficient response.

Step 4. Follow up after the negotiation

- Assess each step of the negotiation process: What worked well? What did not work well? What could you have done differently?

- Look at the results of the negotiation.

  - You can use the tool "Selecting a Strategy to Reach a Negotiated Agreement" to see in what area of the matrix the results fit.

- Consider documenting the process by writing down your reflections. Seek feedback if you wish.

From *Managers Who Lead: A Handbook for Improving Health Services*
Cambridge, MA: Management Sciences for Health, 2005

TOOL   Selecting a strategy to reach a negotiated agreement

PURPOSE

This is a tool to help you select a negotiation strategy. Use it to clarify what you want to accomplish and how to do this. Use the following matrix to determine the stance you want to take so that you can select the right approach to reach your goal.

MATRIX OF NEGOTIATION STRATEGIES

		CONNECTION	
		LOW	**HIGH**
ADVOCACY	**HIGH**	**Bargaining** When you want to get the best possible deal for yourself: ■ start with opening offers that camouflage real desires; ■ bargain back and forth between offers that start far apart. Gradually approach the other's offer, until you both arrive at a compromise (although it may not really be one). **The result:** One party's win is the other's loss, or both lose a little bit through compromise.	**Creative problem solving** When the cost of alienating the other person is high and the relationship is important: ■ use the PICO method of negotiation. (PICO stands for People, Interests, Criteria, Options.) See "Negotiating to Achieve Intended Results." **The result:** If the negotiation concludes well, both parties walk away satisfied that their interests have been served and the relationship is preserved.
	LOW	**Take it or leave it** When you have no significant stake in the negotiation: ■ offer the other a person the choice of taking your offer or not getting an opportunity. **The result:** You withdraw your offer or, sometimes, you unexpectedly win. The relationship may be damaged.	**Mutual learning** When both parties want to move beyond an instrumental concern for the other party *and* beyond enlightened self-interest: ■ explore mutual and separate needs. **The result:** You risk not fully resolving the issue. New perspectives on the issue may make it less or more important and require a new strategy. The relationship is probably strengthened.

From *Managers Who Lead: A Handbook for Improving Health Services*
Cambridge, MA: Management Sciences for Health, 2005

TOOL   Negotiating to achieve intended results

PURPOSE

PICO is a technique for negotiating with another person to solve a problem while maintaining a good relationship with that person. PICO stands for People, Interests, Criteria, Options. Use the PICO Worksheet to plan your negotiation. This method is based on Fisher et al. 1991.

PICO WORKSHEET

People—Separate the people from the problem Consider the background factors that may have contributed to their current positions.	
Interests—Look for the interests hidden behind the positions Put yourself in the others' shoes: what motivates the others, where do your interests agree, and where do they differ?	
Criteria—Agree on objective criteria to test if an agreement has been reached Define objective criteria for evaluating possible options, for example, what would be a fair outcome?	
Options—Look for alternative solutions If anything is possible, what are the best solutions, and how would these benefit you and the other person?	

From *Managers Who Lead: A Handbook for Improving Health Services*
Cambridge, MA: Management Sciences for Health, 2005

EXERCISE   Renegotiating roles among health system levels

PURPOSE

For the public sector, this exercise provides an opportunity
for adjacent levels in the health pyramid to explore, negotiate,
and agree on the kinds of activities and roles each level has
in relation to the other. It can also be used in large private
organizations that have multiple branch or field (country) offices
that they want to become more autonomous. The exercise
produces a set of actions that the participants from various
levels can agree on to support one another. It also clarifies for
lower levels what the real constraints are at the central level.

This exercise is best used when:

- decentralization is the official policy but the levels aren't
  clear about how their roles and the requirements have
  changed;

- new roles have been imposed without any conversation;

- people from different levels are not comfortable or skilled
  in talking together in ways that go against cultural norms.

RESOURCES NEEDED

- ❏ flipchart and markers for each
  group
- ❏ copies of Handout: Shifting the
  Health System to Serve Local
  Needs

PROCESS

Preparation

- Go over the exercise with key stakeholders at the most central level and make sure
  they understand the exercise and you have their support.

- Invite people from adjacent levels in the health system, four or five people per level.

- Prepare copies of Handout: Shifting the Health System to Serve Local Needs.

- Use an ice-breaker to build trust and help create a safe space for conversation, a
  space in which cultural norms and taboos can be temporarily suspended (such as
  those that prevent people from lower levels from raising issues with higher levels).

Step 1. Identify management levels

- In plenary, ask the participants to help you draw their current health system pyramid
  or structure.

- Identify the various management/administrative levels and what each level currently
  does.

Step 2. List activities of the different levels

- Seat participants from the same level together.

- Separate the groups enough so their conversations do not interfere with each other
  but keep the groups in the same room if possible.

- Have each group's members write on a flipchart:
    - activities they do that support the other levels present in the room;
    - things they require or expect from the other levels (such as reports).

Step 3. Present lists of activities

- In plenary, have each group present its lists.
    - Compare lists and clarify meanings of words if necessary.
    - Note discrepancies.
    - Keep a running list of items and issues that need further attention.

Step 4: Discuss the health system pyramid with the central level at the bottom

- In plenary, briefly present the Handout showing the pyramid turned upside down (with the central level at the bottom).
- Explore how the roles change. For example, the center now supports the entire pyramid.
- Check that everyone understands the concept of the upside-down pyramid.

Step 5: Find out what kind of support is needed

- Ask the participants to return to their separate groups.
- Have each group write on a flipchart for each level:
    - the support it would like to receive from the other levels present in the room;
    - the support it is willing to give to the other levels.

Step 6: Present support needs

- In plenary, have each group present its list of needs for support from the other levels.
- Check for clarity. Groups may be using vague and abstract words that hide their intentions.
- Push to find out what actions the groups want from each other.
- Create a running list of agreements that the various levels are committing themselves to.

Wrap up and plan next steps

- Do a check for consensus at the end.
- Ask if everyone is clear about the next steps in the process, whether anyone needs to sign off on it, and, if so, how will that happen.
- Find out what else is needed to make sure these agreements are implemented and determine a date after which they will be implemented.
- Set a date and time for reviewing progress on commitments made.

From *Managers Who Lead: A Handbook for Improving Health Services*
Cambridge, MA: Management Sciences for Health, 2005

HANDOUT   **Shifting the Health System to Serve Local Needs**

Reorienting a health system toward the local level turns the traditional organizational pyramid upside down and changes the way staff need to think and work.

Centrally oriented health system

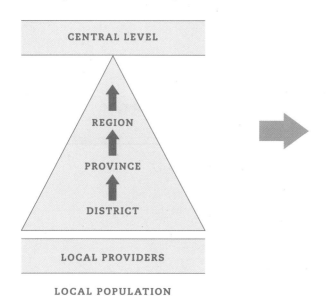

Locally oriented health system

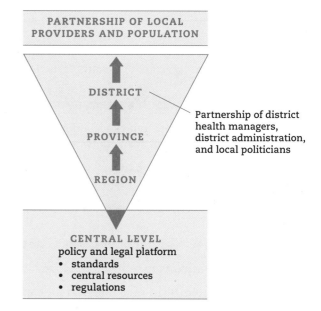

Partnership of district health managers, district administration, and local politicians

EXERCISE   "Renegotiating roles among health system levels"   From *Managers Who Lead: A Handbook for Improving Health Services*
Cambridge, MA: Management Sciences for Health, 2005

EXERCISE   Making requests for better coordination

PURPOSE

This exercise is most useful in coordination meetings in which multiple parties are present. It enables the groups to be explicit with one another about the support and information they need from each other, as well as respond to other groups' requests.

RESOURCES NEEDED

❑ flipchart and markers
❑ removable self-stick notes in several colors
❑ copies of Handout: Complaints versus Requests

PROCESS

Preparation

- Make copies of Handout: Complaints versus Requests.

- Determine how many different groups there are (for interagency coordination, groups may consist of government agency, donor agency, private sector, volunteer organization, facility; for intra-organizational organization consider groups of managers, service providers, board members, and volunteers). It is better to limit the number of groups, so if some smaller groups have a similar role and similar requests, consider grouping them together.

- Post one flipchart for each group on the wall, and mark it clearly with the group's name and preferably with a distinct color that will identify each group.

- Have pads of removable self-stick notes in corresponding colors for each of the groups, or cut pieces of paper and color-code them to match the various flipcharts.

- Show which group is which color and then hand out the pads of self-stick notes or pieces of paper.

Step 1. Create requests for other groups

- Distribute copies of Handout: Complaints versus Requests, to each group, and explain the concept of requests versus complaints.

- Ask each group to make a list of requests for each of the other groups.

- Requests may be for:

  - information

  - facilitating or unblocking something

  - changing a deadline

  - different kinds of behavior

  - feedback.

- Ask the members of each group to determine no more than five requests that they have for each of the other groups in the room. If they have more than five, ask them to prioritize and pick the five most important requests.

- Have them write each request on a separate self-stick note or piece of paper that is color-coded for their group.

- Have them post their requests on the flipchart of the group to which they are making the request.

- Repeat this process for all the other groups in the room.

Step 2. Read the requests others have made of your group

- When each group has finished posting its requests, have the members of each group get their designated flipchart and read the requests from the other groups. The color of the note or piece of paper indicates from which group the request came.

- Have the participants return to their tables and ask them to formulate a response to each request.

- Write a response to each request (on separate self-stick notes if you have these) next to each request.

Step 3. Share the responses

- In plenary, have each group take a turn reading the requests made to it and responding directly to the requesting group with an answer.

- Keep a running list of all agreements made or mark them on the relevant flipchart. Mediate or intervene if the commitment or agreement is unclear or too vague and push for resolution.

- Responses should include:

  - dates or time

  - deliverables where appropriate

  - a temporary "parking lot" for things that require more negotiation

  - dates and times for further discussions.

Wrap up and plan next steps

- Review all commitments made to make sure there is full agreement. You can then use this list when the group convenes again to check on progress and explore obstacles to progress (and make new agreements).

From *Managers Who Lead: A Handbook for Improving Health Services*
Cambridge, MA: Management Sciences for Health, 2005

HANDOUT   Complaints versus Requests

Complaints and requests: Principles in effective organizations

- People complain only to someone who can do something about the situation.

- People state their complaint in the form of a request.

- If you receive a complaint you cannot do anything about, you decline to listen to it, and refer it to someone who can do something about it (avoid gossip).

- If you receive a request, you are free to respond in the three ways (yes, no, or counteroffer).

Take one complaint and transform it into a request using the following format

1. Will you _____ (specific person)

2. please do this _____ (specific action)

3. by this time _____? (specific time)

Three ways to respond to a request

- Yes

- No

- Make a counteroffer: "No, I can't do that, but I can do something else, or I can do it by some other time."

E X E R C I S E   "Making requests for better coordination"   From *Managers Who Lead: A Handbook for Improving Health Services*
Cambridge, MA: Management Sciences for Health, 2005

EXERCISE   Understanding the process of leading change

PURPOSE

This exercise helps participants draw lessons from their own experience about leading change. Use it with a group whose members have to function as change agents. It can also be used in conjunction with a conversation about breakdowns (see the exercise "Coaching Your Team through Breakdowns").

RESOURCES NEEDED

❑ flipchart and markers

PROCESS

Preparation

- Write the following on a flipchart, leaving spaces between the questions:
  - Think of a change you have experienced.
  - How did you feel during that change?
  - What do you wish others had done during that change?
- Cover the flipchart, which will be revealed later (or for a large group make a handout to distribute during Step 1).

Step 1. Reflect on a past experience of change

- Discuss people's responses to the questions.
- Remind participants that leading people through change requires managing the transition.
- Reveal the flipchart with the questions (see above).
- Ask participants to write down their thoughts about these questions.

Step 2. Share reflections on change

- Divide the participants into pairs or small groups, and have them share their responses.
- In plenary, invite participants to share responses they heard to the questions.
- Write down responses on a flipchart.
- Discuss how the participants can support others in going through change.

Wrap up and plan next steps

- Close the conversation by discussing what principles should guide change agents.
- Write these principles and ideas on a flipchart.
- Discuss how the participants are going to apply the principles to their current change efforts.

From *Managers Who Lead: A Handbook for Improving Health Services*
Cambridge, MA: Management Sciences for Health, 2005

EXERCISE   Applying the factors of success in leading change

PURPOSE

This exercise is based on the eight factors of success in leading change (see chapter 6 of the handbook). Use this exercise if you are the team leader responsible for a change initiative. The checklist helps teams discuss their change process, focusing on the key factors that will help them to be successful in leading the change initiative.

RESOURCES NEEDED

❏ flipchart and markers
❏ Handout: Checklist for Successful Change Initiatives

PROCESS

Preparation

- Review the list of questions in the checklist and make adjustments as necessary to fit the particular situation.

- Make and distribute copies of Handout: Checklist for Successful Change Initiatives (or modified checklist) to each member of the change team.

Step 1. Fill in the checklist

- Have each member of the team fill in the checklist, providing an explanation for their answers in the column marked "Comments." (To save time it is best to have each team member fill it in before the meeting.)

Step 2. Discuss the requirements of success

- Discuss each question with the team along with the comments made by each member of the team.

Step 3. Plan new and follow-up actions

- Agree on priority actions and who is responsible for implementing each action.

Wrap up and plan next steps

- Keep a running list of things that the team needs to do to stay on track.

From *Managers Who Lead: A Handbook for Improving Health Services*
Cambridge, MA: Management Sciences for Health, 2005

HANDOUT   **Checklist for Successful Change Initiatives**

QUESTIONS	COMMENTS
Have we communicated the urgency of the change effort by framing the challenge clearly?	
Have we built a strong core team?	
Do we have a shared vision of the end result of the change initiative?	
Are we including key stakeholders in planning and implementation activities?	
Do we have examples of obstacles that we have overcome together as a result of the change initiative?	
Are we sufficiently focused on results?	
Do we have periodic celebrations of short-term wins?	
Do we have continued senior leadership support for facing ongoing challenges?	
Are new behaviors and values becoming increasingly visible at work?	
Are changes incorporated in routine organizational processes and systems?	

EXERCISE   "Applying the factors of success in leading change"

Source: Adapted from Kotter 1996

EXERCISE   Learning from experience: The after-action review

PURPOSE

The after-action review provides a process for thinking about and discussing what went well in implementing a project or set of activities and what didn't go well. The exercise helps people think in a different way about mistakes, failures, and breakdowns without blaming or finger-pointing. It also provides an opportunity to recognize successes. The lessons are then fed back into the group (and the larger organization) and combined with other lessons to create organizational knowledge and improved solutions.

An after-action review should take place after an event or series of events have concluded that were intended to produce a specific result. The meeting also can be held after key milestones have been achieved even if the whole initiative has not yet been completed. Those who were critical to the project or assignment should be in the meeting.

> ### RESOURCES NEEDED
>
> ❑ flipchart and markers

PROCESS

Step 1. Explain the purpose of the after-action review

- Explain to the group that the after-action review is separate from an evaluation and should serve as a collective learning experience, not to find fault with or evaluate a specific individual's performance.

  - Everyone in the conversation should feel free to speak up, without fear of reprisal.

  - Everyone, no matter how junior or senior in the hierarchy, has the opportunity to offer direct feedback about the process and the results of the work.

Step 2. Reflect on individual role and commitment

- Write the following questions on a flipchart and ask each participant in the meeting to think about how they would respond to each question:

  - What am I most proud of in this project?

  - What was my individual role? What did I contribute?

  - What do I still need to communicate? (Explain that responses to this question might include, for example, acknowledgment of others or regrets.)

Step 3. Share individual responses

(For groups of more than six people)

- Ask participants to share their responses with the person sitting next to them.
- Have each pair report to the whole group.
- Record the responses on a flipchart.

(For groups of 6 people or fewer)

- Ask participants to share their responses with the whole group.

Step 4. Reflect on group commitment and accomplishments

- Write the following questions on a flipchart
- Ask each participant to write down his answers individually on a piece of paper.
  - What was the commitment of the group in this work?
  - What was the result we intended to accomplish?
  - Did we accomplish that result?
  - If we did not accomplish the result, what is missing?
  - What aspects of the process worked well?
  - What aspects of the process could have been improved?
  - What lessons did we learn?
  - What actions can we take now?

Wrap up and plan next steps

- Walk around and take answers to each question from the group.
- Record the answers on flipchart.
- Ask a few people to share what they learned from this exercise.
- Document the lessons learned for distribution to the group and any other people or groups in the organization that need to have the information.

From *Managers Who Lead: A Handbook for Improving Health Services*
Cambridge, MA: Management Sciences for Health, 2005

Annotated bibliography

Advance Africa. Project funded by the US Agency for International Development and led by Management Sciences for Health. *Best Practices Compendium for Family Planning and Reproductive Health.* Boston: Management Sciences for Health, 2003. http://erc.msh.org

    Searchable online database of best practices in the delivery of reproductive health and family planning services.

Aitken, Iain. "Decentralization and Reproductive Health: Opportunities and Challenges." In Riitta-Liisa Kolehmainen-Aitken, ed. *Myths and Realities about the Decentralization of Health Systems.* Boston: Management Sciences for Health, 1999, pp. 111–36.

    Concludes that decentralization has had both advantages (such as greater district and community involvement) and disadvantages (such as lack of planned and coordinated implementation) for the achievement of integrated reproductive health services.

American Society for Training and Development. "Succession Planning." *Infoline* no. 9312, 1993.

    Emphasizes systems and procedural aspects.

April, Kurt, Robert Macdonald, and Sylvia Vriesendorp. *Rethinking Leadership.* Capetown: University of Capetown Press, 2000.

    Topics covered include essential leadership skills (such as awareness and openness), leaders' roles (stewardship and followership), communication, organizational strategy, and dealing with complexity and ambiguity.

Arrangoiz, David C. *Líderes y educadores.* Mexico City: Fondo de cultura económica, 2000.

Beerel, Annabel. *Leadership through Strategic Planning.* London: International Thomson Business Press, 1998.

Bennis, Warren, and Patricia Ward Biederman. *Genius: The Secrets of Creative Collaboration.* Reading, MA: Addison-Wesley, 1997.

Bennis, Warren, and Edgar H. Schein, eds. *Leadership and Motivation.* Cambridge, MA: MIT Press, 1966.

Block, Peter. *Stewardship: Choosing Service over Self-Interest.* San Francisco: Jossey-Bass, 1983.

Explains how to integrate the management of work and the doing of work to redistribute purpose and power within an organization. The book discusses how this integration can affect work flow, quality control, performance appraisal, pay systems, supervisory methods, job design, and human resources.

Bragar, Joan. "Influence Behaviors for Managers." Boston: Forum Corporation, 1991.

Bridges, William. *Managing Transitions: Making the Most of Change.* 2nd ed. Cambridge MA: Perseus Publishing, 2003.

Bryant, Malcolm. "Planning for and within Decentralized Health Systems." In Riitta-Liisa Kolehmainen-Aitken, ed. *Myths and Realities about the Decentralization of Health Systems.* Boston: Management Sciences for Health, 1999, pp. 11–26.

Stresses that planning *for* decentralization must take into account the forces motivating it, and planners should define what decentralization means in the local context and what its objectives are. Planning *within* a decentralized system requires clarity about roles and responsibilities. Managers must take the lead in shaping the new health system and gather good information on which to base their decisions.

Buckingham, Marcus, and Coffman, Curt. *First Break All the Rules: What the World's Greatest Managers Do Differently.* New York: Simon and Schuster, 1999.

A very readable book that summarizes the research conducted by Gallup worldwide and identifies 12 practices that successful managers perform. Although some of these practices seem counterintuitive, the authors claim that these insights are solidly research based.

Chambers, Robert. *Whose Reality Counts: Putting the First Last.* London: ITDG Publishing, 1997.

Charan, Ram, Stephen Drotter, and James Noel. *The Leadership Pipeline: How to Build the Leadership-powered Company.* San Francisco: Jossey-Bass, 2001.

Written for audiences in the Western corporate world. Provides the notion of a pipeline and a framework for thinking through the requirements of growing leaders from within.

Charoenparij, Sriracha, et al. "Thailand Health Financing and Management Study Project—Final Integrated Report." Unpublished. Bangkok: Health Systems Research Institute, Ministry of Public Health, and Boston: Management Sciences for Health, 1999.

Report of research findings—from interviews with leaders in the health sector and review of documents—that were presented to an expatriate Technical

Advisory Group, a Steering Committee, and subject-specific Working Groups. Based on technical reports prepared by the research team, the Ministry developed action plans for health personnel deployment and hospital autonomy. This report also presents larger issues of reform of the organization and financing of the health sector.

Covey, Stephen. *The Seven Habits of Highly Effective People: Powerful Lessons in Personal Change.* New York: Simon and Schuster, 2004.

An internationally respected authority on leadership on the importance of balancing personal and professional effectiveness. The seven habits enable one to make a shift from being reactive to being proactive and productive in one's life and work. The habits are: Be proactive, Begin with the end in mind, Put first things first, Think win/win, Seek first to understand, then to be understood, Synergize (creative cooperation), and Sharpen the saw (self-renewal).

Cripps, Gilbert, et al. *Guide to Designing and Managing Community-based Health Financing Schemes in East and Southern Africa.* Partnerships for Health Reform Plus and USAID/Regional Economic Development Services Office in East and Southern Africa, 2000. http://www.phrplus.org/Pubs/hts8.pdf (accessed March 2, 2005).

Outlines steps that community-based health financing (CBHF) schemes have implemented successfully to bridge the wide gap between the health care needs of the rural poor and limited local resources for health. The manual provides information to help community partners initiate successful programs, such as: basic components of a CBHF scheme; roles and responsibilities of key stakeholders in the community; tools to assess the feasibility and long-term sustainability of schemes; and financial and management guides to cost services, determine payment levels, and design cost-efficient programs.

De Pree, Max. *Leadership Is an Art.* Rev. ed. New York: Currency, 2004.

Looks at leadership as a kind of stewardship, stressing the importance of building relationships, initiating ideas, and creating a lasting value system within an organization. De Pree asserts that the artful leader must stimulate effectiveness by enabling others to reach both their personal potential and their institutional potential; take a role in developing, expressing, and defending civility and values; and ensure the continuation of the corporate culture by nurturing new leaders.

Eastman, Lorrina J. *Succession Planning: An Annotated Bibliography and Summary of Commonly Reported Organizational Practices.* Greensboro, NC: Center for Creative Leadership, 1995.

Summarizes 56 works from a wide variety of sources, which provide access to, and a general understanding of, the nature and extent of the practical literature on succession planning.

EngenderHealth. *COPE® Handbook: A Process for Improving Quality in Health Services.* Revised ed. New York: EngenderHealth, 2003.

A process that empowers local-level service providers to address issues within their control that improve client services and work climate alike. COPE has been used successfully for over a decade to wake up passive staff who felt unable to deal with persistent service delivery problems. This revision of the classic 1995 handbook focuses on how to perform COPE exercises and contains more information on orienting key managers and helping facilitators prepare for the COPE process.

Esque, Timm J. "Managing to Lead." *Performance Improvement* vol. 39, no. 2, 2000: 45–47.

Farrell, Timothy. "An Evaluation of the Effects of Re-engineering for Sustainability." Unpublished. Boston: Management Sciences for Health, 2003.

> Assessment of the impact of sustained and integrated management development on service delivery, income generation, and overall sustainability in APROFAM, a Guatemalan NGO. This report focuses on two main points: (1) organizational change, or the incorporation of management inputs into APROFAM's management structure; and (2) the impact of change on management effectiveness, financial sustainability, and the delivery of family planning services and products.

Fisher, Roger, William Ury, and Burce Patton. *Getting to Yes: Negotiating Agreement without Giving In.* 2nd ed. New York: Penguin Books, 1991.

Fradette, Michael, and Steve Michaud. *The Power of Corporate Kinetics: Create the Self-Adapting, Self-Renewing, Instant-Action Enterprise.* New York: Simon and Schuster, 1998.

Friedman, Thomas L. *The Lexus and the Olive Tree.* Rev. ed. New York: Farrar, Straus, Giroux, 2000.

Fritz, Robert. *The Path of Least Resistance for Managers: Designing Organizations to Succeed.* San Francisco: Berrett-Koehler, 1999.

Galford, Robert M., and Anne Seibold Drapeau. "The Enemies of Trust." *Harvard Business Review* Feb. 2003. 6 pp.

Gardner, Howard. *Changing Minds.* Boston: Harvard Business School Press, 2004.

Gilmore, Thomas N. *Finding and Retaining Your Next Chief Executive: Making the Transition Work.* Governance Series No. 16. Washington, DC: National Center for Nonprofit Boards, 1993.

> Easy-to-read booklet that walks board members through the process of hiring a chief executive who can lead a nonprofit organization effectively. Sections include new leadership concepts, mistakes to avoid, screening, interviewing, and determining priorities.

———. *Making a Leadership Change: How Organizations and Leaders Can Handle Leadership Transitions Successfully.* San Francisco: Jossey-Bass, 1989; Philadelphia: Center for Applied Research, 2000.

> Out of print but contains much more detail than the 1993 Gilmore book.

Goleman, Daniel. "An EI Based Theory of Performance" in Cary Cherniss and Daniel Goleman. *The Emotionally Intelligent Workplace: How to Select for, Measure, and Improve Emotional Intelligence in Individuals, Groups, and Organizations.* San Francisco: Jossey-Bass, 2001, pp. 27–44.

> From a collection of articles by specialists in the field of emotional intelligence and competency development.

———. "Leadership That Gets Results." *Harvard Business Review* March–April 2000: 78–90.

Goleman, Daniel, Richard Boyatzis, and Annie McKee. *Primal Leadership: Realizing the Power of Emotional Intelligence.* Boston: Harvard Business School Press, 2002.

Describes the impact of leadership styles on drivers of work climate and also discusses how leadership styles are related to emotional intelligence competencies. Goleman holds that a leader's primal task is setting a productive emotional climate. In other words, before leaders can turn to setting strategy, fixing budgets, or hiring staff, they must first attend to the impact of their moods and behaviors. In times of turbulence and setbacks, people look to leaders for clarity and support. Leaders must be aware of how they set the organizational climate.

Gottman, John M. *Why Marriages Succeed or Fail: What You Can Learn from the Breakthrough Research to Make Your Marriage Last.* New York: Simon and Schuster, 1994.

Haines, Stephen. *The Manager's Pocket Guide to Strategic and Business Planning.* Human Resource Development Press, 1999.

Hay Group. "Research into Teacher Effectiveness: A Report by Hay/McBer for the Department for Education and Employment—June 2000." http://www.teacher-net.gov.uk/_doc/1487/haymcber.doc (accessed March 4, 2005).

Describes the impact classroom climate has on educational outcomes and how teachers can impact climate and the relationship between climate and motivation.

Heifetz, Ronald A. *Leadership without Easy Answers.* Cambridge, MA: Belknap Press, 1994.

Introduces a view of leadership as a function that seeks to give responsibility back to those who will ultimately be responsible for facing challenges and achieving real change. Heifetz distinguishes between "formal authority," or positional power, and leadership as an activity that can be carried out by people without formal authority. He distinguishes between technical and adaptive change, with the latter requiring people to make a shift in their values, expectations, attitudes, or habits of behavior.

Heifetz, Ronald A., John V. Kania, and Mark R. Kramer. "Leading Boldly: Foundations Can Move Past Traditional Approaches to Create Social Change through Imaginative—and Even Controversial—Leadership." *Stanford Social Innovation Review* Winter 2004: 21–31.

Heifetz, Ronald A., and Donald L. Laurie. "The Work of Leadership." *Harvard Business Review* Jan.–Feb. 1997: 123–34.

Emphasizes that adaptive challenges cannot be solved by the use of authority alone. The leader's job is to set an effective climate for learning in the organization so that people can own and face the challenges and learn their way through them. Getting people to take greater responsibility and the initiative in defining and solving challenges means that leaders needs to learn to support rather than control.

Helfenbein, Saul, and Catherine Severo. *Scaling Up HIV/AIDS Programs: A Manual for Multisectoral Planning.* Boston: Management Sciences for Health, 2004.

Hume, Margaret, Riitta-Liisa Kolehmainen-Aitken, Eireen Villa, and Taryn Vian. "Planning and Implementing Health Programs under Decentralization: The Case of the Philippines." Paper presented at the annual meeting of the American Public Health Association. New York, Nov. 1996.

> Examines decentralization in the Philippines health sector, particularly from the vantage point of the USAID-funded Local Government Performance Program. The paper focuses on lessons learned from that program as they relate to the implementation issues that emerged from the process of decentralizing health services.

Imai, Masaaki. *Kaizen: The Key to Japan's Competitive Success.* 1st ed. New York: Random House Business Division, 1986.

> The source of the Five Whys technique

Jaffe, Dennis T., and Cynthia D. Scott. *Getting Your Organization to Change: A Guide for Putting Your Strategies into Action.* San Francisco: Crisp Publications, 1999.

Jaques, Elliott, and Kathryn Cason. *Human Capability: A Study of Individual Potential and Its Application.* Falls Church, VA: Cason Hall, 1994.

> A controversial book, demonstrating the results of a three-year study that individuals process information in only four ways which recur in a series of higher orders of information complexity. The author argues that this hierarchy of mental processing methods corresponds with levels of individual capability and is congruent with levels of work complexity, explaining, at last, the very nature of managerial systems. The book discusses managerial procedures that enable companies to match people with roles, and to develop programs that effectively meet the organization's future human resource requirements.

Kanter, Rosabeth Moss. *Rosabeth Moss Kanter on the Frontiers of Management.* Boston: Harvard Business School Press, 1997.

Kantor, David. In William Isaacs, *Dialogue and the Art of Thinking Together: A Pioneering Approach to Communicating in Business and in Life.* New York: Doubleday, 1999. See pp. 192–99 and 418–19 on Kantor's Four Player System and pp. 199–202, "Listening for the Underlying Intent."

Katz, Daniel, and Robert L. Kahn. *The Social Psychology of Organizations.* New York: John Wiley & Sons, 1966.

> A classic

Kenya National Council of NGOs. *A Guide to Leader Transition and Building the Successor Generation.* NGO Leadership Development Series No. 2. Nairobi: Kenya National Council of NGOs, 2001.

> Booklet describing the steps of leadership transition in Kenyan NGOs, with emphasis on the role and tasks of the governing body. The booklet offers suggestions on preparing the next generation of senior leaders.

Kets de Vries, Manfred. "Organizations on the Couch: A Clinical Perspective on Organizational Dynamics." *European Management Journal* vol. 22, no. 2, 2004: 183–200.

Kiefer, Charles. "Leadership and the Learning Organization." *Prism* 3rd quarter 1995: 87–96.

Kolehmainen-Aitken, Riitta-Liisa. "Decentralization and Human Resources: Implications and Impact." Paper presented at the annual meeting of the American Public Health Association. New York, Nov. 1997.

———. "Decentralization's Impact on the Health Workforce: Perspectives of Managers, Workers and National Leaders." *Human Resources for Health* vol. 2, no. 5, May 2004. http://www.human-resources-health.com/content/2/1/5 (accessed April 12, 2005).

———, ed. *Myths and Realities about the Decentralization of Health Systems.* Boston: Management Sciences for Health, 1999.

An anthology with three parts. The first focuses on decentralization's impact on critical technical support areas (health planning, financing, human resources, pharmaceuticals, management information, and the improvement of service quality). The second examines the relationship of decentralization to reproductive health and hospital services. The third part reviews the evolution of decentralization in Indonesia.

Kolehmainen-Aitken, Riitta-Liisa, and Elizabeth Lewis. "Decentralization Mapping Tool (DMT)." Boston: Management Sciences for Health, 2004. http://erc.msh.org

A practical tool that policy makers and managers can use to understand how managers in their country perceive their new roles under decentralization. Policymakers and managers can use the DMT to examine managers' perceptions at different points in time to see whether management roles become clearer and whether the distribution of management responsibility and authority shifts in the desired direction; and compare health managers' current perception of their responsibility and authority with the country's decentralization design.

Kotter, John P. *Leading Change.* Boston: Harvard Business School Press, 1996.

Presents Kotter's thesis that strategies for change often fail because the changes do not alter behavior. Describes the most common mistakes and eight steps to avoid them: (1) establishing a sense of urgency; (2) putting together a powerful team to lead change; (3) creating a vision; (4) communicating the new vision, strategies, and expected behavior; (5) removing obstacles to the change and encouraging risk taking; (6) recognizing and rewarding short-term successes; (7) identifying people who can implement change; and (8) ensuring that the changes become part of the institutional culture.

———. "What Leaders Really Do." *Harvard Business Review* May–June 1990: 1–12.

Explores how leadership and management are complementary systems of action, both of which are essential for organizational success. Management is about coping with complexity, while leadership is about coping with change. Both systems of action involve decision-making, but each in a different way. Leadership functions include setting direction, aligning people, and motivating people. Management functions include planning, budgeting, organizing, staffing, implementing, and controlling.

Kotter, John P., and Dan S. Cohen. *The Heart of Change: Real Life Stories of How People Change Their Organization.* Boston: Harvard Business School Press, 2003.

Kouzes, James M., and Barry Z. Posner. *Encouraging the Heart: A Leader's Guide to Rewarding and Recognizing Others.* San Francisco: Jossey-Bass, 1999.

———. *The Leadership Challenge: How to Get Extraordinary Things Done in Organizations.* 3rd ed. San Francisco: Jossey-Bass, 2002.

Based on extensive research on more than 3,000 people achieving "individual leadership standards of excellence." The authors identified five leadership practices that are key to success: model the way, inspire a shared vision, challenge the process, enable others to act, and encourage the heart. "What we have discovered, and rediscovered, is that leadership is not the private reserve of a few charismatic men and women," writes Kouzes.

Laschinger, Heather K. Spence, Joan Finegan, and Judith Shamian. "The Impact of Workplace Empowerment, Organizational Trust on Staff Nurses' Work Satisfaction and Organizational Commitment." *Health Care Management Review* vol. 26, no. 3, 2001: 7–23.

Describes the impact of empowerment on satisfaction, commitment, and performance in a health care environment in Ontario, Canada.

Levine, Rick, Christopher Locke, Doc Searls, and David Weinberger. *The Cluetrain Manifesto: The End of Business as Usual.* Cambridge, MA: Perseus Books, 2000.

Written for the fast-paced Western world, full of questions about things people take for granted. The book generates ideas on how to change the way we work. A primer on the information age and what it means for how they relate to clients, this book helps people rethink how they see their organization as a business, who their customers are, how they can serve them well, how information travels, and thus how to scan a much wider horizon.

Lindenberg, Marc, and Benjamin Crosby. *Managing Development: The Political Dimension.* W. Hartford, CT: Kumarian Press, 1981.

Litwin, George H., and Robert A. Stringer, Jr. *Motivation and Organizational Climate.* Cambridge: Harvard University Press, 1968.

The seminal work on organizational climate, which describes research conducted at Harvard Business School in the 1960s. Litwin and Stringer define the concept of organizational climate, discuss the relationships between motivation and behavior, and between managerial style and organizational climate, and identify a process to measure climate.

Management Sciences for Health (MSH). "Achieving Functional HIV/AIDS Services through Strong Community and Management Support." *The Manager* vol. 11, no. 4, 2002.

The Manager is a continuing education quarterly for health program managers; each issue includes a case scenario with questions, for use in training.

———. "Business Planning to Transform Your Organization." *The Manager* vol. 12, no. 3, 2003.

———. "Clinic Supervisors' Manual." Version 3, 2004. http://erc.msh.org

———. "Communities Taking Charge of Their Health: The India Local Initiatives Program." Boston: Management Sciences for Health, 2002.

———. "Conducting Local Rapid Assessments for the District Level." *The Manager* vol. 7, no. 1, 1998.

———. "Convergence Strategy: A Report on the Process Documentation of Health Sector Reform Agenda and Best Practices, Draft Final Report." Boston: Management Sciences for Health, 2002.

Discusses how interventions and key players in the Philippines were aligned around a common vision of what these stakeholders wanted to see in their local area. The strategy was designed to bring such groups as the Department of Health, health insurance programs, local government, civil society groups, and the local beneficiaries together to pool their efforts and resources to implement health reforms.

——. "Coordinating Complex Health Programs." *The Manager* vol. 12, no. 4, 2003.

——. *CORE, A Tool for Cost and Revenue Analysis: User's Guide.* Version 1.0. Boston: Management Sciences for Health, 1998.

A tool that helps managers analyze a facility's current and projected costs and revenues per service, and compare costs and revenues among several facilities within the same organization. Managers can see how costs and revenues would be affected by changes in prices, staff utilization, service volume, and service mix. Includes diskette with electronic spreadsheets.

——. "Creating a Work Climate That Motivates Staff and Improves Performance." *The Manager* vol. 11, no. 3, 2002.

Explains what work climate is and why it is important. It also explains how to measure work climate and then what to do after climate is measured.

——. "Decentralizing Health and Family Planning Services." *The Family Planning Manager* vol. 4, no. 2, 1995.

The Family Planning Manager is the former title of *The Manager* periodical.

——. "Developing Managers Who Lead." *The Manager* vol. 10, no. 3, 2001.

——. "Exercising Leadership to Make Decentralization Work." *The Manager* vol. 11, no. 1, 2002.

——. "Leading Changes in Practices to Improve Health." *The Manager* vol. 13, no. 3, 2004.

——. "Managing Performance Improvement of Decentralized Health Services." *The Manager* vol. 13, no. 1, 2003.

——. "Mobilizing Local Resources to Support Health Programs." *The Manager* vol. 11, no. 2, 2002.

A participatory approach for scanning, focusing, planning, implementing, and monitoring and evaluation. Developed in the Philippines and Indonesia, based on WHO's district team problem-solving methodology, this learning-by-doing process builds the skills of district teams to identify local health needs and develop interventions to address them. Teams mobilize resources and implement and monitor their plans.

——. *MOST—Management and Organizational Sustainability Tool: A Guide for Users and Facilitators.* 2nd ed. Boston: Management Sciences for Health, 2004.

A participatory, rapid-assessment process for identifying an organization's management needs and making plans for improvement. This second edition of MOST highlights the key role played by an organization's leaders and emphasizes the importance of having managers who lead at all levels. It incorporates new components on organizational values, lines of authority and accountability, communication, decision-making, and monitoring and evaluation. The guide provides all the information needed to facilitate the MOST process, including complete session plans, materials for participants' workshop binders, and suggestions for follow-up activities. Includes a CD-ROM.

——. "Planning for Leadership Transition." *The Manager* vol. 10, no. 1, 2001.

———. "Service Delivery Assessment and Management Protocol." Unpublished. Boston: Management Sciences for Health, 2004.
   English and French.

———. "Tackling the Crisis in Human Capacity Development for Health Services." *The Manager* vol. 13, no. 2, 2004.

———. "Using Evaluation as a Management Tool." *The Family Planning Manager* vol. 6, no. 1, 1997.

———. "Using National and Local Data to Guide Reproductive Health Programs" and "Supplement: Guide to National and Local Reproductive Health Indicators." *The Family Planning Manager* vol. 6, no. 2, 1997.

———. "Using Performance-Based Payments to Improve Health Programs." *The Manager* vol. 10, no. 2, 2001.

———. "Working with Boards of Directors." *The Family Planning Manager* vol. 3, no. 5, 1994.

Management Sciences for Health and the World Health Organization. *Managing Drug Supply.* 2nd ed., rev. and exp. W. Hartford, CT: Kumarian Press, 1997.

Mbigi, Lovemore, and Jenny Maree. *Ubuntu, the Spirit of African Transformation Management.* Randburg, South Africa: Knowledge Resources, 1995.

McCauley, Cynthia D., Russ S. Moxley, and Ellen Van Velsor, eds. *The Center for Creative Leadership Handbook of Leadership Development.* Greensboro, NC: Center for Creative Leadership; San Francisco: Jossey-Bass, 1998.

   From the Center for Creative Leadership (CCL), the world's largest institution devoted to leadership research and education. CCL staff present an updated handbook summarizing research and practical information on programs, processes, and contexts of leadership development. The book examines changing views of leadership, organizational climates that support leadership development, leadership development for nontraditional managers, crosscultural leadership development, and leadership assessment.

McClelland, David C. *Human Motivation.* Glenview, IL: Scott, Foresman, 1985.

McGregor, Douglas. *The Human Side of Enterprise: 25th Anniversary Printing.* Foreword by Warren Bennis. New York: McGraw-Hill, 1985.

Mind Tools. "Force Field Analysis: Understanding the Pressures for and against Change." http://www.mindtools.com/forcefld.html (accessed March 4, 2005).

Mumford, Michael D., Ginamarie M. Scott, Blaine Gaddis, and Jill M. Strange. "Leading Creative People: Orchestrating Expertise and Relationships." *The Leadership Quarterly* vol. 13, no. 6, 2002: 705–50.

   Posits that the influence of leaders on workers' creativity and innovation has been underestimated because of the notion that creative ideas should be credited only to the work of the individual. The authors found that studies indicated a positive correlation between creative output and particular styles of leadership in real-world settings. Leaders must have both technical expertise and skills in communication and problem-solving.

Newbrander, William, and Elizabeth Lewis. *HOSPICAL: A Tool for Allocating Hospital Costs: User's Guide.* Version 3.1. Boston: Management Sciences for Health, 2001.

Oshry, Barry. *The Possibilities of Organization*. Boston: Power & Systems, 1992.

Ostroff, Frank. *The Horizontal Organization: What the Organization of the Future Looks Like and How It Delivers Value to Customers*. New York: Oxford University Press, 1999.

Pan American Health Organization (PAHO). *Teoría y técnicas de desarrollo organizacional* [Theory and Techniques of Organizational Development]. Vols. I–VI. Washington, DC: PAHO, 2000.

    Describes a work climate assessment tool developed by PAHO for use in Latin America.

Partners for Health Reform*plus*. *NHA Training Manual: Guide for Trainers*. Abt Associates: Bethesda, MD, 2003. http://www.phrplus.org/nhatm.html (accessed March 4, 2005).

Paxman, John M., Abu Sayeed, Ann Buxbaum, Sallie Craig Huber, and Charles Stover. "The India Local Initiatives Program: Expanding Services through Behavior Change and Resource Mobilization." *Studies in Family Planning* 36, forthcoming [2005].

Peppard, Joe, and Philip Rowland. *The Essence of Business Process Re-engineering*. New York: Prentice-Hall, 1995.

Pike, Robert W. *Creative Training Techniques Handbook: Tips, Tactics, and How-to's for Delivering Effective Training*. Minneapolis, MN: Lakewood Books, 1989.

    A classic reference for trainers. This handbook covers presentation preparation, presentation techniques, learner motivation, visual aids, group involvement, creative materials, resource materials, and classroom management techniques. It also deals with customized training, instrumented learning, transformation of existing training programs, participant-centered techniques for technical training, and the myths and methods of e-learning.

Pillay, Yogan. "The Impact of the South African Constitutional Arrangement on the Organisation of Health Services in Post Apartheid South Africa." Boston: Management Sciences for Health, 2000.

    A 29-page paper that analyzes the impact of the political settlement in South Africa as manifested in the constitution passed in 1996 on the transformation of the health system during the first five years after apartheid. This period witnessed a change in the roles of the central and provincial governments but not without the problems related to decentralization seen elsewhere in the world. The importance of effective intergovernmental relations to the creation of a national health system is highlighted. Negotiation, contracting and coordination skills and mechanisms needed to be strengthened to build a more effective national health system within a decentralized political system.

Quick, James C., Jonathan D. Quick, Debra L. Nelson, and Joseph J. Hurrell. *Preventive Stress Management in Organizations*. Rev. ed. Washington, DC: American Psychological Association, 1997.

    Describes a model for preventing and managing job stress at both the individual and organizational levels. Discusses sources of stress, the mechanics of the (eu)stress/distress response, the consequences of stress, and how to diagnose organizational stress. Includes a discussion of the characteristics of healthy organizations.

Quick, Jonathan, and Carmen Urdaneta. "Achieving Lasting Impact: Local Leaders for Health." *Global HealthLink* no. 129, 2004.

Rogers, Everett. *Diffusion of Innovations.* New York: Free Press, 2003.

Rohde, Jon, and John Wyon, eds. *Community-Based Health Care: Lessons from Bangladesh to Boston.* Boston: Management Sciences for Health, 2002.

> Perspectives from 36 health experts on how to reach more people with sustainable, high-quality health services. This anthology highlights lessons from Bangladesh, Bolivia, Germany, Haiti, India, Nepal, and Vietnam. Chapters on the United States describe programs in environments as different as rural West Virginia and Boston.

Rummler, Geary. "Geary Rummler: Training Skills Isn't Enough." *Training* vol. 20, no. 8, 1983: 75–76.

Schein, Edgar H. *Organizational Culture and Leadership.* 3rd ed. San Francisco: Jossey-Bass, 2004.

> "Transforms the abstract concept of culture into a tool that managers and students can continually use to better shape the dynamics of organization and change." Schein "draws on a wide range of contemporary research to . . . demonstrate the crucial role leaders play in successfully applying the principles of culture to achieve their organizational goals. He tackles the complex question of how an existing culture can be changed—one of the toughest challenges of leadership. The result is a vital aid to understanding and practicing organizational effectiveness." The third edition has updated examples.

Schwartz, Peter. *The Art of the Long View.* New York: Currency Doubleday, 1991.

> A primer and step-by-step guide on how to use and develop scenarios for strategic planning purposes.

Schwartz, Roger M. *The Skilled Facilitator.* San Francisco: Jossey-Bass, 1994.

> A classic and basic reference for anyone whose role is to guide groups toward realizing their creative and problem-solving potential. The book provides a diagnostic approach for identifying and solving problems that can undermine group process. It also covers such topics as setting and maintaining ground rules, starting and ending meetings right and ensuring that they are productive, and handling emotions in groups.

Senge, Peter M. *The Fifth Discipline: The Art and Practice of the Learning Organization.* New York: Doubleday, 1990.

> Introduces the notion of "The Learning Organization" and the five disciplines upon which it is based (systems thinking, personal mastery, mental models, shared vision, and team learning). Relevant for individual and group learning. Senge explains why the learning organization matters, summarizes his management principles, offers some basic tools for practicing them, and shows what it's like to operate under this system. This book was groundbreaking in its integration of systems thinking and organizational and personal development. Organizations are effective when their members hold personal and shared visions and are able to learn together to produce their desired results.

Senge, Peter M., et al. *The Fifth Discipline Fieldbook: Strategies and Tools for Building a Learning Organization.* New York: Doubleday, 1994.

Sonnenfeld, Jeffrey. *The Hero's Farewell: What Happens When CEOs Retire.* New York: Oxford University Press, 1988.

> Examines the critical role a CEO's departure style plays in helping or hindering the transfer of power. Based on interviews and on a survey of 300 top managers (most from US companies), Sonnenfeld identifies four major types of leadership departure styles: monarchs (who choose not to leave voluntarily but either die in office or are overthrown); generals (who leave reluctantly and spend their retirement planning a comeback); ambassadors (who retain close ties with their former firms); and governors (who willingly serve a limited time and leave to pursue new interests). The book helps senior executives and board members to think through ways of facilitating the inevitable transfers of power that organizations must face.

Spencer, Laura. *Winning through Participation.* Dubuque, IA: Kendall/Hunt, 1989.

Stover, Charles C., and Gerald Rosenthal. "Health Financing, Health Sector Delivery, and Decentralization in the Health Sector." Paper presented at the annual meeting of the American Public Health Association. New York, Nov. 1997.

> Examines experience in Kenya showing that charging fees in public health facilities paved the way for decentralization in the health sector. In Kenya, steps needed to administer funds in a decentralized manner preceded steps to decentralize administrative responsibility for health services. By contrast, experience in the Philippines is cited to show how the devolution of health services was the major factor causing significant changes in the fiscal systems in the health field.

Stringer, Robert A. *Leadership and Organizational Climate: The Cloud Chamber Effect.* Upper Saddle River, NJ: Prentice Hall, 2002.

> Summarizes Stringer's thinking on work climate and illustrates climate-related issues through short case studies. The book builds the groundbreaking research described in Motivation and Organizational Climate, which Stringer co-authored with George Litwin.

Sullivan, Eleanor J., and Phillip J. Decker. *Effective Leadership and Management in Nursing.* 4th ed. Menlo Park, CA: Addison Wesley Nursing, 1997.

Taylor, Carl E., and Henry G. Taylor. "Scaling Up Community-based Primary Health Care." In Jon Rohde and John Wyon, eds. *Community-based Health Care: Lessons from Bangladesh to Boston.* Boston: Management Sciences for Health, 2002, pp. 113–27.

> Reviews experiences in Tibet, Peru, Nepal, and India.

Texiera, Paulo. Interview. May 2002.

Thomason, Jane A., William C. Newbrander, and Riitta-Liisa Kolehmainen-Aitken, eds. *Decentralization in a Developing Country: The Experience of Papua New Guinea and Its Health Service.* Pacific Research Monograph No. 25. Canberra: Australian National University, National Centre for Development Studies, 1991.

Tichy, Noel. *The Leadership Engine.* New York: Harper Business, 1997.

> Illustrates the process winning organizations use to teach and develop future leaders. This book describes how to build dynamic leaders at every level within an organization. Tichy holds that "winning organizations are teaching organizations." Senior leaders take direct responsibility for developing and teaching other leaders. Great leaders use stories to teach and communicate their ideas. "Every person in a key position has to see himself or herself as a mini-CEO. They

have to conceptualize what has to be done in the same way the CEO has. Then it cascades."

Van der Heijden, Kees. *Scenarios: The Art of Strategic Conversation.* Chichester, UK: John Wiley and Sons, 1996.

A book that helps readers understand the basis of an organization's success, break out of a restrictive "thinking box," and see beyond their current range of vision. By creating scenarios, organizational decision-makers learn together to connect many apparently unrelated developments and build a systemic framework using a story line. The book proposes a practical methodology to nurture and sustain an ongoing strategic conversation throughout the organization.

Vriesendorp, Sylvia. *Strategic Planning: Reflections on Process and Practice.* Boston: Management Sciences for Health, 1999.

Waldrop, M. Mitchell. "Dee Hock on Management." *Fast Company* Oct. 1996: 79.

Wheatley, Margaret J. "The Real Work of Knowledge Management." *IHRIM Journal* [April–June 2001, vol. 5, no. 2]: 29–33. www.berkana.org/articles/management.html (accessed March 2, 2005).

A short article that describes beliefs that impede knowledge management and principles that will facilitate it.

Wolff, James, Linda Suttenfield, and Susanna Binzen, eds. *The Family Planning Manager's Handbook: Basic Skills and Tools for Managing Family Planning Programs.* W. Hartford, CT: Kumarian Press, 1991.

Wong, Paul T. P. "The Positive Psychology of 'Climate Management.'" International Network on Personal Meaning. President's column, August 2001. http://www.meaning.ca/articles/presidents_column/climate_management.html (accessed March 2, 2005).

A short article that explores the seven dimensions of a positive workplace and the seven pathways to meaning.

World Bank. *World Development Report 1997: The State in a Changing World.* Washington DC: World Bank, 1997.

Index

About Management Sciences for Health

Management Sciences for Health (MSH) is an international nonprofit organization, dedicated to closing the gap between what is known about the overwhelming public health challenges facing many nations and what is done to address those challenges.

Since 1971, MSH has worked in more than 100 countries with policymakers, health professionals, and health care consumers to improve the quality, availability, and affordability of health services. We work with governments, donors, nongovernmental organizations, and health agencies to respond to priority health problems such as HIV/AIDS, tuberculosis, malaria, child health, and reproductive health. Our publications and electronic products augment our assistance in these technical areas.

MSH's staff of more than 1,100 from almost 70 nations work in its Cambridge, Massachusetts, headquarters; offices in the Washington, DC, area; and more than 30 country offices. Through technical assistance, research, training, and systems development, MSH is committed to making a lasting difference in global health.

For more information about Management Sciences for Health, please visit our Web site at www.msh.org. For a catalog of MSH's publications, please contact:

MSH Bookstore
784 Memorial Drive
Cambridge, MA 02139-4613 USA

Telephone: 617.250.9500
Fax: 617.250.9090
E-mail: bookstore@msh.org